Fundamentals OF
Managerial Statistics

DAVID Heinze
NORTHERN ARIZONA UNIVERSITY

Published by

M30 **SOUTH-WESTERN PUBLISHING CO.**

CINCINNATI   WEST CHICAGO, ILL.   DALLAS   PELHAM MANOR, N.Y.   PALO ALTO, CALIF.

PREFACE

The modern manager continually faces situations where uncertainty exists. Probability and statistics provides management with a formal method of handling those situations where uncertainty prevails. Therefore we would expect probability and statistics to become increasingly important in management's attempt to understand its environment and make satisfactory decisions in the face of uncertainty.

This text, which has a single course in algebra as a prerequisite, covers probability, descriptive statistics, and inferential statistics. In this context, the objectives of this text are

1. To familiarize the reader with the vocabulary of probability and statistics.

2. To acquaint the reader with the capabilities of probability and statistics as tools for analysis and decision-making in a management context.

3. To develop in the reader the ability to properly use probability and statistics for the sake of analyzing simple problems and making decisions in simple decision situations.

4. To enable the reader to understand the basic concepts of probability and statistics thereby making possible a meaningful interpretation of the results of statistical analyses.

5. To provide the background necessary for the reader who wishes to take a course in fields such as management science and marketing research.

In an attempt to accomplish these objectives, this text follows an intuitive approach which usually moves from a concrete illustration to the general principle. A conscious effort has been made to use colorful examples and illustrations which encourage the student to read the text.

With regard to the organization of this text, probability is presented first and is followed by descriptive statistics, thus paving the way to inferential statistics. It is believed that this is a more natural approach than beginning with descriptive statistics only to be interrupted with probability in order to finally study inferential statistics. With regard to the breadth of coverage, it should be noticed that many of the small tributaries leading into the mainstream of probability and statistics are not explored. Many elementary texts are so loaded with minor topics that the student is not exposed to the full spectrum of important statistical techniques. Having excluded many of these minor topics, it is hoped that a one-semester course in statistics based on this text will cover nearly all the chapters. In so doing, this will provide the student with a *complete* course in elementary statistics.

Finally, I wish to thank those who offered suggestions for improving this text and I wish to thank Daniel Brooks of Arizona State University for contributing an excellent chapter on time series analysis.

David Heinze

CONTENTS

1.1

SKETCHES

Jupiter Probe

A well-known writer has claimed that the planet Venus originated from Jupiter. Devotees of this theory were delighted to hear that the Australian government was going to soft-land a satellite on the surface of Jupiter. Their delight changed to ecstasy when the Australians told the Venus-Jupiter Society that it could place 60 pounds of test equipment on the satellite for the purpose of determining if Venus could have come from Jupiter. The Venus-Jupiter Society immediately began to employ scientists to develop the test equipment. Of all the test equipment ideas suggested, the ideas of Gerhunz and Gerhilda Webb caught the fancy of the Society.

Gerhilda Webb developed a 60 pound piece of test equipment which had a 99 percent chance of functioning correctly on Jupiter's surface. Gerhunz developed a radically different type of equipment. He designed a 20 pound piece of equipment and proposed that three of these identical pieces of equipment be placed on the satellite. Gerhunz reasoned that it would be better to have three pieces of identical equipment, so that if one or two failed, perhaps the third would work. If Gerhilda's single piece of test equipment failed, then there would be no chance to run this all-important test. The only problem with Gerhunz' idea is that his 20 pound piece of equipment is not as reliable as Gerhilda's 60 pound piece. In particular, Gerhunz' 20 pound piece has a reliability of only 90 percent; that is, there is a 90 percent chance that it will work. This is to be compared to Gerhilda's 60 pound piece, which has a 99 percent reliability. However, Gerhunz pointed out that with the 60 pound weight limit imposed, three of his pieces of test equipment could be placed on board the satellite. Gerhunz stated that he is sure that three pieces of equipment, each of which is 90 percent reliable, would be better than one piece which is 99 percent reliable. Gerhilda disagreed with Gerhunz. It was therefore left to the Venus-Jupiter Society to determine whether to go with the Gerhunz plan or Gerhilda's.

Since the officers of the Venus-Jupiter Society knew little about *probability theory*, they hired a statistician to determine which plan would offer the greatest chance of a successful test. Though the statistician was working with less than a full load of bricks, he had read Chapter 2 of this text and was thus able to crack the problem in less than a minute.

Buffalo Snow Bank

When Tammy Paticlepitcher was hired as a new teller by the Buffalo Snow Bank, she immediately began to wonder what she would be doing at the bank during the period from December to May. It was then that the bank's manager indicated that the boredom of facilitating an occasional deposit by a walrus would be broken by the excitement of descriptive statistics. Not only would working with descriptive statistics be a delightful way to spend a winter, the manager went on to say, but the New York State Bank Examiner might interrupt a Florida vacation at any time to make a visit to the bank. If this should happen, the bank must be able to convince the examiner that the bank is as financially strong as the City of New York. To prove this, the bank must have available a number of charts and tables which depict its financial status. Tammy then learned that descriptive statistics has to do with the collection and presentation of numerical data such as the bank examiner would require.

Tammy's first winter with the Buffalo Snow Bank proved to be most productive in terms of the tabulation of financial data. Tammy was able to prepare one table or chart for each foot of snow that fell. Figure 1.1 shows four of the 200 charts and tables that Tammy produced. These illustrate some of the methods by which statistical data can be presented. It is seen, for example, that the Buffalo Snow Bank had $50,000,000 in consumer loans as of December 31; time deposits were below $200,000,000; 25 percent of the bank's expenditures went for employee salaries and benefits; and the bank had a total of 132,679 time depositors, of which 48,432 had savings accounts from $0 to $999.99 at year's end. In addition, Tammy computed several averages. For example, the average size of all the demand deposits on December 31 was $386.42. Chapter 5 of this text provides exposure to a number of the methods within the domain of *descriptive statistics* that Tammy used to describe the operations and status of the bank.

FIGURE 1.1

Charts and Tables for Buffalo Snow Bank (December 31, 19––)

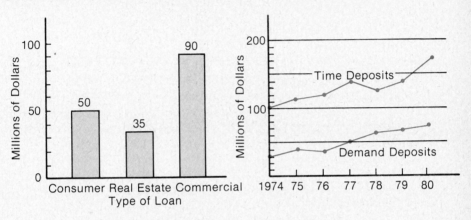

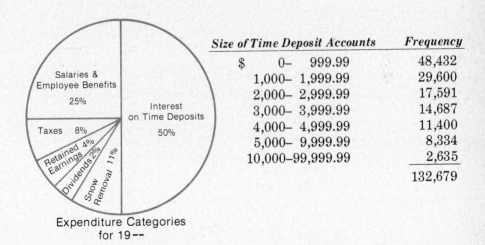

Size of Time Deposit Accounts	Frequency
$ 0– 999.99	48,432
1,000– 1,999.99	29,600
2,000– 2,999.99	17,591
3,000– 3,999.99	14,687
4,000– 4,999.99	11,400
5,000– 9,999.99	8,334
10,000–99,999.99	2,635
	132,679

Expenditure Categories
for 19––

Scenic Highways

M. Gookin was a cub statistician in pursuit of employment. Gookin was especially pleased to see an ad in the newspaper placed by the *Scenic Highways* magazine. The ad indicated that the editor of the magazine was looking for a cub statistician, and so Gookin made a trip to Chicago to apply for the position. In time, Gookin was notified that he had received the job and was told to report to work in a week. Upon arriving, Gookin was given his first assignment.

Bethany Eden, the editor-in-chief, told Gookin that the magazine wanted to do a feature story on the Million Dollar Highway. Eden went on to say that the Million Dollar Highway is perhaps the most scenic stretch of highway in the United States, as it winds around the spectacular San Juan mountains of southwestern Colorado between Ouray and Silverton. Gookin then asked Eden how he fitted into the situation, as it seemed that the magazine would want either a writer or photographer for such a story. Eden retorted that finding writers and photographers was no problem; however, the task at hand would require a species of inductive reasoning which is not usually found within the skull of a writer or photographer. For this reason, a statistician was hired.

The problem confronting the magazine dealt with the origin of the name of the highway. Eden told Gookin that she has heard of two explanations of why the highway is called the "Million Dollar" Highway. The first explanation or theory is that the highway had originally cost about a million dollars to construct. The second theory explains that there is about a million dollars worth of gold within the crushed rock which forms the bed for the highway. It is Gookin's task to determine which of these two theories is correct.

Within hours Gookin was flying west. After touching down at Stapleton Airport in Denver, Gookin rented a car and drove over the Rockies to Ouray. There he began to question some of the old-timers about why the Million Dollar Highway has such a name. Each of the six old-timers told Gookin the same story. They said that in the old days it cost a million dollars to cut the highway out of the mountains; that is why it bears its name. Gookin then decided to drive the highway. The first sign he approached while traveling south toward Silverton told the same story. The sign said that this highway had been constructed at a cost of a million dollars. After seeing the sign Gookin was essentially convinced that this was the truth, and so continued on to Silverton merely to enjoy the scenery.

While eating an ice cream cone in Silverton, Gookin started chatting with another old-timer. Before long, this old-timer was telling Gookin that the Million Dollar Highway is so-called because it has a million dollars of gold in its roadbed. The old-timer went on to admit that this was not the popular theory, but asked Gookin to figure it out for himself. If the truth ever got out, every tourist coming along would swipe a rock from the roadbed, and before long they'd be digging out the blacktop in order to get at the gold below. This would cost the state of Colorado and the local residents all kinds of expense and inconvenience. Hence, the state and residents have a vested interest in maintaining that the highway cost a million to construct, rather than admitting that it is loaded with gold.

With the last old-timer's thoughts ringing in his ears, Gookin headed back to Chicago. He told Eden of his indecision. Eden then reminded him that he had been hired to solve this problem, and therefore, he better get to it or he'd be looking for another job. A great plan then came to Gookin, after giving serious thought to the matter.

In late November there are few people roaming around Ouray and the immediate countryside. It was at this time that Gookin returned to the tiny town and checked in at a motel. Next, he rented a truck. Then the curtain of darkness settled over the Switzerland of America, as Ouray is called. What Gookin did next is unknown. However, the Colorado highway maintenance crew encountered strange phenomena the next day. Along the 23 miles of the Million Dollar Highway, the crew reported that there were 100 chuckholes, each of which went through the blacktop down to the bottom of the crushed rock roadbed. Furthermore, the chuckholes seemed to occur in a purely random pattern.

You, of course, know what happened. Gookin had sampled 100 chunks of roadbed from the highway. Though there were hundreds of thousands of square foot chunks of roadbed in the highway, Gookin decided that he would only have to sample 100 of them in order to accurately determine how much gold was in the entire highway roadbed. A casual observer might be somewhat skeptical of whether Gookin could make any reliable statements about how much gold was in the entire highway based on a mere sample of 100 chunks. However, Gookin was quite confident of his findings, as he had properly applied a powerful form of inductive reasoning which he had learned in Chapter 8 of this text. The kind of method Gookin used is known as *inferential statistics*.

1.2
PROBABILITY AND STATISTICS

Probability and *statistics* comprise the subject matter of this text. Before beginning the study of these two related subjects, it would be useful to give a very general description of them. The three sketches in the first section of this chapter expose certain aspects of both probability and statistics. Let us now briefly consider the character of probability and statistics. In so doing, mention will be made of the three introductory sketches.

Probability

In the seventeenth century, there was interest in various games of chance. For instance, a duke might have wanted to know what the chances were of drawing two successive aces from a deck of cards. Problems of this sort caught the attention of mathematicians like Blaise Pascal and Pierre de Fermat. These men used a mathematical approach to solve a number of problems which involved the operation of chance. In doing this, they introduced the field of study known as *probability*. Since then, a number of axioms, definitions, and theorems have been developed in the field of probability. Probability theory is now a well-defined branch of mathematics. By applying probability theory to real world events, a host of problems, where chance or uncertainty plays an important role, can be solved. Because uncertainty is pervasive in the world of management, we would rightly expect that probability theory would have many managerial applications. Some of these applications will be studied in this text.

In the first sketch of Section 1.1, the case of determining whether the Gerhunz or the Gerhilda system is the more reliable is a situation where probability theory can be applied in order to reach a decision. Recall that probability entered into the picture since Gerhilda's test equipment had a 99 percent chance of operating correctly, whereas one of Gerhunz' pieces had a 90 percent probability of working. Chapters 2 through 4 of this text are devoted to introducing the basic concepts of probability. These basic concepts make solving the Gerhilda-Gerhunz problem an easy matter. Not only does probability theory provide a method by which a wide variety of problems involving chance can be directly solved, but it also forms the theoretical foundation upon which statistics is based. Therefore, probability is an important subject.

Descriptive Statistics

Statistics can be broken into two areas of study. The first area is known as descriptive statistics; the second is known as inferential statistics. Before commenting on the nature of descriptive statistics, it should be noted that the term "statistics" can be used in either a plural sense or in a singular sense. It is used in the plural sense in the following sentence: "Here are the statistics on the Dallas Cowboys." The statistics in this case are all the numerical data referring to the performance of the football team known as the Dallas Cowboys. The plural use of "statistics" means nothing more than a collection of numerical data. The singular use of "statistics" is illustrated when a prospective employer asks a college graduate, "Do you know statistics?" Here statistics refers to a field of study which concerns the methods of describing and analyzing numerical data. Statistics in this sense can be segmented into two areas, namely, descriptive statistics and inferential statistics.

Descriptive statistics deals with the collection, tabulation, presentation, and interpretation of numerical data. Descriptive statistics is, therefore, just about as old as human history. In the Old Testament, for example, descriptive statistics was applied whenever a census was taken. Political states within the past few centuries have kept elaborate records on trade, deaths, revenues, and the like. All this comes under the aegis of descriptive statistics. Today descriptive statistics is a part of just about every human enterprise. Numerical data are being collected, tabulated, presented, and interpreted in baseball, finance, real estate, hospitals, government, and so on.

In the second sketch of Section 1.1, Tammy Paticlepitcher was applying descriptive statistics as she collected various quantitative data relating to the operation of the bank and then tabulated and presented them in the charts and tables of Figure 1.1. In this text descriptive statistics is introduced in Chapter 5 and then is woven throughout the remainder of the text.

Inferential Statistics

Inferential statistics is the second area of statistics. Whereas descriptive statistics is almost as old as history, inferential statistics is primarily a product of the twentieth century. In order to understand inferential statistics, a distinction must initially be made between a *population* and a *sample*. To illustrate this distinction, consider the entire collection of people who will vote in Ohio on election day. This entire collection of voters is called the population. From this population of hundreds of thousands of voters, a random sample of 50 voters might be taken. A sample is therefore a selected portion of the entire population. The sample is taken from the population for the sake of drawing some conclusion concerning the population. Inferential statistics deals with determining the types of conclusions that can be drawn concerning the population on the basis of sample evidence. It is by inferential statistics that a pollster can make certain inferences regarding how the entire population of Ohio voters will vote if only a small sample of voters is taken. Likewise, inferential statistics is important to the auditor who wishes to draw a conclusion (inference) regarding the total value of a firm's accounts receivable on the basis of only a sample of the accounts.

The third sketch in Section 1.1, where Gookin was seeking to determine the gold content in the roadbed of the Million Dollar Highway, involved an application of inferential statistics. Gookin took a sample of 100 chunks of the roadbed and on the basis of this sample was able to make an inference regarding the gold content of the entire highway, which is composed of hundreds of thousands of chunks of roadbed. Inferential statistics will be treated in Chapters 6 through 11. Therefore, a major part of this text is devoted to this important subject.

1.3

OBJECTIVES AND PEDAGOGY

As has been indicated, this text deals with probability, descriptive statistics, and inferential statistics. In view of this subject matter, the objectives of this text are:

1. To familiarize the reader with the vocabulary of probability and statistics.

2. To acquaint the reader with the capabilities of probability and statistics as tools for analysis and decision-making in a management context.

3. To develop in the reader the ability to properly use probability and statistics for the sake of analyzing simple problems and making decisions in simple decision situations.

4. To enable the reader to understand the basic concepts of probability and statistics, thereby making possible a meaningful interpretation of the results of statistical analysis.

5. To provide the background necessary for the reader who wishes to take a course in fields such as management science and marketing research.

In order to optimally accomplish the foregoing objectives, this text follows the intuitive approach to the presentation of probability and statistics. Furthermore, the presentation will usually move from a concrete illustration to the general principle rather than from the general principle to the illustration. Such an approach is best suited to the reader who lacks a strong foundation in mathematical courses. Finally, the focus of the text will be on the broad principles of probability and statistics.

1.4

NOTATION

The mathematical prerequisites for this text consist merely of a basic course in algebra. However, several types of notation are used in this text which are sometimes new to the reader. These notations will be briefly discussed here.

Summation notation is merely a bit of mathematical shorthand which is occasionally used in this text. Suppose the collection of possible values for the variable X is given by $-2, 4, 5, 6$, and 9. A shorthand way of describing the sum of these values is ΣX. Here the capital sigma, Σ, means "Sum up the values of X." Therefore,

$$\Sigma X = -2 + 4 + 5 + 6 + 9$$
$$= 22$$

Following this convention, ΣX^2 would refer to the sum of all the squared values of X, that is,

$$\Sigma X^2 = (-2)^2 + 4^2 + 5^2 + 6^2 + 9^2$$
$$= 162$$

Similarly, the expression $\Sigma(X - 5)$ would equal

$$\Sigma(X - 5) = (-2 - 5) + (4 - 5) + (5 - 5) + (6 - 5) + (9 - 5)$$
$$= -3$$

Another bit of mathematical shorthand involves the *factorial notation*. When an exclamation point is placed after an integer, like 5!, this is called "five factorial" and represents

$$5! = 5 \cdot 4 \cdot 3 \cdot 2 \cdot 1$$
$$= 120$$

Similarly,

$$8! = 8 \cdot 7 \cdot 6 \cdot 5 \cdot 4 \cdot 3 \cdot 2 \cdot 1$$
$$= 40{,}320$$

$$2! = 2 \cdot 1$$

$$1! = 1$$

Finally, by definition

$$0! = 1$$

The reader should also be familiar with *exponents*. For example,

$$3^4 = 3 \cdot 3 \cdot 3 \cdot 3$$
$$X^4 = X \cdot X \cdot X \cdot X$$

In statistics, several Greek letters are used in addition to English letters. Figure 1.2 presents a list of these Greek letters and shows how each is pronounced.

FIGURE 1.2

Commonly Used Greek Letters

α	alpha	ν	nu
β	beta	ρ	rho
δ	delta	σ	sigma
λ	lambda	χ	chi
μ	mu		

PROBLEMS

1.1

The term "statistics" can be used as a plural noun and as a singular noun. Explain what each of these uses of the term means.

1.2

Briefly describe the field of study known as probability. Why might probability be useful for the manager?

1.3

Briefly describe the field of study known as descriptive statistics.

1.4

Briefly describe the field of study known as inferential statistics.

1.5

Which system, the Gerhunz or the Gerhilda, appears *to you* to offer the greater chance of success?

1.6

Two of the four charts and tables of Figure 1.1 prepared by Tammy Paticlepitcher are inconsistent. What is the inconsistency?

1.7

Give three situations where descriptive statistics is used in the world of business.

1.8

Give three examples where a business corporation might use inferential statistics.

1.9

Distinguish between a population and a sample.

1.10

What are the five objectives of this text?

1.11

If the values of X are 0, 2, 4, and 6, find
(a) ΣX
(b) ΣX^2
(c) $\Sigma (X - 3)$
(d) $\Sigma (X - 3)^2$
(e) $[\Sigma (X - 3)]^2$
(f) $\Sigma (X/10)$
(g) $(.1) \Sigma X$
(h) $(\Sigma X)/10$

1.12

Evaluate each of the following:
(a) $4!$
(b) $0!$
(c) $\dfrac{6!}{4!\,2!}$
(d) $\dfrac{8!}{3!\,5!}$
(e) $\dfrac{5!}{5!\,0!}$

1.13

If $p = .3$, find the numerical value of
(a) p^3
(b) $p^4 (1 - p)^3$

1.14

Identify each of the following lowercase Greek letters:
(a) δ
(b) β
(c) ν
(d) α
(e) λ
(f) μ
(g) ρ
(h) χ
(i) σ

2.1

INTRODUCTION

The language of probability is commonplace today as we seek to adequately express our thoughts concerning the uncertainties which face us. "It's not very likely that she would forget — something must be wrong." "There's a good chance that ASU will win the game tomorrow night." "The lion will probably be sleeping." "This picture probably won't turn out." "There's very little chance that he'll get sick." Such general statements of uncertainty or probability are sometimes replaced with more specific statements. For example, "The probability of measurable precipitation tomorrow is thirty percent." "There is one chance in ten that Beetle Balm will win the triple crown." "About 20 percent of the Rocky Mountain Spotted Fever cases are fatal." Such specific statements convey more information than general statements like "If you get Rocky Mountain Spotted Fever, there is a pretty good chance that you will make it."

Statements containing probabilistic information occur more and more because we desire to think and speak precisely about the many uncertainties we face. Not only is the future uncertain, but the past is also uncertain in the sense that our present knowledge of many past events is uncertain. Hence we might say "I'm pretty sure that it was the *left* shoe which Nicky Kruschev slammed on the table." In reality it either was or wasn't the left shoe, but my memory leaves me in a state of some uncertainty as to which shoe it in fact was and thus I can only say "I'm pretty sure."

The decision maker operating within the context of management is also faced with many uncertainties. For example, consider the marketing firm of Marsh & Scott. Marsh & Scott is considering the introduction of a home burglar alarm system which will be sold exclusively through television advertising. After the television viewer is exposed to the new burglar alarm, the viewer will be invited to call a toll-free number in order to place a C.O.D. order for the alarm. In such a situation Marsh & Scott is confronted with several uncertainties of crucial importance. For example, how many alarms will be ordered as a result of each thousand dollars spent in advertising? No one knows how the viewers will respond to the ads; nevertheless, Marsh & Scott must make a decision to either go ahead with the project or scrap it. But you might reply that Marsh & Scott should test market the product by advertising it in a limited area like Phoenix. However, even if the response of Phoenicians is known, Marsh & Scott still cannot know with certainty how Bostonians would respond — uncertainty still exists.

Another kind of uncertainty confronting Marsh & Scott concerns the refusal rate. Out of every hundred alarms ordered, how many persons will refuse the alarm when the mail carrier seeks to deliver it C.O.D.? Will 10 percent, or 15 percent, . . . , or 40 percent of the orders end in refusals? Obviously Marsh & Scott will be quite concerned about this uncertainty. Through the use of probability, Marsh & Scott can formally express the degree of uncertainty regarding the number of orders generated and the refusal rate. In so doing Marsh & Scott can better analyze the situation.

Other situations where management faces various uncertainties are everywhere. Will the union strike? What will be the cost of construction next year? What will be the prime rate of interest? Will we run out of stock? Such questions are best answered probabilistically. This sets the stage for the incorporation of probability into the manager's decision-making processes.

In this chapter the nature of probability will be discussed and then attention will be focused on the matter of working with these probabilities which are essential to coping intelligently with many managerial decision situations.

2.2

INTERPRETATIONS OF PROBABILITY

Probabilities are numbers from zero through one which express how likely an event is to occur. There have been three different interpretations of what probabilities really are and how they may be legitimately derived. These three historical interpretations will now be briefly considered.

Classical Interpretation

In the eighteenth century, mathematicians sought to mathematically express the likelihood of certain events associated with games of chance. Probability was used to accomplish this task. The probabilities associated with the games of chance were determined *a priori*; that is, they were determined by pure reason prior to any experimentation. For example, what is the probability of heads on the flip of a coin? Without actually flipping the particular coin in question, this probability may be determined. By reason alone it can be seen that upon flipping a coin there are only two possible outcomes, heads and tails. Since a coin is symmetrical, there is no reason for heads to occur any more than tails. Therefore, the probability of heads is 1/2; that is, there is one chance in two that heads will occur. Consider the roll of a die instead. What is the probability of getting an odd number of spots? Since the die is symmetrical with six equally likely sides, and since three of the sides have an odd number of spots, the probability is determined *a priori* to be

$$P(\text{Odd number}) = \frac{3 \text{ sides with an odd number of spots}}{6 \text{ equally likely sides}} = \frac{3}{6} = .5$$

In like manner, according to the classical approach, the probability of drawing an ace from a shuffled deck of 52 playing cards is

$$P(\text{Ace}) = \frac{4 \text{ ace cards}}{52 \text{ cards}} = \frac{4}{52}$$

The classical approach is quite adequate as long as one is dealing with such things as games of chance where there are coins being flipped, dice rolled, cards chosen, and roulette wheels spun. However, suppose that we wish to know the probability that the next bluefish caught in Chesapeake Bay will weigh over 10 pounds. No amount of armchair reasoning will give us an answer here unless it is known that bluefish never grow to more than two or three pounds. Another way of determining and interpreting probabilities is therefore needed.

Relative Frequency Approach

The second approach to probability has appeared in conjunction with the development of science. Science is concerned with experimentation and observation and so it would be expected that the scientist would use the concept of probability in order to precisely describe phenomena where uncertainty is present. What is the probability, for example, that a female of age 60 will die within the next year? The classical approach cannot be of help in answering this question; empirical evidence is needed. Thus, an actuarial scientist observes that out of 100 females of age 60, 3 die within the following year. This means that the relative frequency of deaths, based on 100 observations, is .03 or 3 percent. It could therefore be stated that

$$P(\text{Female aged 60 dying in a year}) = 3/100 = .03$$

However, you might question this procedure by asking why exactly 100 women were observed — why not more? For instance, if a group of 1000 females aged 60 were observed, perhaps 27 would die, yielding a relative frequency or probability of .027 rather than .03. Most people would agree that .027 should be preferred since it is based on 1000 observations rather than 100. If this be the case, we might wonder how many observations are required to find the "true" probability. The only answer is, "The more observations the better."

In conclusion, the relative frequency approach states that the probability of an event equals the relative frequency of that event based on an ever increasing number of observations.

Management might use a relative frequency approach to the derivation of probabilities in certain situations like the following: Dayspring Electrical Supply manufactures rolls of #12 romex. The quality control department has inspected 120 rolls and has found that 8 of these rolls are defective. Therefore, Dayspring might assume that currently the probability of producing a defective roll of #12 romex is 8/120 or .067.

Subjective Approach

The relative frequency approach to probability cannot deal with certain situations for which we would like to be able to use probabilities. Suppose we are sitting at the Ford Motor Company headquarters a number of years ago when the Edsel was initially being considered. At that point in time Ford was interested in the potential profitability of the Edsel. One executive might have claimed, "I think there is an 80 percent chance that the Edsel will be profitable." Where did this probability come from? Certainly it was not determined by the relative frequency approach since there never was a series of past instances on which to base the relative frequency where companies just like Ford introduced automobiles just like the Edsel into similar marketplaces. The Edsel case is unique and hence one cannot appeal to past relative frequencies in determining probabilities. Neither was this probability determined *a priori* in the sense that the probability of .80 is apparent to everyone on the basis of some well-defined pattern of reasoning. Another executive might have responded, "I disagree. I believe the probability is .10 that the Edsel will make a profit." These same two executives could be convinced that the probability of drawing an ace from a deck of cards is 4/52, but there is no reason to believe that they could both be convinced to agree on the probability in the Edsel case. The two executives might in all honesty see things differently in this regard. Hence, the probability assessed in such a situation is not "objective"; rather, the probability reflects the executive's personal belief concerning the possibility of the Edsel making a profit. This is the third approach to probability and is called the subjective approach.

According to the subjectivist view, a probability expresses the strength of a person's belief. If a person gives a probability of 1 for some event, that person is convinced (believes with certainty) that the event will occur. If a person gives a probability of 0 for some event, that person is convinced that the event will not happen. If the person assigns a probability of .5, this means that he or she believes that the likelihood of the event is the same as the chance of getting heads on a single flip of a coin. To the subjectivist, probability does not objectively exist. Rather, probability expresses a person's uncertainty concerning the occurrence of some event. It could be said that probabilities exist only in the mind.

The subjective approach to probability arose in the twentieth century and is especially useful to the manager who is often confronted with unique situations where uncertainty exists. It should be noted that in a sense the subjectivist approach encompasses all the situations that the classical and relative frequency approaches deal with. For example, my subjective probability for getting heads on the flip of a coin is .5; this is my belief concerning the flip of a coin. This belief, though personal, is rooted in the fact that I know something of the nature of a coin (symmetrical) and I have seen coins flipped many times and noted that heads seem to occur about half the time. The subjective approach sees probability as representing my belief concerning the occurrence of an event; there is no reason why my belief cannot be based fully or partially on *a priori* thought or empirical observation. Thus, the subjective approach may yield probabilities which are identical to those determined by either of the other two approaches. The difference between the approaches in these cases resides in the fact that the subjectivist sees the probability as a personal statement of belief, whereas the other two approaches or schools view the probability as having some sort of objective existence apart from the beliefs of the person.

Regardless of the approach espoused, probabilities are still numbers and they are mathematically treated in the same way. Therefore all of the theorems and operations to be discussed in this chapter have universal application.

2.3

EXPERIMENTS AND PROBABILITY

An *experiment* is an action which, according to chance, results in any of several outcomes. If a coin is flipped, there are two possible outcomes, either of which may occur. Furthermore, the occurrence of heads or tails is said to be determined by chance. Therefore, this coin flipping exercise constitutes an experiment. Consider now another example of an experiment. You station yourself at a spot on the Snake River for an hour for the purpose of counting the number of rafts which pass. This is an experiment where the outcomes are: No rafts pass, one raft passes, two rafts pass, three rafts pass, ... The outcome which materializes is determined by chance as far as you are concerned. As a final example, suppose we are interested in the prime rate of interest two months from now because we are anticipating a cash shortage at that time. In two months we will make a call to our banker (an action) and our banker will inform us of the prime rate. At that time the prime rate may be 6.00 percent, or 6.25 percent, or 6.50 percent et cetera; these are the various outcomes. Since the prime rate in two months is uncertain as far as we are concerned, we express this by saying that it is determined according to chance. Thus, this situation may be considered to be an experiment in the probabilistic sense.

The outcomes of an experiment are often listed. The set of outcomes in the coin-tossing experiment is shown as

$$\{H, T\}$$

The set of outcomes in the Snake River experiment is

$$\{0, 1, 2, 3, 4, 5, \ldots\}$$

Finally, the set of outcomes in the interest-rate experiment may be shown as

$$\{\ldots 6.00\%, 6.25\%, 6.50\%, \ldots\}$$

The set of all possible outcomes in an experiment is called the *sample space* for that experiment. A portion or subset of the sample space is called an *event*. For example, in the Snake River experiment an even number of rafts might pass. This event is represented by the following subset

$$\{0, 2, 4, 6, \ldots\}$$

which is a subset of the sample space in this experiment. Another event might be "less than four rafts pass." This event is represented by the subset

$$\{0, 1, 2, 3\}$$

Consider now another experiment which is quite familiar, the rolling of a die. The set of outcomes or sample space is given by

$$S = \{1, 2, 3, 4, 5, 6\}$$

The sample space in this case is represented by S. The event "an even number of spots" is given by

$$E = \{2, 4, 6\}$$

and the event "an odd number of spots" is given by

$$D = \{1, 3, 5\}$$

Both of these events are nothing more than subsets (portions) of the sample space which is the set of all possible outcomes. Furthermore, the events E and D are said to be *collectively exhaustive*. This means that when considered together, all the outcomes in the sample space are to be found in E or D or both. If the event "less than three spots" is now defined, that is,

$$L = \{1, 2\}$$

it should be apparent that E and L taken together are not collectively exhaustive. A die could be rolled and neither E nor L might occur. When several events are collectively exhaustive, at least one of them is sure to occur.

Two or more events are said to be *mutually exclusive* if only one of them can occur in the experiment. In the die-rolling example, E and L are not mutually exclusive since both could occur when the die shows two spots. However, the events E and D are mutually exclusive because if one of them occurs we can be sure that the other will not. There is no overlap between these two events which have no outcomes in common. The concepts of mutual exclusiveness and collective exhaustiveness will come into use later in this chapter as progress is made in the study of probability.

It has been stated that in an experiment any one of several outcomes may occur and that the outcomes are controlled by chance. In the first two sections of this chapter it was explained that probability is used to express the degree of chance associated with uncertain events. Thus, it would seem appropriate that we seek to make probabilistic statements concerning the outcomes of an experiment. For example, with the roll of a die where the sample space S is

$$S = \{1, 2, 3, 4, 5, 6\}$$

the probability of the event $\{1\}$ is $P(1) = 1/6$, the probability of getting two spots is $P(2) = 1/6$, the probability of getting three is $P(3) = 1/6$, $P(4) = 1/6$, $P(5) = 1/6$, and $P(6) = 1/6$. In this context several things might be said about probabilities. *First*, probabilities are numbers which are never less than zero nor more than one. A probability of 1.3 or $-.2$ is meaningless: it's like saying that purple weighs ten inches. *Second*, the probabilities of each of the outcomes in the sample space when summed, add to one. In the roll of a die case we see that this is true since

$$P(1) + P(2) + P(3) + P(4) + P(5) + P(6) = 1/6 + 1/6 + 1/6$$
$$+ 1/6 + 1/6 + 1/6$$
$$= 1$$

Notice that the outcomes of an experiment, when taken individually, are mutually exclusive. In the *third* place, probabilities can be attached to events which are not the individual outcomes of an experiment. For example, for the event E which was earlier defined as $\{2, 4, 6\}$, the probability of E is given by $P(E) = 3/6$. This follows from the fact that E is a subset of S, which is composed of the three individual outcomes of 2, 4, and 6. These three outcomes each have a probability of 1/6. When these are added, they then yield 3/6 which is the probability of E. *Finally*, it might be noted that the probability of S is unity, that is, $P(S) = 1$. One of the outcomes which makes up the sample space is sure to happen, since by definition the sample space S includes all of the possible outcomes of the experiment.

Even though the above discussion does not appear to be profound, it is of extreme importance because it gives us insight into how probabilities may be linked with experiments. More will be said concerning the probabilities of various events and how they relate to each other in succeeding sections of this chapter. Before leaving this discussion, however, it should be indicated that the probabilities attached to each of the individual outcomes in a sample space might be determined by any of the three approaches to probability discussed in Section 2.2. For example, in the roll of the die where the probability was 1/6 for each side, this probability might have been determined according to the classical approach. In the Snake River experiment the classical approach is of no use. In this case you may have spent a number of hours observing rafts on the Snake and have found that in about 10 percent of the hours, there were 0 rafts which passed you; in 20 percent of the hours, one raft passed; in 30 percent of the hours, two rafts passed; in 25 percent of the hours, three passed; and in 15 percent of the hours, four rafts passed you. Thus, these relative frequencies might become the probabilities for this experiment, that is, $P(0) = .10, P(1) = .20, P(2) = .30, P(3) = .25, P(4) = .15, P(5) = 0, P(6) = 0$, etc. In the prime rate of interest experiment the probabilities would be subjectively determined, thereby representing a manager's beliefs concerning the prime rate two months hence. For a given manager the probabilities associated with the sample space for this experiment might be $P(6.00 \text{ percent}) = .33, P(6.25 \text{ percent}) = .34$, and $P(6.50 \text{ percent}) = .33$.

2.4

TYPES OF PROBABILITIES

In these days considerable attention is being given to matters involving corporate social responsibility. Within the domain of corporate social responsibility activities, employment practices may come to mind first as an area where much change is taking place. The roots of equal employment opportunity and the like go back in history to that famous, but rarely cited, suit known as Susan Bladder Timphany v. Rocky Mountain Fur Company. This case is cited here not because of its implications for employment practices, but because it graphically illustrates the basic types of probability statements, and because one of the laws of probability proved to be critical in the resolution of the suit.

In the 1820s a number of mountain men roamed the West in search of beaver. Once each year the trappers would gather at a prearranged spot, like Jackson Hole in the shadow of the Tetons, and at this time would trade their beaver pelts to fur companies like the Rocky Mountain Fur Company. Quite a bit of excitement was generated at these yearly rendezvous as the trappers gathered to do their trading. As the mountain men swapped tales of encounters with hostile Indians and grizzlies, often a journalist would show up to record some of these wild adventures of the past year. One tale, true mind you, was that of Cannibal Phil (as in Philadelphia from whence he came). It seems that while snowed in with his squaw in the high Rockies the previous winter, Phil ran out of venison, beaver meat, bear meat, and in fact almost all edible items. It was at this juncture in time that hungry Phil became Cannibal Phil. Thanks to the journalist, this story got back to New York where one Susan Timphany read it. Susan was incensed, as were many people, and so she sought to bring the Rocky Mountain Fur Company to court on charges that the company permitted one of its male employees to convert one of its female employees into food.

Before formally bringing a charge, Susan's lawyer (Ralph Earp) counselled her that neither Cannibal Phil nor his former squaw were actually employees of the fur company. Ralph did say, however, that he thought he knew a way to get the company on a related matter if that was Susan's pleasure. In particular, it seems that at each rendezvous the Rocky Mountain Fur Company would give away something of a door prize; the purpose of this practice was to induce trappers to deal with the Rocky Mountain Fur Company rather than a competing company which was holding its rendezvous at another spot. Since the door prize was of substantial value, the choosing of a winner was a big event at each rendezvous. Supposedly the Rocky Mountain Fur Company *randomly* chose the winner each year. However, for the past three years when there were door prizes, mountain men always seemed to win. A woman had never won. Ralph felt that this was sure evidence that Rocky Mountain Fur Company was "fixing" the selection of the winner. He therefore apprised Susan of this fact. It was then that Susan brought formal charges against the company for discriminating against mountain women.

In order to see how the court resolved this case it must first be recognized that the selection of a winner at the rendezvous is essentially an experiment; review the definition of an experiment as given at the beginning of Section 2.3. The sample space for this experiment is pictorially displayed by means of an Euler diagram as shown in Figure 2.1. Several characteristics of the participants at a typical rendezvous are apparent from Figure 2.1. First, it is assumed that there are ten people present. Of these ten, four are English, seven are young, five are illiterate, seven are men, and three are women. The company is now going to randomly select one person from among the ten. Consider now some probabilities concerning the characteristics of the person who is selected.

What is the probability that a young person will win the prize? Since seven of the people are young, and since there are a total of ten people, all of whom stand an equal chance of winning (assuming a random selection process), it can be concluded that the probability of a young person winning is

$$P(Y) = 7/10$$

The probability that a woman will win is

$$P(W) = 3/10$$

since exactly three of the ten persons present are women. This sort of probability is called a *simple probability* or sometimes a *marginal probability*. Other simple probabilities associated with this experiment are $P(E) = 4/10, P(I) = 5/10, P(M) = 7/10$, and $P(S) = 1$.

Sometimes it is desirable to speak of the probability of *not* getting a young person as winner, or *not* getting an illiterate person. The event "not young" is denoted by the symbol $\overline{Y}$. The probability in this experiment of not getting a young person is $P(\overline{Y}) = 3/10$, since only three of the ten are not young. $\overline{Y}$ is called the *complementary event* of Y. Some other simple probabilities involving complementary events are $P(\overline{I}) = 5/10, P(\overline{M}) = 3/10$, and $P(\overline{E}) = 6/10$.

FIGURE 2.1_____

Euler Diagram for Rendezvous Door Prize Experiment

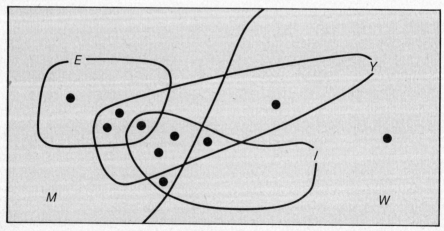

E = English (4), Y = Young (7), I = Illiterate (5),
M = Man (7), W = Woman (3), S = Sample Space (10)

Another type of probability is the *joint probability*. Suppose we wish to know what chance a person who is illiterate and young has of winning. This probability is .4 since four of the ten persons are both illiterate and young as seen in the Euler diagram. A joint probability is written as

$$P(I, Y) = 4/10$$

In some texts joint probabilities are written as $P(I \cap Y)$ instead of $P(I, Y)$. In either case, a joint probability represents the probability that *both* events, I and Y in this case, will occur. In the experiment at hand it should be noted that $P(Y, I)$ means the same thing as $P(I, Y)$. Some other joint probabilities in this experiment are $P(E, Y) = 3/10$, $P(Y, \overline{W}) = 5/10$, $P(Y, W) = 2/10$, $P(I, E, M) = 1/10$, and $P(W, I) = 1/10$. If the two events in a joint probability statement are mutually exclusive, then the joint probability will always equal zero. For example, the probability of getting a winner who is English and a woman is zero since none of the ten are both English and a woman.

Another type of probability that may be encountered could be called a *union probability*. What, for example, is the probability that the winner will be English and/or young? In other words, we are asking for the probability that the winner is English or young or both. According to Figure 2.1, there are eight people who are English and/or young. Thus the probability is

$$P(E \cup Y) = 8/10.$$

The numerator of this probability is found by counting all of the dots within the E and Y sets, being careful to never count a dot twice. Other union probabilities in this experiment are $P(I \cup M) = 8/10$, $P(\overline{I} \cup Y) = 9/10$, $P(W \cup E) = 7/10$, and $P(E \cup Y \cup I) = 9/10$; the reader should verify these probabilities. Notice that if the events being considered are collectively exhaustive, then the union probability is one. For example, M and W are collectively exhaustive events and thus $P(M \cup W) = 1$.

The last type of probability is a *conditional probability*. What is the probability that the winner will be illiterate, given that the winner is a man? If it is known that a man has won, and there are seven men, then the probability that the winner will also be illiterate must be 4/7 since four of the seven men are illiterate. The conditional probability is written as

$$P(I|M) = 4/7$$

where the vertical line separating the I and M is read "given that." Some other conditional probabilities follow. The probability that an English person will win, given that the winner is young, is 3/7, that is, $P(E \mid Y) = 3/7$. Also, $P(W \mid \overline{Y}) = 1/3$, $P(E \mid M) = 4/7$, $P(Y \mid I) = 4/5$, $P(I \mid E) = 1/4$, and $P(E \mid W) = 0/3 = 0$.

Getting back to the Susan Timphany v. Rocky Mountain Fur Company suit, can we see any merit to Susan's charge that the company has been discriminating because a woman has not won the prize in the three years that the company has been supposedly randomly selecting a winner? So far we can only state that the probability of a woman winning in one year is the simple probability $P(W) = 3/10$. How are we to be able to extend this result to three successive years? Presently we do not know how to do this. In the next section some laws of probability will be introduced which will enable Susan to determine the chance of having a male winner in each of three successive years. Before considering these laws of probability, some more attention will be devoted to finding simple, joint, union, and conditional probabilities.

The Internal Revenue Service is ready to select a company for the sake of making a tax audit. Presently there are 50 companies in a given file at the IRS. It is from these 50 companies that a random selection will be made for an audit. Table 2.1 indicates the types of companies found in the file. As you might suspect, it is more common to get information in the form of a table as in Table 2.1 than in the form of an Euler diagram as in Figure 2.1. Based on the random selection of one company from the 50, the following *simple* probabilities may be derived: $P(L) = 14/50$, $P(M) = 24/50$, $P(S) = 12/50$, $P(O) = 30/50$, $P(A) = 2/50$, $P(C) = 14/50$, and $P(R) = 4/50$. Notice that each of these probabilities may be determined by referring only to the margins of the table. This is why they are sometimes called marginal probabilities instead of simple probabilities.

TABLE 2.1_____

IRS File of Fifty Corporations

		Oil (O)	Auto (A)	Computer (C)	Rail (R)	
	Large (L)	8	2	3	1	14
Size of Company	Medium (M)	12	0	9	3	24
	Small (S)	10	0	2	0	12
		30	2	14	4	50

The probability that the IRS will audit a company that is a small oil company (both small and oil) is 10/50 since 10 of the 50 companies are small oil companies. Some other *joint probabilities* are $P(A, M) = 0$, $P(L, R) = 1/50$, $P(\overline{M}, O) = 18/50$, and $P(\overline{R}, S) = 12/50$.

The probability that an oil and/or a large company will be audited is $P(O \cup L) = 36/50$. The "36" is found by adding all the entries in the first row and column. Other *union probabilities* are $P(A \cup C) = 16/50$, $P(R \cup M) = 25/50$, and $P(\overline{S} \cup C) = 40/50$. The "40" in the last probability is found by adding $14 + 24 + 2$ where the last 2 are small computer companies.

Given that a computer company will be audited, the probability that it will be large is $P(L|C) = 3/14$. In other words, of the 14 computer companies, 3 are large. Other *conditional probabilities* are $P(A|L) = 2/14$, $P(R|M) = 3/24$, $P(O|S) = 10/12$, and $P(O|\overline{S}) = 20/38$.

The four types of probabilities which have been identified will now be related one to another by means of several laws of probability. These laws enable us to solve a wide variety of problems which involve probabilities.

2.5

LAWS OF PROBABILITY

Having defined several types of probabilities, it is now time to express relationships between these types of probabilities. These relationships are called laws or rules of probability. By using the laws of probability, a number of problems can be solved with relative ease. Four laws of probability will be presented and illustrated.

Complement Law

A particular airliner has 100 passenger seats and it is nearly full. Before takeoff the stewardess must count the number of passengers on board. Typically, the stewardess will merely count the number of empty seats, say 7, and then report that 93 people are aboard. Such a procedure is much more efficient than individually counting the 93 people. This same principle which the stewardess used may be employed in probability theory. It is called the *complement law of probability.*

If A represents an event and $\overline{A}$ represents the complementary event (recall that $\overline{A}$ means "not A"), then

$$P(A) = 1 - P(\overline{A})$$ COMPLEMENT LAW

Similarly, the complement law may be written as

$$P(\overline{A}) = 1 - P(A)$$

or as

$$P(A) + P(\overline{A}) = 1$$

In the experiment where a coin is to be flipped, let A represent heads and $\overline{A}$ represent tails. Since $P(A) = .5$, it follows that $P(\overline{A}) = 1 - .5$. If the probability that a cereal purchaser will buy Puritan Oats is .4, then the probability is .6 that the cereal purchaser will not buy Puritan Oats. As one more example of the complement law, if there is a probability of .20 that 0 or 1 defective will be found in a batch of printed circuits, then the probability is .80 that there will be more than 1 defective in the batch.

Addition Law

If in an experiment two events are denoted by A and B, then the *addition law* states

$$P(A \cup B) = P(A) + P(B) - P(A, B) \qquad \text{ADDITION LAW}$$

For example, a marketing manager states that there is a 20 percent chance that sales for a new product will be low, a 45 percent chance that sales will be medium, and a 35 percent chance that sales will be high. In view of these subjective probabilities, what is the probability that sales will be low and/or medium? Letting L represent low sales and M represent medium sales, the addition law states

$$P(L \cup M) = P(L) + P(M) - P(L, M)$$

From the marketing manager's statement it is known that $P(L) = .20$ and $P(M) = .45$. But what is $P(L, M)$? This is the joint probability that sales will simultaneously be both low and medium. Since L and M are mutually exclusive, this probability is 0. Therefore,

$$\begin{aligned} P(L \cup M) &= .20 + .45 - 0 \\ &= .65 \end{aligned}$$

Whenever the events A and B are mutually exclusive, their joint probability is 0, and so the addition law reduces to

$$P(A \cup B) = P(A) + P(B)$$ ADDITION LAW FOR
MUTUALLY EXCLUSIVE
EVENTS

Before leaving the marketing manager example, it should be noted that this same problem could have been solved by the complement law. The probability that sales will be low and/or medium is one minus the probability that sales will be high, or $1 - .35$.

For the second example, refer to Figure 2.1. What is the probability of getting a person who is English or young? By the addition law,

$$P(E \cup Y) = P(E) + P(Y) - P(E, Y)$$
$$= 4/10 + 7/10 - 3/10$$
$$= 8/10$$

Notice that three of the people who are both English and young were counted for the sake of determining $P(E)$ and counted again for the sake of determining $P(Y)$; hence, they were double counted and thus are subtracted out once by the joint probability.

As another example, suppose that you are interested in determining what proportion of American adults are investors; that is, own either stocks or bonds or both. So far you have been able to find only the following information: 30 percent of American adults own stocks, 20 percent own bonds, and 10 percent own both stocks and bonds. It would be incorrect to conclude that $30\% + 20\% + 10\%$ or 60% are investors. The reason is that a person who owns both stocks and bonds is counted among those 30 percent who own stock and among the 20 percent who own bonds as well as separately as owning both. The addition law is helpful in finding the desired answer. Let $P(S)$ represent the probability or proportion of American adults who own stocks, $P(B)$ represent the probability that an American adult owns bonds, and $P(S, B)$ the probability that both stocks and bonds are owned. Then,

$$P(\text{Investor}) = P(S \cup B) = P(S) + P(B) - P(S, B)$$
$$= .30 + .20 - .10$$
$$= .40$$

Thus, it may be concluded that 40 percent of American adults are investors.

As a final example, suppose that you have just moved to Phoenix where there are 20 different banks. You have heard that five of the Phoenix banks offer free checking, seven offer a free safety deposit box, and ten of the banks offer free checking and/or a free safety deposit box. What is the probability that the closest bank to your new home offers both free checking and a free safety deposit box? In order to solve this problem, it is necessary to first define symbols. Let C represent the event that a bank has free checking and let B represent the event that a bank offers a free safety deposit box. From the information given above, if a single bank is randomly chosen, then

$$P(C) = 5/20$$
$$P(B) = 7/20$$
$$P(C \cup B) = 10/20$$

Two simple probabilities and a union probability are known. The question asks for the probability that the closest bank will offer both C and B, that is, $P(C, B)$ is desired. By the addition law,

$$P(C \cup B) = P(C) + P(B) - P(C, B)$$

By substitution,

$$10/20 = 5/20 + 7/20 - P(C, B)$$

Solving this yields

$$P(C, B) = 5/20 + 7/20 - 10/20$$
$$= 2/20$$

Multiplication Law

The *multiplication law* links simple, joint, and conditional probabilities. For the events A and B, the law states

$$P(A, B) = P(A) P(B|A) \qquad \text{MULTIPLICATION LAW}$$

Alternative ways of stating this law are

$$P(A, B) = P(B) P(A|B)$$

and, providing that $P(B)$ is not zero,

$$P(A|B) = \frac{P(A, B)}{P(B)}$$

In the section to follow, Section 2.6, a special form of the multiplication law will be given. First, a number of examples of the law in its general form as given above will be presented.

Return again to the Euler diagram of Figure 2.1. What is the probability of getting a person who is both illiterate and young, that is, what is $P(I, Y)$? This probability can be directly read from Figure 2.1; it is 4/10. However, it can also be obtained by the multiplication law

$$P(I, Y) = P(I) P(Y|I)$$
$$= (5/10)(4/5)$$
$$= 4/10$$

Look back now to the IRS example of Table 2.1. What is the probability that an auto company will be audited, given that a large company is to be audited? Again, this conditional probability can be determined by using the multiplication law

$$P(A|L) = \frac{P(A, L)}{P(L)}$$

$$= \frac{2/50}{14/50}$$

$$= 2/14$$

As another example, suppose that you wish to get a job at Pigment Paints. As you currently evaluate your situation, you feel that there is a 70 percent chance that you will get a job at Pigment Paints. While interviewing with Pigment, you learned that 30 percent of those who get a job must make a move within the first five years of employment. Where you currently stand, what is the probability that you will get a job at Pigment Paints and will have to move within five years? To begin, define the appropriate symbols. Let J represent the event of getting a job at Pigment Paints and let M represent the necessity of making a move within five years. The information given implies that $P(J) = .70$ and $P(M|J) = .30$. You now seek the joint probability expressed by $P(J, M)$. By the multiplication law,

$$P(J, M) = P(J) P(M|J)$$
$$= (.70)(.30)$$
$$= .21$$

Thus, there is a probability of .21 that you will get the job and move.

Webster Electronics reports that of all their large customers, 90 percent of them are satisfied, that is, $P(S|L) = .90$. Furthermore, Webster states that 45 percent of their customers are large satisfied customers, $P(S, L) = .45$. From this information, what proportion of Webster's customers are large? By the multiplication law the probability $P(L)$ is sought.

$$P(S, L) = P(L) P(S|L)$$
$$.45 = P(L) \cdot (.90)$$
$$P(L) = .45/.90$$
$$= .50$$

Hence, 50 percent of Webster's customers are large customers.

Timothy Paticlepitcher works at Borror International. Timothy is one member of a team of five workers. Each year it is the policy of Borror to randomly select two workers from each group of five for the sake of giving the two selected workers a free physical examination. Most folks would be delighted to get a free physical examination, but not Timothy. Timothy knows that a complete physical involves blood tests, and he also knows that the blood tests are not done, as said in Latin, *in veino* but rather *ex veino*. Because the usual method of getting the blood from *in veino* to *ex veino* leaves Timothy less than excited, he is interested in determing the probability that he will be passed over this year. Timothy begins by picturing the five workers in his groups as five marbles in a can, four are green and one is yellow. The probability that Timothy escapes is the same as the probability of randomly selecting two green marbles from the can in two successive draws. This probability is also the same as not getting the yellow marble in two draws. In symbols,

$$P(\text{Timothy does not get chosen}) = P\left(\begin{array}{c}\text{Yellow marble does}\\\text{not get chosen}\end{array}\right)$$
$$= P\left(\begin{array}{c}2 \text{ green marbles}\\\text{get chosen}\end{array}\right)$$
$$= P(G_1, G_2)$$

Before proceeding, note that $P(G_1, G_2)$ represents the successive events of getting a green on the first draw and then getting another green on the second draw from the can. This probability is logically similar to someone else getting selected for the first physical and someone else getting selected for the second physical exam.

By the multiplication law,

$$P(G_1, G_2) = P(G_1) P(G_2|G_1)$$

Thinking for the moment only about the can which contains four greens and one yellow, the probability of drawing a green initially is $P(G_1) = 4/5$. The probability of getting a green on the second draw, given that a green was removed on the first draw, is $P(G_2|G_1) = 3/4$. This is because only four marbles are left after the first draw, of which three are green. Therefore,

$$P(G_1, G_2) = (4/5)(3/4)$$
$$= 3/5$$

This means that the probability is .60 that Timothy will not have to endure the rigors of blood extraction this year. Just as Timothy was relaxing, Borror announced a new employee benefit package. Now three instead of two out of every group of five workers will get the free physical. By an extension of the multiplication law, the probability of getting three green marbles in a row is

$$P(G_1, G_2, G_3) = P(G_1)P(G_2|G_1)P(G_3|G_1, G_2)$$
$$= (4/5)(3/4)(2/3)$$
$$= .40$$

Now Timothy has only a .40 chance of escaping.

Elimination Law

The last law of probability to be presented is the *elimination law*. If in an experiment the events $A_1, A_2, A_3, \ldots,$ and A_n are mutually exclusive and collectively exhaustive, and if B is another event, then

$$P(B) = P(A_1)P(B|A_1) + P(A_2)P(B|A_2) + \ldots + P(A_n)P(B|A_n)$$

ELIMINATION LAW

By applying the multiplication law to each term on the right, a second form of the elimination law appears:

$$P(B) = P(A_1, B) + P(A_2, B) + \ldots + P(A_n, B)$$

This law will now be illustrated by two examples.

Refer again to the Rocky Mountain Fur Company example of Figure 2.1. From the Euler diagram it is apparent that the probability that a young person will win the door prize is 7/10. This may be confirmed using the elimination law. The events M and W are mutually exclusive and collectively exhaustive. Thus they are like A_1 and A_2 as defined above. The event "is young" is another event.

It may be likened to B in the original statement of the elimination law. Then,

$$P(B) = P(A_1)P(B|A_1) + P(A_2)P(B|A_2)$$
$$P(Y) = P(M)P(Y|M) + P(W)P(Y|W)$$
$$= (7/10)(5/7) + (3/10)(2/3)$$
$$= 5/10 + 2/10$$
$$= 7/10$$

In essence, the elimination law says that the probability of getting a young person is the probability of getting a young man (5/10) plus the probability of getting a young woman (2/10).

   Brim Lumber of the Pacific Northwest has three plywood plants located in Eugene, Seattle, and Boise. One percent of the plywood sheets from the Eugene plant are defective, 4 percent of the output from the Seattle plant is defective, and 3 percent of the sheets of plywood from Boise are defective. Furthermore, the Eugene plant produces 60 percent of the total output of Brim Lumber, the Seattle plant produces 30 percent of the total, and Boise produces 10 percent of the plywood that bears the Brim trademark. If a builder purchases one sheet of Brim plywood from a local lumber yard in Atlanta, what is the probability that the sheet will be defective?

   The events "came from Eugene," "came from Seattle," and "came from Boise" are mutually exclusive and collectively exhaustive. That is, a given sheet could have originated from only one of these plants, and a given sheet could not have come from anywhere else since there are no other Brim plywood plants. Since these three events are mutually exclusive and collectively exhaustive, they may be represented by A_1, A_2, and A_3, respectively. Now let the event "is defective" be represented by D. The elimination law says

$$P(D) = P(A_1)P(D|A_1) + P(A_2)P(D|A_2) + P(A_3)P(D|A_3)$$

From the information supplied in the previous paragraph, the probability that a sheet comes from Eugene is $P(A_1) = .60$, since Eugene produces 60 percent of the total output. The probability that the sheet is defective given that it came from Eugene is $P(D|A_1) = .01$, since it was stated that 1 percent of the sheets from Eugene are defective. Following this approach,

$$P(D) = (.60)(.01) + (.30)(.04) + (.10)(.03)$$
$$= .021$$

This means that there is a probability of .021 that a piece of Brim plywood, whose plant origin is unknown, is defective.

2.6

STATISTICAL INDEPENDENCE

Consider an experiment where a coin is to be flipped and a die is to be rolled. Knowing what happens with the coin gives no clue as to what event occurs with the die. If heads occurs with the coin, this tells us nothing about what side turned up with the die, and vice versa. Letting H represent heads on the coin and E represent an even number of spots on the die, it is said that the events H and E are *statistically independent* since the occurrence of either gives absolutely no information as to the occurrence of the other. Mathematically, it could be said that the probability of heads is $P(H) = .5$, and that the probability of heads is still .5 even if it is given that the die turned up with an even number of spots, that is, $P(H|E) = .5$. The occurrence of E in no way changes the probability of H; therefore, H and E are statistically independent.

Now let U represent the event "the stock market is up today" and C represent the event "it's a cool day in Manila." Are U and C statistically independent? If someone indicated that C had occurred, does this give even a miniscule amount of information as to whether U occurred? No! C and U are totally unrelated and hence would be independent.

I am sitting at the entrance of the Chief Yellow Horse trading post on Interstate 40 near Gallup, New Mexico. In so doing I am engaged in an experiment which consists of merely noticing the next person to walk into the trading post, where noticing consists in identifying the sex and the eye color of the entering person. Let F refer to the event "is female" and B refer to the event "has blue eyes." Are F and B statistically independent? F and B are statistically independent because blue eyes are no more nor less common among females than among males. A person just now enters the trading post and I tell you that the person has blue eyes. This does not at all help you in determining the probability that the person is female. This means that F and B are statistically independent. This may be expressed with probabilities as follows. Assume that the probability that the next person entering will be female is $P(F) = .5$. The probability that the next person will be female given that the person has blue eyes is $P(F|B) = .5$. Since $P(F) = P(F|B)$, we may conclude that eye color is unrelated or independent of a person's sex.

Now assume that I am sitting at the doorway of the Steuben Glass Center in midtown New York. Again I will notice the next person to pass through the door except that this time I am interested in the event "is a female" and in the event "weighs over 220 pounds;" these two events are represented by F and W. What is the probability that the next person passing through the door will be a female? Let us again assume that it is $P(F) = .5$. But what if I tell you that the person passing through weighs over 220 pounds. What is the probability now that this person is a female? You would probably reason that since very few females weigh over 220 pounds and that since quite a few males do weigh over 220 pounds, the person who just passed through the door is more likely to be a male, or is less likely to be a female. You might now say $P(F|W) = .02$. Knowing the weight of a person does give us information, though not perfect information, as to their sex. It is therefore said that F and W are not statistically independent; they are statistically dependent.

There are many pairs of events which are statistically dependent. The events "is a heavy smoker" and "has contracted lung cancer," the events "very profitable company" and "strong performance in the stock market," and the events "large advertising expenditures" and "high toothpaste sales," are three pairs of events which in each case are typically dependent events.

Instead of having to rely on intuition in order to determine if two events are statistically independent, a mathematical definition of statistical independence is useful. In particular, two events are *statistically independent* if

$$P(A|B) = P(A)$$

where A and B are the two events being considered. Refer now to Figure 2.1 as we ask whether being illiterate is independent of whether a person is a woman. Among the ten people gathered at the rendezvous, the probability of being a woman is $P(W) = 3/10$ and the probability of being a woman given the person is illiterate is $P(W|I) = 1/5$. Since these two probabilities are not equal, it may be concluded that in this assembly of ten people, W and I are not statistically independent. The same thing could have been proved by comparing $P(I|W)$ and $P(I)$.

Having defined what is meant by statistical independence, it is now useful to see if this concept has any implications for the multiplication law of probability. The multiplication law states that for any two events A and B,

$$P(A, B) = P(A) P(B|A)$$

If A and B were statistically independent, then $P(B|A) = P(B)$. When $P(B)$ is substituted for $P(B|A)$ in the multiplication law, it results in

$$P(A, B) = P(A) P(B) \qquad \text{MULTIPLICATION LAW FOR INDEPENDENT EVENTS}$$

A more general expression of this multiplication law for statistically independent events is

$$P(A, B, C, \ldots) = P(A) P(B) P(C) \ldots$$

Consider some illustrations of this law now.

A coin is to be flipped three times in succession. What is the probability of getting three tails in a row? First it is noticed that what happens on one flip of a coin is totally unrelated to what happens on another flip: the outcomes are independent from flip to flip. Therefore, by the multiplication law for independent events,

$$\begin{aligned}
P(T_1, T_2, T_3) &= P(T) P(T) P(T) \\
&= (.5)(.5)(.5) \\
&= .125
\end{aligned}$$

It is known that 20 percent of the households in Detroit are watching the new television series entitled "The Adventures of Gunga Din." If four households are randomly called by phone, what is the probability that none of them will be watching Gunga? Notice first that what one family is watching does not influence what another family is watching at some other home: the responses from phone call to phone call are independent. Therefore, according to the multiplication law

$$\begin{aligned}
P(\text{None of the 4 watching}) &= P(\overline{W}_1, \overline{W}_2, \overline{W}_3, \overline{W}_4) \\
&= P(\overline{W}) P(\overline{W}) P(\overline{W}) P(\overline{W}) \\
&= (.8)(.8)(.8)(.8) \\
&= .4096
\end{aligned}$$

In the market for canned asparagus there are three competitors, Del Monkey, Wibbie, and Blue Dwarf, which capture 50 percent, 30 percent, and 20 percent of the market, respectively. Considering the next three cans of asparagus to be purchased, what is the probability that their brands are Del Monkey, Wibbie, and Del Monkey in that order? By the multiplication law for independent events,

$$\begin{aligned}
P(D_1, W_2, D_3) &= P(D) P(W) P(D) \\
&= (.5)(.3)(.5) \\
&= .075
\end{aligned}$$

Next, what is the probability that out of the next three cans sold, two of them will be Wibbie and one will be Blue Dwarf? In order to solve this it is important to see that there are several ways or

orders in which two Wibbies and one Blue Dwarf may be purchased. Specifically, there are three distinct ways:

$$(W, W, B) \qquad (W, B, W) \qquad (B, W, W)$$

Thus, the probability of selling two Wibbies and one Blue Dwarf is

$$P[(W, W, B) \cup (W, B, W) \cup (B, W, W)]$$

By the addition law for mutually exclusive events this is equal to

$$P(W, W, B) + P(W, B, W) + P(B, W, W)$$

Each of these terms may be broken down by the multiplication
law:

$$\begin{aligned}
P(W, W, B) + P(W, B, W) + P(B, W, W) &= P(W)P(W)P(B) \\
&+ P(W)P(B)P(W) \\
&+ P(B)P(W)P(W) \\
&= (.3)(.3)(.2) \\
&+ (.3)(.2)(.3) \\
&+ (.2)(.3)(.3) \\
&= .054
\end{aligned}$$

According to this procedure, there is a probability of .054 of selling
two Wibbies and one Blue Dwarf.

As a final example we return to the Susan Timphany v. Rocky
Mountain Fur Company suit. Susan, as you recall, claims that the
fact that men have won the door prize for the past three years
indicates that the company is fixing the selection to insure that a
woman does not get the prize. The company claims that it was by
pure chance that three men have won. It was at this time that the
judge asked the court statistician, Doncella Fudd, to enter. Given
that the composition of persons at each rendezvous was essentially that of Figure 2.1, Fudd determined what the probability is
that a woman would not win in three years if the company was
using a purely random selection procedure. From Figure 2.1 it is
apparent that at any rendezvous there were seven men and three
women. The probability that a woman would never win in three
years is given by $P(\overline{W}, \overline{W}, \overline{W})$. This probability may be found by the
multiplication law for independent events:

$$\begin{aligned}
P(\overline{W}, \overline{W}, \overline{W}) &= P(\overline{W}) P(\overline{W}) P(\overline{W}) \\
&= (.7)(.7)(.7) \\
&= .343
\end{aligned}$$

Upon being advised of this probability, the judge concluded that the evidence against the company was not great enough to prove that the company had fixed the selection of winners for the past three years. In other words, the company is considered innocent until proven guilty, and the awarding of three prizes to men is not that unusual under purely chance conditions. Thus, the court is not justified in ruling that the company is guilty.

2.7

PROBABILITY TREES

ORW Copper of the Netherlands has a big smelting plant down in Amazonia, a somewhat volatile South American country. The plant is in need of modernization, and so ORW must come to a decision as to whether or not to go ahead with the expenditures necessary to modernize. If Amazonia would not nationalize the copper industry and if the same tax structure prevailed, ORW would not hesitate to go ahead with the modernization. However, the crumbling of the current government, nationalizations, new taxes, and the like loom large on the horizon. Based on the opinions of ORW's political consultants, ORW has constructed a *probability tree* which depicts the events which may successively occur. Figure 2.2 presents this probability tree, which is a sequence of connected forks and branches depicting a multistage probabilistic situation or experiment. The branches are typically arranged in chronological fashion.

In the tree of Figure 2.2 there are three tiers of branches, indicating three successive types of events which may occur with the passage of time. This tree indicates that ORW believes there is a 30 percent chance that there will be a coup d'etat in Amazonia. If the coup does materialize, thus ousting the current government, there is a .90 probability that the new government will nationalize the copper industry. If nationalized, there is only a 20 percent chance that Amazonia will make reparations for its seizure of the smelting plant. Other sequences of events are also evident from this probability tree, such as C–$\overline{N}$–T, C–N–$\overline{R}$, and so on. The probability that any specified succession of three events will take place may be determined by means of the multiplication law. Notice that the events associated with ORW's predicament are typically dependent. For example, the probability of nationalization given that there is a coup is $P(N|C) = .9$, whereas the probability of nationalization given that there is no coup is $P(N|\overline{C}) = .2$. This means that the multiplication law in its original general form as

FIGURE 2.2
Probability Tree for ORW Copper

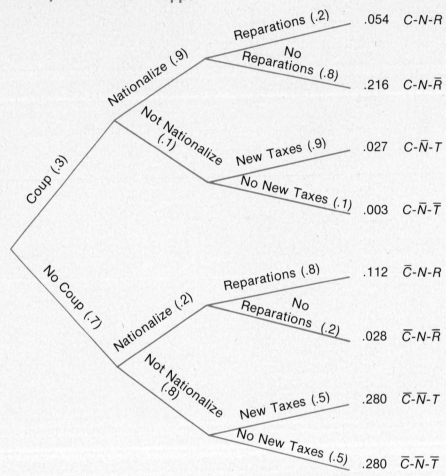

given in Section 2.5 is to be used. To find the probability of the
C–N–R succession, the law states

$$P(C, N, R) = P(C)\,P(N|C)\,P(R|C, N)$$
$$= (.3)(.9)(.2)$$
$$= .054$$

In general, the probability of any succession of three events
that are listed in the probability tree may be found by merely multiplying the probabilities attached to each of the branches which
form the path from the left to the right. This is an application of
the multiplication law. Therefore, $P(C, \overline{N}, T) = (.3)(.1)(.9) = .027$

and $P(\overline{C}, N, \overline{R}) = (.7)(.2)(.2) = .028$. The probabilities of the eight paths have been placed at the ends of these paths in Figure 2.2. These eight probabilities must add to unity since the paths are mutually exclusive and collectively exhaustive. Such will be the case in every probability tree that is constructed properly.

Based on the probability tree, what is the probability that ORW's smelting plant will end up being nationalized? This sort of question can be answered quite easily. Nationalization occurs if any of the following four paths take place: C–N–R, C–N–$\overline{R}$, $\overline{C}$–N–R, $\overline{C}$–N–$\overline{R}$. The probabilities of these four mutually exclusive paths are .054, .216, .112, and .028. Adding these four probabilities yields .41, which is the probability of being nationalized.

PROBLEMS

2.1

(a) Describe each of the three interpretations of probability.
(b) Which of the interpretations of probability are inappropriate for expressing the likelihood of each of the following events:
   (i) Heads on the flip of a coin
   (ii) Inflation rate below 7 percent next year
   (iii) A blemished tire coming off the assembly line
   (iv) Rainfall in Dallas will exceed 25 inches next year
   (v) Coal will supply 50 percent or more of the United States' energy needs by 2000 A.D.

2.2

An urn contains seven blue marbles, three green marbles, and ten red marbles. What is the probability of getting a blue marble according to the classical interpretation of probability? according to the relative frequency interpretation? What is your subjective probability of getting a blue marble on a random draw of one marble?

2.3

Define the following terms:
(a) experiment
(b) sample space
(c) event
(d) collectively exhaustive events
(e) mutually exclusive events

2.4

You are going to shoot an arrow at a bull's-eye target. Is this an experiment? If so, what is the sample space?

2.5

A free ferry in North Carolina has a capacity of 8 vehicles. An experiment consists of observing how many vehicles are being carried by the next ferry to arrive.
(a) List the sample space.
(b) List three events which are collectively exhaustive and mutually exclusive.
(c) List three events which are collectively exhaustive but not mutually exclusive.
(d) List three events which are mutually exclusive but not exhaustive.

2.6

A pair of dice are simultaneously rolled. List the sample space.

2.7

A die is to be rolled and then a coin flipped. Show all of the outcomes in the sample space of this experiment.

2.8

An urn contains seven blue marbles, three green marbles, and ten red marbles.
(a) If an experiment consists of randomly drawing one marble from the urn, list the sample space.
(b) If an experiment consists of randomly drawing two marbles from the urn, list the sample space.

2.9

If the sample space in a given experiment is

$$S = \{1, 2, 3, 4, 5, 6, 7, 8\}$$

and the following events are defined:

$$E = \{2, 4, 6, 8\} \qquad D = \{1, 3, 5, 7\} \qquad L = \{6, 7, 8\}$$
$$K = \{1, 2, 7, 8\} \qquad M = \{2, 3, 4, 5, 6\}$$

state whether the following events are mutually exclusive, collectively exhaustive, both mutually exclusive and exhaustive, or neither.

(a) E, D (e) K, L, D
(b) E, M (f) L, D
(c) D, L (g) K, D
(d) K, M (h) L, K, E, D

2.10

A person is to be randomly chosen from a large group of people. Are the following events mutually exclusive? collectively exhaustive?
(a) blue eyes, brown hair
(b) male, female
(c) over 100 pounds, male
(d) college graduate, senior citizen
(e) has red blood, always smiling
(f) owns bonds, owns stocks
(g) buys Texaco gas, buys any other brand of gasoline

2.11

A sample space is given by $S = \{6, 7, 8, 9\}$ and several events are defined as $L = \{8, 9\}, E = \{6, 8\}, M = \{6, 7, 8\},$ and $A = \{6, 7\}$. Are the probabilities in each of the parts given below possible or impossible?
(a) $P(L) = .5, P(E) = .5, P(M) = .75,$ and $P(A) = .5$
(b) $P(L) = .7, P(E) = .7, P(M) = .9,$ and $P(A) = .3$
(c) $P(L) = .4, P(E) = .6, P(M) = .5,$ and $P(A) = .3$

2.12

One object is to be selected randomly from a population described by the following Euler diagram. Find each of the probabilities on the following page. Also, identify each as being either a simple, union, joint, or conditional probability.

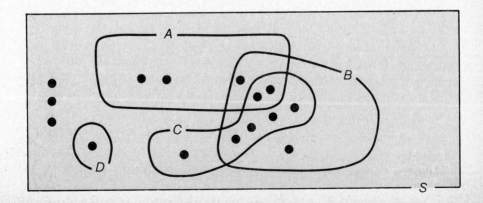

(a) $P(A)$

(b) $P(B, C)$

(c) $P(D, A)$

(d) $P(\overline{D})$

(e) $P(C \cup D)$

(f) $P(C \cup B)$

(g) $P(A, B, C)$

(h) $P(\overline{B})$

(i) $P(S)$

(j) $P(C|A)$

(k) $P(D|B)$

(l) $P(B|\overline{C})$

(m) $P(\overline{A} \cup C)$

(n) $P(\overline{D}, \overline{A})$

(o) $P(\overline{A}|C)$

2.13

Service stations have been classified as follows:

		Brand			
		Elco (E)	Gant (G)	Alonzo Oil (A)	Others (O)
	Small (S)	3	5	13	10
Size	Medium (M)	5	8	5	24
	Large (L)	2	7	12	6

Find each of the following probabilities if one station is to be randomly selected. Also, identify each probability as being either a simple, joint, union, or conditional probability.

(a) $P(G)$

(b) $P(E)$

(c) $P(L)$

(d) $P(S, A)$

(e) $P(M, E)$

(f) $P(G \cup E)$

(g) $P(G \cup L)$

(h) $P(A|S)$

(i) $P(M|E)$

(j) $P(E, A)$

(k) $P(G|E)$

2.14

If a letter is randomly selected from the alphabet, what is the probability that it is a vowel? What is the probability that it is a vowel if it is given that it is one of the first 10 letters in the alphabet?

2.15

The 200 workers in a community have been classified as below.

	Employed (E)	Unemployed ($\overline{E}$)
Skilled (S)	80	5
Unskilled ($\overline{S}$)	100	15

If one worker is randomly chosen, find the probabilities below.

(a) $P(E)$
(b) $P(\overline{S})$
(c) $P(S \cup E)$
(d) $P(E|S)$
(e) $P(E|\overline{S})$
(f) $P(E, S)$
(g) Does the fact that a worker is skilled have anything to do with whether that worker is employed?

2.16

An analyst studying voting patterns among mine workers has found the following results in a recent mine contract election. 5,000 of the 20,000 Appalacian miners voted yes, 3,000 of the 5,000 Midwestern miners voted yes, 7,000 of the 10,000 Southern miners voted yes, and 4,000 of the 5,000 Western miners voted yes. What is the probability that a miner voted no if the miner were from the Midwest? If a miner voted yes, what is the probability that the miner came from the South?

2.17

The probability that a store will sell 10 or more cans of paint next week is .8. What is the probability that nine or fewer cans will be sold? What law of probability is used to answer this question?

2.18

Sixty percent of the residents of Miami like oranges. Forty percent of the residents like lemons. Fifteen percent like both oranges and lemons. What proportion of Miami's residents like oranges and/or lemons? What law of probability is used to solve this problem?

2.19

If $P(C, D) = .2, P(D) = .5$, and $P(C \cup D) = .7$, find $P(C)$.

2.20

Webster Plastics sells to various companies. Eighty percent of Webster's sales are to toy companies and/or domestic companies. Thirty percent of Webster's sales are to toy companies. Thirty-five percent of sales are to foreign companies. What proportion of sales are to domestic toy companies?

2.21

Of the 500 televisions shipped by rail, 80 were superficially damaged only, 5 had major damages only, 15 had both superficial and major damages, and the rest were not damaged in any way.
(a) What is the probability that a television set will not be damaged?
(b) What is the probability that a set will sustain major damage?
(c) What is the probability that a set will sustain major and/or superficial damage?

2.22

The following is a portion of a mortality table.

Age	Deaths per 1000 persons during that year
30	12.0
31	13.2
32	14.5

Person X is 30 years old and person Y is 32 years old.
(a) What is the probability that X will die within the year?
(b) What is the probability that both X and Y will die within the year?
(c) What is the probability that both will survive the year?

2.23

If $P(M) = .30$, and $P(M, T) = .20$, find $P(T|M)$.

2.24

If $P(S|R) = .30$, $P(R) = .80$, and $P(S) = .60$, find $P(R|S)$.

2.25

The probability that Merck will develop a new antibiotic is .80. The probability that the FDA will approve the drug is .90. What is the probability that Merck will develop a new antibiotic which is approved?

2.26

Sixty percent of the packages handled by the post office get dropped. If three packages are sent through the mail, what is the probability that
(a) all three will get dropped?
(b) none of them will get dropped?

2.27

You are taking a true-false quiz on a subject of which you are totally ignorant. If there are four questions on the quiz, what is the probability that you will get all four right? What is the probability that you would miss at least one question?

2.28

Scott Federal Savings and Loan has found that 40 percent of high income mortgagees move within five years. If 10 percent of Scott Federal's mortgagees are in the high income bracket, what proportion of Scott Federal's mortgagees are high income and will move within five years?

2.29

What proportion of the banks in America are large if the following information is known? 30 percent of America's banks have loaned money to New York City and are large. Of all the large banks in America, 40 percent have loaned to New York City.

2.30

The probability of rain today is .40, the probability of rain tomorrow is .50, and the probability of rain the day after tomorrow is .30. Assuming that the weather from day to day is independent, what is the probability that it will rain at least once in the three days?

2.31

Delgado, Inc., ships batteries in packs of six. If it is known that two of the batteries in a six-pack will be dead, what is the probability that if you select two batteries in succession both will be good? What is the probability that the first will be dead and the second will be good?

2.32

A Florida amusement park has found that 30 percent of its visitors are out-of-state students. Also, 50 percent of its visitors are from outside the state. What is the probability that a visitor is a student, given that the visitor is from outside the state?

2.33

The probability of getting the flu, given that you have been vaccinated, is .10. The probability of getting the flu if you have not been vaccinated is .30. Forty percent of the population has been vaccinated. What is the probability that a randomly chosen person will get the flu? If there are 100,000 persons in the population, how many will not get the flu?

2.34

Fail-Safe Insurance has found that the probability that a person is a good driver, given that the person has received a speeding ticket, is .30. The probability that a person is a good driver, given that the person has never had a speeding ticket, is .80. If 40 percent of the drivers have had a speeding ticket, what is the probability that a randomly selected driver is a good driver?

2.35

Carson Instruments states that there is a .30 probability that future sales of a particular kind of calculator will be low, a .50 probability that sales will be medium, and a .20 probability that sales will be high. Low selling products show poor test market performance about 95 percent of the time, medium selling products show poor test market performance about 45 percent of the time, and high selling products do poorly in test markets about 15 percent of the time. Carson instruments goes ahead and test-markets the new kind of calculator. What is the probability that it will do poorly in the test market?

2.36

The probability that an all-weather cruise missile will miss its target if the weather is bad is .20. The probability of missing the target when the weather is good is .05. The forecast for tomorrow states that there is a 70 percent chance of bad weather and a 30 percent chance of good weather. What is the probability that the cruise missile which will be launched tomorrow will miss the target? will hit the target? If two cruise missiles are independently launched tomorrow, what is the probability that both will miss the target?

2.37

Which of the following pairs of events would typically be statistically independent?

(a) brown eyes, male
(b) heads on a quarter, tails on a penny
(c) hot in Phoenix, hot in Tucson
(d) high toothpaste sales, high advertising expenditures
(e) high family income, own three cars
(f) incorporated in Delaware, very profitable company

2.38

In Problem 2.12, are A and C independent events? Prove it.

2.39

In Problem 2.13, are Gant and Large Station independent events? Prove it.

2.40

Are W and V independent events? Prove it.

		The first credit card a person obtained	
		Master Charge (M)	BankAmericard (V)
Region	West (W)	20%	15%
	East (E)	40%	25%

2.41

A car dealer has found that 30 percent of the cars sold are full-sized, 50 percent are intermediates, and 20 percent are compacts. What is the probability that for the next three cars sold,

(a) the first will be an intermediate; the second, an intermediate; and the third, a compact?
(b) none will be intermediates?

2.42

An electrical switch manufactured by Arnold Electric is composed of component A and component K. The probability that A is defective is .02 and the probability that K is defective is .05. The condition of one component is statistically independent of the condition of the other. What is the probability that

(a) both the components in a single switch will be defective?
(b) A will be defective and K will not be defective?
(c) neither will be defective?

2.43

After a radar unit has been manufactured, it must undergo three independent tests: shock test, accuracy test, and low-temperature test. The probabilities that a newly manufactured radar unit will pass each of these tests are .9, .95, and .8, respectively. What is the probability that a radar unit will
(a) pass all three tests?
(b) fail the shock test and pass the remaining tests?
(c) pass exactly one test (and hence fail the other two)?

2.44

A power plant for Arizona Public Service is constructed in three successive stages. The time it takes to complete one stage is independent of the time it takes to complete any other stage. The probabilities of completing the first, second, and third stages on time are .7, .5, and .9, respectively. What is the probability that the power plant will be completed on time?

2.45

The auditing firm of Broda & Brooda has found that of the accounting graduates that are offered a job, only 30 percent accept. The firm has three new positions it must fill. However, it makes four job offers to qualified accounting graduates. What is the probability that Broda & Brooda will be stuck with too many new auditors?

2.46

The dairy industry claims that consumers can tell the difference between butter and a top quality margarine. A blind-folded consumer is tested four times to see if she can distinguish between the butter and margarine. In each of these tests she made a correct identification. What is the probability that a person with seared taste buds could make four correct identifications by just guessing?

2.47

Consider the probability tree on page 49. Find the following probabilities:
(a) $P(A, B, E_2)$
(b) $P(\overline{A}, \overline{B}, C)$
(c) $P(B)$
(d) $P(\overline{C})$
(e) $P(B|A)$
(f) $P(E_1|A, B)$

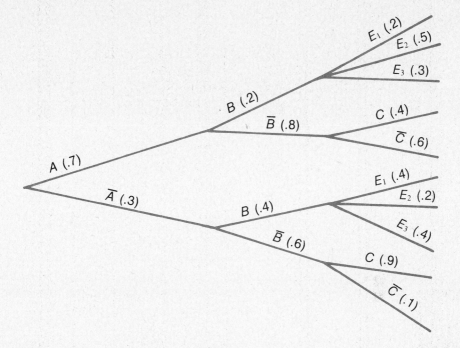

2.48

You are offered the following game. You first randomly draw one marble from a can which contains seven reds and three blues. If you get a red, then you randomly choose a marble out of a bag which contains four yellows and six greens. If you got a blue out of the can, then instead you randomly choose a marble out of a box which contains eight yellows and two greens. If you end up this process with a yellow marble, you will win $20; if you end up with a green marble, you get nothing. Draw a probability tree for this game and determine the probability that you would win the $20. Would you prefer playing the game or getting $10?

2.49

In the next election there is a .60 probability that a Democrat will win and a .40 chance that a Republican will win. If a Democrat wins, there is a 50 percent chance that a strong environmentalist will be appointed as Secretary of the Interior. If a Republican wins, there is a 20 percent chance of getting a strong environmentalist as Secretary. The chance that a new dam will be constructed in Colorado is .10 if a strong environmentalist is appointed as Secretary and .70 if the Secretary is not a strong environmentalist. Draw a probability tree and use it to determine the probability of the dam being built in Colorado.

2.50

Coffee beans grown in Massachusetts can be purchased only on the first day of June, July, and August. The probability that the price of the beans will be exorbitant is .3 and the probability that the price will be high is .7 on any of these three days. As a buyer for Chock-Full-of-Gas coffee, you have decided upon the following purchasing strategy. Buy in June only if the price is high. Buy in July only if you have not previously purchased and the price is high. Buy in August no matter what the price if a purchase has not been previously made. Use a probability tree to model this situation and then determine the probability that you will manage to buy the beans at a high price.

2.51

An oil pipeline is to be constructed by Elco Oil. There are three successive stages to the construction. The probability of the first stage being completed at or below the projected cost is .80. The probability of the second stage being completed at or below projected costs is .90 if the first stage is completed at or below costs, but is .70 if the first stage went over projected costs. The probability that the third stage is completed at or below costs is .60 if the second is completed at or below costs, but is .50 if the second stage goes over projected costs. Use a probability tree to model this situation. Determine the probability that all three stages will be completed at or below projected costs. Also, determine the probability that the first stage will run over projected costs and the remaining two stages will be completed at or below projected costs.

CHAPTER 3

PROBABILITY DISTRIBUTIONS

3.1

RANDOM VARIABLES

In Section 2.3 of the last chapter, the idea of a probabilistic experiment was introduced. In such an experiment any one of a number of different outcomes may occur, and the outcome or event which occurs is determined by chance. Furthermore, the set or collection of all the outcomes for an experiment is called the sample space. With this background, consider another experiment where a mutual fund holds four different stocks: Central National Bank, General Telephone, Vermont Electric & Power, and Farmers Bank. The mutual fund has decided to randomly select one of these four stocks from its portfolio for the purpose of liquidating its holdings in the stock. In this experiment the sample space consists of the four stocks held in the fund's portfolio,

$$S = \{C, G, V, F\}$$

Now suppose that the mutual fund performs the experiment and V or Vermont Electric is chosen. What is the significance of this selection? The intent of the selection was to chose a stock to liquidate. There are many things that can be said about Vermont Electric stock. For example, its yield is 8.3 percent; it pays an annual dividend of $1.24; its current market price is $15; and so on. What is of primary interest here is the stock's current market price, since the fund is about to liquidate its holdings of Vermont Electric stock. In other words, of all the quantitative characteristics of the selected stock, the mutual fund at this time is only interested in its market price. Since price is a quantitative characteristic, let us define it by means of a variable. In particular, let X equal the current price of the stock selected in the aforementioned experiment. Notice that the value of X, when the Vermont Electric stock has been selected, is \$15. However, in this experiment another stock could just as well have been selected. Therefore, X could take on any of four different values since there are four different stocks in the portfolio.

It is important at this point to note two things: First, X is a *variable* since the value that it may take on varies according to the stock that is selected. Second, it is a *random variable* because the value it takes on depends upon chance; that is, it depends upon the random selection of a stock from among the four in the portfolio. Below are listed the outcomes in the sample space and also the corresponding values of the random variable X.

$$\{ \underset{\downarrow}{C} \quad \underset{\downarrow}{G} \quad \underset{\downarrow}{V} \quad \underset{\downarrow}{F} \}$$
$$X = \quad \$43 \quad \$68 \quad \$15 \quad \$19$$

This listing clearly displays that a different value of the random variable X corresponds to each of the different outcomes in the sample space. Once the value of the random variable for each outcome in the sample space has been given, the random variable is appropriately described.

Lest the idea of a random variable still seem unclear, consider another example. Two dice are to be rolled. In this experiment let the random variable T represent the sum of the spots on the up sides of the two dice. Notice that T will take on a different value depending on what happens with the dice. If the first die turns up 3 spots and the second die turns up 4 spots, then T takes on the value of $3 + 4$, or 7. If the first turns up a 6 and the second a 5, then $T = 11$. In this experiment the possible values for the random variable T are $2, 3, 4, 5, \ldots, 11$, and 12.

Consider yet another experiment. We are now at the entrance to a Kampgrounds of Kanada campground in the middle of Saskatchewan. The experiment is to observe the occupants of the next vehicle entering the campground. Let us define the random variable N, where N equals the number of human beings in the entering vehicle. In this experiment it should be clear that the possible values for the variable N are $1, 2, 3, 4, 5, 6$, and so on. N is a random variable because its value will be determined by chance.

A distinction must be made between two different types of random variables. The variables X, T, and N above are called *discrete random variables* since the values they may take on can be specifically listed. X, which represents the price of a stock traded on the New York Stock Exchange, can theoretically take on any of the following prices: $0, $1/8, $1/4, . . . , $15, $15 1/8, $15 1/4, ... A specific list of all the possible prices can be made. T as defined above can take on values of 2, 3, 4, . . . , and 12; hence the list of possible T values is quite small. N can take on values of 1, 2, 3, 4, 5, ... But how about the variable W which represents the true weight of the next person to step on the plane? Can a list of specific possible values for W be made? The person could weigh 135.5768994 pounds or 142.8867685 pounds and so forth. There are an infinite number of possibilities for W between the weights of 135 and 136 pounds. It is impossible to generate a list of all these possibilities for W. In contradistinction to a discrete random variable, W is a *continuous random variable* because it can take on any value along a continuum. Other continuous variables, for example, are G, which is the amount of oil pumped from a particular well in 24 hours, and S, which is the exact speed at takeoff of the next flight. Both these variables can take on any value along a continuum. Such is not the case with the discrete variables such as X, T, and N. For instance, X cannot take on a price like $15.36249 since prices on the New York Stock Exchange are quoted in eighths like $15, $15 1/8, $15 1/4, or $15 3/8. Neither can T assume a value like 7.54, nor N take on a value like 1.3 persons.

3.2

DISCRETE PROBABILITY DISTRIBUTIONS

It has been shown that with a random variable there is a number which may be associated with each outcome in the sample space of an experiment. For instance, if an experiment consists in flipping a coin twice, then the sample space is

$$S = \{(T, T), (T, H), (H, T), (H, H)\}$$

Now let the random variable X be defined such that X equals the number of heads achieved in the foregoing experiment. If (T, T) occurs, then $X = 0$. If (T, H) occurs, then $X = 1$. If (H, T) occurs, then $X = 1$ also. Finally, if (H, H) occurs, then $X = 2$. Next we might ask for the probability that (T, T) will occur. By the multiplication law for independent events,

$$
\begin{aligned}
P(T, T) &= P(T) P(T) \\
&= (.5)(.5) \\
&= .25
\end{aligned}
$$

Now the following conclusion can be drawn. The probabilty that X will take on the value 0 in this experiment is .25. This is because X equals 0 only when (T, T) occurs, and the probability of (T, T) is .25. Following this kind of reasoning, what is the probability that X will take on the value of 1 in this experiment? The answer is $P(X = 1) = .50$, since $X = 1$ occurs when (T, H) or (H, T) occur, and there is a probability of .25 for each of these outcomes. Therefore,

$$P(X = 1) = P(T, H) + P(H, T)$$
$$= .25 + .25$$
$$= .50$$

Finally, the probability of X equaling 2 is $P(X = 2) = .25$.

Table 3.1 shows the four outcomes in the sample space, the probability of each outcome, and the value of X for each outcome. Then all the probabilities associated with a given value of X are combined (added) and displayed in Table 3.2. This display in Table 3.2 is called the *probability distribution* of the random variable X, or simply the distribution of X. A probability distribution of a discrete random variable is a list of all the possible values of the random variable, along with the respective probabilities of each value.

TABLE 3.1
Experiment Where A Coin Is Flipped Twice

Outcomes	Probability	X
(T, T)	.25	0
(T, H)	.25	1
(H, T)	.25	1
(H, H)	.25	2

TABLE 3.2
Probability Distribution of X

X	P(X)
0	.25
1	.50
2	.25
	1.00

Figure 3.1 pictorially displays the probability distribution of X. In this graph of the distribution, the values of the random variable are placed along the horizontal axis and the probabilities are

placed along the vertical axis. The height of the block above each value of the random variable indicates the corresponding probability.

FIGURE 3.1_____
Graph of the Distribution of X

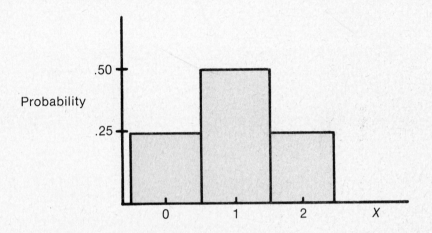

As another example of a probability distribution, assume that we wish to count the number of half-gallon containers of ice cream that are sold at the corner QQQ Market. Let Y equal the number of cartons sold in a day. After observing the purchase of ice cream on 20 different days, we summarize our findings by the following relative frequencies. Zero cartons were sold on one day, hence the relative frequency is 1/20. One carton was sold on 3 of the 20 days, hence the relative frequency for $Y = 1$ is 3/20. Two cartons, $Y = 2$, were sold on 5 of the 20 days, et cetera. The original frequencies and relative frequencies based on the 20 days are given in Table 3.3. By letting the relative frequencies be probabilities, a probability distribution for Y evolves. This distribution of Y is also given in Table 3.3. Figure 3.2 presents the graph of the distribution of Y.

In concluding this section on discrete probability distributions, several characteristics of a probability distribution should be noted. First, each of the probabilities which correspond to the varying values of the random variable is a number which cannot be less than 0 or greater than 1. Second, the probabilities in a distribution, when summed, equal 1. Other characteristics of a probability distribution relating to its shape when graphed will be discussed in later sections of this chapter.

TABLE 3.3
Ice Cream Sales Observations and Probability Distribution

Number of Cartons Sold in a Day, Y	Frequency	Relative Frequency	Probability Distribution Y	P(Y)
0	1	1/20	0	.05
1	3	3/20	1	.15
2	5	5/20	2	.25
3	6	6/20	3	.30
4	3	3/20	4	.15
5	2	2/20	5	.10
	20 days			1.00

FIGURE 3.2
Graph of the Distribution of Y

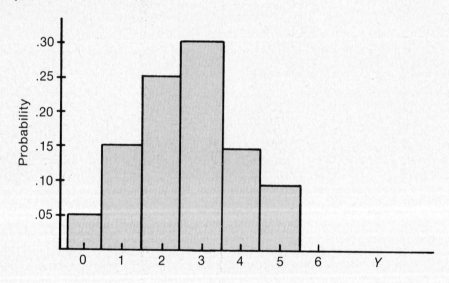

3.3
CUMULATIVE DISTRIBUTIONS

Probability distributions may be displayed in an alternate fashion. Instead of listing the probability that the random variable will take on each specific value, the probability that the random variable will take on a value equal to or less than each specific value may be given. For example, the probability distribution

of U is given in Table 3.4. From this distribution it is seen that
$P(U = 1) = 0, P(U = 2) = .10, P(U = 3) = .30, \ldots$, and $P(U = 6) =$
.10. To construct a *cumulative distribution*, we want first to find
the probability that U will be less than or equal to 1. This probability is 0, hence $P(U \leq 1) = 0$. Next we seek the probability that U
will be less than or equal to 2. This probability is $0 + .10$, which is
$P(U = 1) + P(U = 2)$. Next, the probability that U will be less than
or equal to 3 is $P(U \leq 3) = 0 + .10 + .30$, or .40. By continuing this
process, the following cumulative probabilities may be determined
from the noncumulative distribution: $P(U \leq 4) = .75, P(U \leq 5) =$
.90, and $P(U \leq 6) = 1.00$. When all of these cumulative probabilities
are associated with the various values of U, a cumulative probability distribution is formed. This cumulative distribution for U is
also given in Table 3.4.

TABLE 3.4_____

A Noncumulative and Cumulative Distribution of U

U	$P(U)$	U	*Cumulative Probability* *(less than or equal to)*
1	0	1	0
2	.10	2	.10
3	.30	3	.40
4	.35	4	.75
5	.15	5	.90
6	.10	6	1.00
	1.00	7	1.00

A cumulative distribution contains exactly the same information as a noncumulative distribution. If one type of distribution is
known, the other may be completely determined. In the previous
paragraph, the method of deriving a cumulative distribution from
a noncumulative distribution was illustrated. The reverse method
is also simple. For example, suppose a cumulative distribution for
the random variable Z shows that $P(Z \leq 8) = .85$ and $P(Z \leq 7) =$
.70, where Z can only take on integral values. In order to find the
simple probability $P(Z = 8)$, subtract .70 from .85 yielding .15:

$$P(Z = 8) = P(Z \leq 8) - P(Z \leq 7)$$

Finally, cumulative distributions may also be graphed. When
the random variable is discrete, the cumulative distribution will
be a step function. Figure 3.3 gives the cumulative distribution for

FIGURE 3.3

Graph of Cumulative Distribution of U

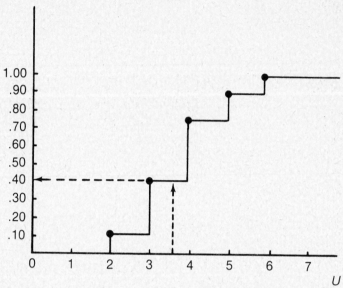

the variable U as found in Table 3.4. From this graph, it can be seen that the probability of U being less than or equal to 3.6 is .40; this is found by moving straight above $U = 3.6$ until the step function is intercepted, and then moving to the left to read the probability. This procedure is indicated by the dotted lines.

3.4

EXPECTED VALUE

In considering a probability distribution, it is often important to know where its center is in terms of the values of the random variable. Take another look at the graph of the random variable X as shown in Figure 3.1. Certainly everyone would agree that the central value for X in this case is $X = 1$. In a case like the graph of the distribution of Y in Figure 3.2, the central value of Y is not so apparent. Instead of leaving the determination of the central value to subjective feelings, a method has been developed which will find such a value mathematically. In Chapter 5 three different views as to what a center of a distribution is will be presented; the three types of centers are called the mean, the median, and the mode. The type of center which is most commonly used and which is to be used here is the mean. We shall therefore proceed to define the mean and will leave the discussion of the median and mode until Chapter 5, where the mean also will be discussed more fully.

The mean of a probability distribution is known as the *expected value* of the random variable. The mean or expected value is defined as

$$\mu = E(X) = \Sigma X\, P(X)$$

where μ or mu refers to the mean, $E(X)$ refers to the expected value of the random variable X, and $P(X)$ is the probability of X. As introduced in Chapter 1, the capital sigma means "sum up." Therefore, the mean is computed by multiplying each value of the random variable by its probability and then summing these products. This definition of the expected value will be used to find the mean of X whose distribution is given in Table 3.2:

$$E(X) = (0)(.25) + (1)(.50) + (2)(.25)$$
$$= 1$$

Now let us find the expected value of Y whose distribution is given in Table 3.3,

$$E(Y) = (0)(.05) + (1)(.15) + (2)(.25) + (3)(.30) + (4)(.15)$$
$$+ (5)(.10)$$
$$= 2.65 \text{ cartons of ice cream}$$

This means that in some sense of the term, 2.65 is the center of the distribution of Y. Recall that Y represented the number of cartons of ice cream sold in a day at the local QQQ Market. Y had been observed to range over several values in the past. To say now that the expected value of Y is 2.65 cartons means that on the average the market sells 2.65 cartons per day.

As a final example, suppose that you are going to play a game where a die is rolled. In this game you will win a payoff equal to the square of the number of spots which turn up. For instance, if you roll a 4, you will receive \$16, which is 4^2. In this game, what are your expected winnings? Let W be the random variable which represents your winnings on one roll. The expected value of W is then

$$E(W) = (1)(1/6) + (4)(1/6) + (9)(1/6) + (16)(1/6) + (25)(1/6)$$
$$+ (36)(1/6)$$
$$= \$15.17$$

This means that if you played the game again and again you would tend to average \$15.17 per game in winnings. This does not imply that in any one game you could win \$15.17.

3.5

VARIANCE AND STANDARD DEVIATION

Two golfers named Xerxes and Yale have been observed numerous times. From a host of scores, a set of relative frequencies and hence probabilities have been established for each of these golfers. Table 3.5 gives the probability distribution for each player, where X is the random variable denoting Xerxes' score on the next round and where Y represents Yale's score on the next round of golf. Figure 3.4 gives the respective graphs.

TABLE 3.5

Two Distributions with the Same Mean or Expected Value

Golfer Xerxes		Golfer Yale	
X	P(X)	Y	P(Y)
70	.20	70	.10
71	.15	71	.10
72	.10	72	.15
73	.10	73	.30
74	.10	74	.15
75	.15	75	.10
76	.20	76	.10
	1.00		1.00

FIGURE 3.4

Graphs of Two Distributions with the Same Mean

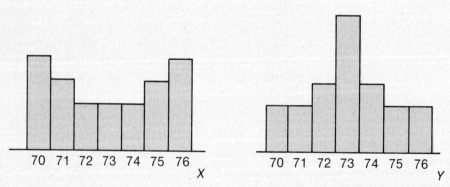

In comparing these two golfers it appears that they have the same average or mean scores. The expected value in each case is a score of 73:

$$E(X) = (70)(.20) + (71)(.15) + (72)(.10) + \ldots + (76)(.20)$$
$$= 73$$

$$E(Y) = (70)(.10) + (71)(.10) + (72)(.15) + \ldots + (76)(.10)$$
$$= 73$$

However, knowing the mean scores does not give a complete description of the two players. Most would agree that Yale is the more consistent player; this is because Yale's probability distribution is more heavily centered about the expected value of 73, while Xerxes' distribution is quite dispersed or spread out.

In an attempt to describe the dispersion of a probability distribution, a measure known as the *variance* has been devised. The variance of a random variable is defined as

$$\sigma_X^2 = \Sigma(X - \mu_X)^2 P(X)$$

where μ_X is the mean or expected value. The variance for Xerxes and the variance for Yale are now calculated; keep in mind that $\mu_X = 73$ and $\mu_Y = 73$.

$$\sigma_X^2 = (70{-}73)^2(.20) + (71{-}73)^2(.15) + (72{-}73)^2(.10) + (73{-}73)^2(.10)$$
$$+ (74{-}73)^2(.10) + (75{-}73)^2(.15) + (76{-}73)^2(.20)$$
$$= 5.00$$

$$\sigma_Y^2 = (70{-}73)^2(.10) + (71{-}73)^2(.10) + \ldots + (76{-}73)^2(.10)$$
$$= 2.90$$

The fact that the variance of X exceeds the variance of Y indicates that the distribution of X is more dispersed than that of Y; there is more variability in the X distribution than in the Y distribution.

Having demonstrated how a variance is computed, it is necessary to see what the variance signifies. It has already been stated that the more dispersed a distribution is, the greater the variance will be. But what else can be said about σ^2? In Table 3.6 a probability distribution is given where the variable G refers to the gain or

TABLE 3.6

Probability Distribution of the Automobile Manufacturer's Gain, G

G	P(G)
$10,000,000	.3
20,000,000	.4
30,000,000	.3

payoff which may be forthcoming if an automobile manufacturer introduces a new car next year. Let us analyze this probability distribution.

The mean or expected value is $20,000,000. The variance may now be determined. In computing the variance, we will not lose sight of the fact that the variable G is expressed in terms of dollar gains as is the mean. The variance is

$$\sigma_G^2 = (\$10,000,000 - \$20,000,000)^2(.3)$$
$$+ (\$20,000,000 - (\$20,000,000)^2(.4)$$
$$+ (\$30,000,000 - \$20,000,000)^2(.3)$$

$$= (-\$10,000,000)^2(.3) + (\$0)^2(.4) + (\$10,000,000)^2(.3)$$

$$= (-10,000,000 \text{ dollars})^2(.3) + 0 + (10,000,000 \text{ dollars})^2(.3)$$

$$= (100,000,000,000,000 \text{ square dollars})(.3)$$
$$+ (100,000,000,000,000 \text{ square dollars})(.3)$$

$$= 60,000,000,000,000 \text{ square dollars.}$$

In order to understand what a variance of 60,000,000,000,000 square dollars means, you must first understand what a square dollar is. Since most people don't catch the significance of things such as square dollars or square points, as in the golfers' example, the variance does not have much meaning. All that can be said is that the larger the variance, the greater the variation or dispersion in the distribution.

Rather than stopping here, someone decided to take the square root of the variance. The result is called the *standard deviation*, which is aptly denoted by σ. Notice what happens if we compute the standard deviation in the automobile manufacturer's case:

$$\sigma = \sqrt{\text{Variance}}$$

$$= \sqrt{\sigma^2}$$

$$= \sqrt{\Sigma(X - \mu)^2 P(X)}$$

$$= \sqrt{60,000,000,000,000 \text{ square dollars}}$$

$$= 7,750,000 \text{ dollars}$$

The standard deviation ends up being expressed in the same units (dollars in this case) as the random variable.

Something can be said concerning the meaning of the standard deviation, since it is a value which is expressed in the same units as the random variable and mean. In the first place, the greater the standard deviation is, the greater the dispersion of the probability distribution; the same is true with regard to the variance.

Referring again to the two distributions of Figure 3.4, the standard deviation of X would be greater than the standard deviation of Y, because the distribution of X is more spread out or more dispersed. Though the general relationship between greater standard deviations and more dispersion is true, more can be said concerning the standard deviation in relationship to the dispersion of a distribution. This brings us to the next point in the discussion regarding the meaning of the standard deviation.

In the second place, something quite specific can be said concerning the standard deviation in the common case where the probability distribution follows the shape of a bell-shaped curve. Figure 3.5 shows a distribution with this familiar shape. In these cases it may be stated that essentially all of the probability will lie

FIGURE 3.5_____
The Standard Deviation and the Bell-Shaped Distribution

(a) $\sigma = 10$

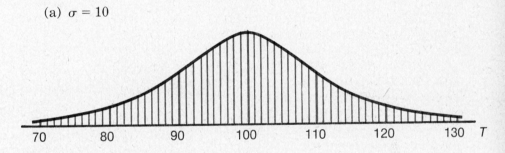

(b) $\sigma = 5$

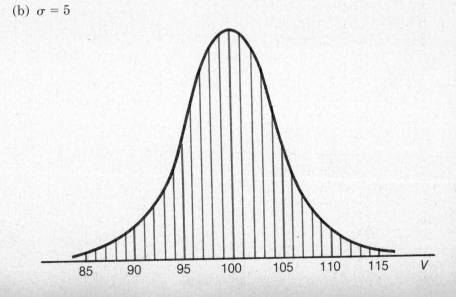

within a distance of three standard deviations of the mean. To illustrate this, assume that the random variable T represents the total number of automobile accidents occurring in one week in Dallas. Suppose that T is known to have a probability distribution where the expected value or mean of T is $\mu = 100$ accidents and the standard deviation is $\sigma = 10$ accidents. Furthermore, the probability distribution of T when graphed has the bell shape. Knowing this, the following can be concluded concerning the dispersion of the distribution of T: "Essentially all of the distribution (probability) will fall within the range between 70 and 130 accidents." In other words, the number of accidents in any week is almost certain to be between 70 and 130 accidents. Notice that the 70 is three standard deviations below the mean of 100, that is,

$$70 = \mu - 3\sigma$$
$$= 100 - (3)(10)$$

and 130 is three standard deviations above the mean:

$$130 = \mu + 3\sigma$$
$$= 100 + (3)(10)$$

The foregoing conclusion can be seen by looking at Figure 3.5a. It is apparent here that essentially the entire distribution lies within three standard deviations of the expected value. Suppose now that the weekly number of accidents in Atlanta is denoted by the random variable V, where $E(V) = 100$ accidents and $\sigma_V = 5$ accidents. Since the standard deviation in Atlanta is half that of Dallas, we would expect the probability distribution of V to be much less dispersed than that of T. In particular, the probability distribution will be squeezed into the region from 85 to 115 since these are the values of V which are three standard deviations in either direction from the mean of 100. Figure 3.5b pictures this more compact distribution for the Atlanta area. As long as the probability distribution takes the familiar bell shape, the distribution will fall entirely within three standard deviations of the mean (this covers a total span of six standard deviations). With bell-shaped distributions it is also the case that about 2/3 of the probability will lie within one standard deviation of the expected value. In the Dallas case this means that T will take on a value between 90 and 110 accidents in about 67 percent of the weeks. This may be symbolically stated as

$$P(\mu - \sigma \le T \le \mu + \sigma) = 2/3$$
$$P(90 \le T \le 110) = 2/3$$

Likewise, in the case of Atlanta the probability is about .67 that V will fall between 95 and 105. This sort of thing gives a little more information for the sake of trying to understand what a standard deviation means if the distribution is bell-shaped.

But what if the probability distribution is not bell-shaped? What then can be said concerning the relationship between the standard deviation and the spread of the distribution? According to a theorem developed by Chebyshev,

> No matter what the shape of the probability distribution, the amount of probability which lies within h standard deviations of the mean is at least $1 - 1/h^2$.

Chebyshev's theorem may be stated more mathematically as

$$P(\mu - h\sigma \leq X \leq \mu + h\sigma) \geq 1 - 1/h^2$$

Suppose that X, the weekly number of accidents in Milwaukee, has a probability distribution whose mean is 100 accidents and whose standard deviation is 10 accidents. Furthermore, suppose that the distribution of X does not have the bell shape, but nothing more of its shape is known. In this case, what is the probability that X will fall between 70 and 130 accidents? According to Chebyshev, since 70 and 130 are $h = 3$ standard deviations away from the mean,

$$P(70 \leq X \leq 130) \geq 1 - 1/3^2$$
$$\geq 8/9$$

Therefore the probability is at least 8/9 that the number of accidents in a week will fall between 70 and 130. Through the use of Chebyshev's theorem you should be able to verify that the number of accidents next week in Milwaukee will fall between 80 and 120, with a probability of at least .75.

In Chapters 4 and 5 more will be said concerning the meaning and relevance of the standard deviation. Throughout the text the standard deviation and the variance will be the primary methods of measuring the dispersion of a probability distribution.

3.6

SKEWNESS AND KURTOSIS

Usually the two most important characteristics of a probability distribution are its mean, which measures the location of its center, and its standard deviation, which measures its dispersion. Two other characteristics relating to the shape of a distribution will now be considered.

A *skewed distribution* is one which has a pronounced tail in one direction or the other. The distribution in Figure 3.6, for example, is a distribution which is skewed to the right, or *positively skewed*. A *negatively skewed* distribution would have the pronounced tail to the left. If the random variable G represents the gross annual income of a randomly selected worker in the United States, G would have a distribution like that of Figure 3.6 which is positively skewed. Although G can only go down to zero, there is no upper limit on G. Also, a great number of people earn just over the minimum wage. There are also many people, yet in decreasing numbers, in the higher income brackets. When all this is put together, the distribution of G proves to be skewed to the right.

FIGURE 3.6

Distribution which is Skewed to the Right (Positively Skewed)

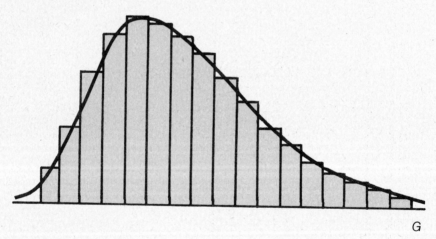

G

Another characteristic of a probability distribution concerns the *kurtosis* or peakedness of the distribution. Figure 3.7 presents three distributions which, though symmetrical, differ in peakedness. The profile of the distribution of Figure 3.7a resembles the silhouette of Stone Mountain in Georgia. Distributions like this, with a relatively flat top, are called *platykurtic*. In Figure 3.7b, there is the likes of Grand Teton in Wyoming. Distributions such as this, with a steep peak, are called *leptokurtic*. Finally, Figure 3.7c presents a distribution with a profile akin to Mount Rainier; this distribution is *mesokurtic*.

The concepts of skewness and kurtosis are useful since they enable us to more accurately describe a probability distribution. Skewness and kurtosis can be mathematically measured, just as the center and dispersion of a distribution can be measured by the mean and standard deviation. The mathematical measures, however, will not be presented in this text.

FIGURE 3.7_____
Examples of Kurtosis

(a) Platykurtic

(b) Leptokurtic

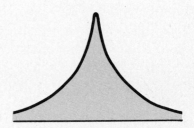

(c) Mesokurtic

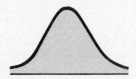

3.7_____
FUNCTIONS OF A RANDOM VARIABLE

To this point we have discussed random variables, their probability distributions, their expected values and their standard deviations. Sometimes a new random variable is defined which is based on the initial random variable. In these cases we may ultimately be interested only in the expected value and standard deviation of the new random variable. For example, let X be the random variable representing the number of tickets that will be purchased for this year's Blubber Bowl to be held December 31 in Fairbanks. Also assume that Blubber Bowl tickets sell for $5 each, the expected value of X is 20,000 tickets, and the standard deviation of X is 3,000 tickets. Though the Blubber Bowl promoters are interested in ticket sales X, the ultimate interest is in revenues. Let R equal the revenues generated from this year's game. It is obvious that the relationship between X and R is

$$R = 5X$$

Notice that since X is a random variable, R must also be a random variable because R is directly linked to X through this simple equation. As X varies, so R will also vary. What then can be said concerning the expected value and the standard deviation of R? A theorem to follow will make an answer to this question possible.

Two variables, X and Y, are said to be *linearly related* if the equation or function relating them is of the following form, where a and b are constants:

$$Y = a + bX$$

If the relationship between the variables were something like

$$Y = a + bX^2$$
or $\quad Y = e^X$

or some such, the relationship is termed *nonlinear*. The following theorem is appropriate only in linear cases.

Theorem 1

If the two random variables X and Y are related by

$$Y = a + bX$$

then the expected value of Y may be found by

$$E(Y) = a + b \cdot E(X)$$

where $E(X)$ is the expected value of X. Furthermore, the variance of Y may be found according to

$$\sigma_Y^2 = b^2 \, \sigma_X^2$$

where σ_X^2 is the variance of X.

Since in the Blubber Bowl the variable R is related to X by means of a linear function, $R = 0 + 5X$, and since $E(X) = 20,000$ and $\sigma_X^2 = 3,000^2$ or $9,000,000$, it follows by *Theorem 1* that the expected value of R is

$$E(R) = 0 + (5)(20,000)$$
$$= \$100,000$$

and the variance of R is

$$\sigma_R^2 = 5^2 \, \sigma_X^2$$
$$= (25)(9,000,000)$$
$$= 225,000,000$$

which means that the standard deviation of R is

$$\sigma_R = \sqrt{225,000,000}$$
$$= \$15,000$$

If several variables are linearly related, there is another theorem which is of use.

Theorem 2

If three or more random variables are related by

$$T = a + bX + cY + dZ + \dots$$

where a, b, c, d, ... are constants, then the expected value of T is found by

$$E(T) = a + b \cdot E(X) + c \cdot E(Y) + d \cdot E(Z) + \dots$$

"Old Ranger Elixir" is sold in two western territories, Tombstone territory and the Yukon territory. Gross sales for the elixir is given by the ensuing relationship, where T represents the number of bottles sold in Tombstone and Y the number sold in the Yukon territory:

$$G = 3T + 2Y$$

This is because Old Ranger gets \$3 per bottle sold in Tombstone and only \$2 per bottle in the Yukon territory. Since the expected sales in Tombstone is 500 bottles and $E(Y) = 400$ bottles, expected gross sales is

$$E(G) = 3\,E(T) + 2\,E(Y)$$
$$= (3)(500) + (2)(400)$$
$$= 2300 \text{ dollars}$$

This is an application of *Theorem 2*.

Thinking back to *Theorem 1*, you might wonder what can be done if two variables are not linearly related. Handling such a case is a little bit more troublesome than the linear case, but it is not difficult. According to Zusapelski's Theory (which no one believes except perhaps the big Z herself), the price F of a gold mining stock ten years hence is related to its projected price T two years hence, according to the following relationship:

$$F = 3^T - T^2$$

Let's apply this relationship to determine the expected value of the price of Homestake Mining stock ten years from now. From the intermediate term prediction department of the Lynch, Lynch, Lynch, Inc. stock brokerage firm comes the probability distribution for the price T of Homestake stock two years hence. This distribution is presented in Table 3.7. From Lynch, Lynch, Lynch's

TABLE 3.7
The Distributions of *T* and *F* for Homestake Mining

T	$P(T)$	F	$P(F)$
$2	.3	$ 5	.3
3	.4	18	.4
4	.3	65	.3

perspective, there is a .3 probability that the price will be $2 per share in two years, a probability of .4 that T will be $3, and $P(T = \$4) = .3$. From this distribution, the expected price two years hence is easily computed to be

$$E(T) = (2)(.3) + (3)(.4) + (4)(.3)$$
$$= \$3$$

In order to find the expected price in ten years, $E(F)$, it is *wrong* to proceed as follows:

$$E(F) = 3^{E(T)} - E(T)^2 \qquad \text{WRONG!}$$
$$= 3^3 - 3^2$$
$$= \$18$$

This sort of procedure where T is replaced by $E(T)$ in order to find $E(F)$ is only legitimate if F and T are linearly related.

The correct way to proceed is to first construct a probability distribution for F. This distribution of F is given in Table 3.7 along with that of T, and was determined in the following manner from the distribution of T. If $T = 2$, then substituting into the equation for F yields

$$F = 3^T - T^2$$
$$= 3^2 - 2^2$$
$$= \$5$$

Since the probability of T equaling $2 is .3, the probability of F equaling $5 must be .3 also since $F = \$5$ is directly linked to $T = \$2$. In like fashion, if $T = \$3$, then according to the equation, F will equal $18. Since $P(T = 3) = .4$, it follows that $P(F = 18) = .4$ also. This is how the distribution of F is constructed.

With the distribution of F constructed, it is now a trivial exercise to find the expected value of F. Proceeding directly from the distribution of F,

$$E(F) = (5)(.3) + (18)(.4) + (65)(.3)$$
$$= \$28.20$$

This is a different value than that which was computed by the *wrong* method a few paragraphs earlier.

3.8

AN APPLICATION

The usefulness of random variables, probability distributions, expected values, and the like has no bounds. This stuff is certainly not the private property of analysts in the European and North American cultures. This may be demonstrated by considering a case directly from the heart of Central America.

It was General Moremore Tortillas, commander and chief of the Banama Canal, that most recently made use of a probability distribution. General Tortillas was principally interested in determining the expected profit of next year's operation of the canal. The General was planning to install a central heating system in his palace at a cost of $.5 million if he thought canal profits would be sufficient to underwrite such a heating system.

The General's new toll was $3,000 per vessel passing through the canal. Direct labor expenses involved in getting a vessel from one end of the canal to the other were anticipated to be $1,000 per vessel. Furthermore, overhead expenses to keep the canal open for a year would total $500,000. In order to determine the expected profit, some idea of the number of vessels which would use the canal was needed. Tortillas, by imperial fiat, declared that

X = the number of vessels which will pass
through the canal next year

Tortillas then asked his Ministress of Economics, Lotsa Cheesa, to assess a probability distribution for X. In so doing, Tortillas informed Cheesa that she should exclude Yankee Clippers from consideration since Yankee Clippers would not be permitted to use the canal. (As a matter of historical interest, the reason General Tortillas would not allow Yankee Clippers was quite simple. It seems that the Yankee Clipper is not equipped with holding tanks. Now it was the General's pleasure that all vessels passing through the canal give the General the 21 gun salute. The Americanos sailing the Clippers were prone to add a little something to the 21 gun salute as they passed through. This little something extra in honor of the General was termed the 21 toilet flush.) Getting back to the probability distribution of X, Cheesa finally came up with the distribution as shown in Table 3.8. From this distribution it appears that the probability of 700 vessels passing through is .2, and $P(X = 800) = .5$, and $P(X = 900) = .3$.

TABLE 3.8

Annual Usage of the Banama Canal

X	$P(X)$
700 vessels	.2
800	.5
900	.3

With all this information in hand, Tortillas with Lotsa Cheesa went to work. First they formulated an equation which relates Neto Incomo (the Americanos would have called it profits) to X. The equation evolved as follows: $3,000 is collected from each vessel passing through; but from this amount, $1,000 must be subtracted, which is the direct labor and equipment cost to get the vessel through. Thus $2,000 is made per vessel passing. If X is the number of vessels passing, then $2,000X$ is the gross revenue from which the overhead of $500,000 must be subtracted. This leaves the net income N of

$$N = (3,000 - 1,000)X - 500,000$$
$$= 2,000X - 500,000$$

Next the General found that the expected number of vessels using the canal is

$$E(X) = (700)(.2) + (800)(.5) + (900)(.3)$$
$$= 810 \text{ vessels}$$

Because N and X are related by a linear equation, the General proceeded to find the expected net income:

$$E(N) = 2,000 \, E(X) - 500,000$$
$$= (2,000)(810) - 500,000$$
$$= \$1,120,000$$

With that kind of expected net income, the General proceeded with his initial plans exclaiming "Chili today, but hot tamale."

PROBLEMS

3.1

Identify each of the following random variables as being either discrete or continuous.

(a) amount of fuel consumed in a flight by a 747
(b) number of microwave ovens sold in a week by a certain company
(c) temperature in a freezer
(d) width of a shoe as commonly measured
(e) dollar sales of Southwest Forest Industries
(f) distance a truck can travel on a tank of fuel
(g) number of defective sheets of plywood in a stack of 50 sheets
(h) the life of a projector bulb

3.2

Three coins are to be tossed. If X equals the number of heads achieved, find the probability distribution of X.

3.3

Two dice are to be rolled. If T equals the total number of spots that turn up, find the probability distribution of T. (Hint: Use the multiplication law for independent events to find the probability of some particular combination like a six on the first die and a two on the second die.)

3.4

Colorado River Rafters takes people through the Grand Canyon for a fee. The number of people seeking a raft trip on each of the past twenty days may be summarized as follows. On 2 days no one showed up, on 6 days two people showed up, on 3 days exactly three people showed up, on 7 days exactly four showed up, and on 2 days five people showed up seeking a raft trip.

(a) Determine the probability distribution of d where d equals the number of people seeking a raft trip in a day.
(b) Draw a graph of the distribution of d.
(c) What is the probability that four or more people will show up tomorrow?
(d) What is the probability that d will equal three or less?

3.5

Sometimes a probability distribution is given in condensed form by means of an algebraic equation. For example, $P(X) = X/10$ is a probability distribution where X may take on the values 1, 2, 3, or 4. Therefore, $P(X = 1) = 1/10$, $P(2) = 2/10$, $P(3) = 3/10$, and the probability that X will equal 4 is 4/10. Determine which of the following meet all the requirements for being a probability distribution.

(a) $P(X) = .5X$ for $X = -1, 0, 1, 2$
(b) $P(X) = X^2/14$ for $X = 0, 1, 2, 3$
(c) $P(X) = (10 - X)/30$ for $X = -1, 0, 1$
(d) $P(X) = 1/X$ for $X = 1, 2, 3$

3.6

Find the cumulative distribution of the "less than or equal to" type for each of the following distributions. Then graph the cumulative distributions.

(a)

X	P(X)
1	.20
2	.10
3	.05
4	.10
5	.15
6	.40

(b)

Y	P(Y)
10	.15
11	.22
12	0
13	.48
14	.05
15	.10

3.7

Find the corresponding noncumulative distribution for each of the cumulative distributions below.

(a)

W	Cumulative Probability
1	.10
2	.25
3	.40
4	.50
5	.85
6	1.00

(b)

U	Cumulative Probability
20	0
21	.35
22	.35
23	.60
24	.80
25	1.00

3.8

If $P(X \leq 8) = .40$ and $P(X \leq 5) = .10$, what is $P(5 < X \leq 8)$? What is $P(X > 8)$? What is $P(X > 5)$?

3.9

For the following distribution, find (a) the mean, (b) the expected value of X, (c) the variance, and (d) the standard deviation.

X	P(X)
60	.3
70	.4
80	.2
90	.1

3.10

The number of computers which break down in Minneapolis in a day has the following probability distribution:

B	20	25	30	35	40
P(B)	.2	.4	.2	.1	.1

(a) Find the mean.
(b) Find the expected value of B.
(c) Find the variance of B.
(d) Find the standard deviation.
(e) Graph the distribution of B.
(f) Determine the cumulative distribution of B.
(g) What is the probability of 30 or fewer breakdowns in a day?

3.11

The number of industrial accidents which occur in a month at a large chemical plant is given by the following distribution.

N	P(N)
0	.1
1	.2
2	.3
3	.2
4	.2

Determine the following:

(a) Mean
(b) Expected value of N
(c) Variance of N

(d) Standard deviation of N

(e) $P(N \geq 2)$

(f) Probability that N will exceed $E(N)$

3.12

The Yummy Yogurt Company states that if their yogurt is soured, they will give you double your money back. Yummy sells for $.90 per pint. About 10 percent of the pints of Yummy turn out to be soured at the time of purchase and hence are returned. Letting C equal the cash flow experienced by the company in dealing with the sale of one pint of yogurt, give the probability distribution of C and then determine its mean.

3.13

There are ten chips in a bag. The first chip has a "1" on it, the second has a "2" on it, . . . , and the tenth has a "10" on it. You are going to randomly select a chip.

(a) If you receive a number of dollars equal to the number on the chip, what is your expected gain?

(b) If you receive nothing if the chip is odd and dollars according to the number of the chip if the chip is even, what is your expected gain?

(c) If you receive the square of the number on the chip if the chip is even, and if you will lose the value of the chip if it is odd, what is your expected gain?

3.14

A tire dealer offers a potential customer a free road atlas if the potential customer will take a look at a five-minute film on tires. Let the random variable X equal the profit to the dealer in this situation. If the potential customer only gets the atlas (and buys nothing), then the profit to the dealer is $X = -\$2$. If the customer gets the atlas and also buys a set of tires, the profit to the dealer is $X = \$30$. If 80 percent of the potential customers merely pick up the atlas and watch the film, and only 20 percent go on to buy a set of tires, what is the expected profit for the dealer. Also, find the standard deviation of X.

3.15

The number of checks cleared by the Bank of Arizona in a week is a random variable with a mean of 100,000 checks and a standard deviation of 15,000 checks. Assuming that the distribution has the bell-shape, in what proportion of weeks will the bank clear be-tween 85,000 and 115,000 checks? The number of checks cleared in a week is almost certain to fall between what two values (or ex-tremes)?

3.16

The number of gallons of sewer effluent processed at a certain treatment plant in Hartford in a day has a bell-shaped distribu-tion with a mean of 40,000 gallons and a standard deviation of 8,000 gallons. On what proportion of the days are more than 48,000 gallons processed?

3.17

Stocks traded on a stock exchange have a mean price of $30 per share with a standard deviation of $10. The shape of the price dis-tribution is unknown and cannot be assumed to be bell-shaped. At least what proportion of the stocks have a price between $10 and $50? between $15 and $45?

3.18

The ages of the employees at a large corporation have a highly skewed distribution with a mean of 40 and a standard deviation of 8 years. At least 75 percent of the employees have ages between what two values?

3.19

Considering all of the families in Virginia, let X equal the amount a family pays in federal income taxes and let Y equal the amount a family pays in state sales taxes.

(a) Would the distribution of X be skewed? if so, in what direction?
(b) Would the distribution of Y be skewed? if so, in what direction?
(c) Which would be more skewed?

3.20

A probability distribution is given below where the probabilities have not been supplied. Make up some probabilities in order to make the distribution skewed to the left (negatively skewed). Now make up some probabilities so that the distribution is symmetrical with a fairly large standard deviation — you need not compute the standard deviation. Now make up some probabilities which will yield a leptokurtic distribution.

X	P(X)
1	
2	
3	
4	
5	
6	
7	

3.21

The number of cars crossing the Delaware Memorial Bridge in an hour late at night has the following distribution.

N	100	120	140	160
P(N)	.3	.4	.2	.1

Each car pays a toll of $.50.
(a) Write an equation which expresses revenue, R, in terms of the number N of cars crossing.
(b) What is the expected value of R?
(c) What is the standard deviation of revenues?

3.22

The profit a company makes is given by $P = 20X - 500$. If X has a mean of 40 and a standard deviation of 10, find the mean and standard deviation of P.

3.23

Texy sells hot pretzels for $.40 each. The cost to make a pretzel is $.15. It costs $600 to keep the store open for a month. If X is the number of pretzels sold in a month,
(a) Give the equation for the monthly profit.
(b) If $E(X) = 40,000$, what is the expected profit?

3.24

If X has the distribution as given,

X	P(X)
10	.3
20	.4
30	.3

(a) find $E(Y)$ if $Y = 10 + 4X$
(b) find $E(Z)$ if $Z = 10 + 4X^2$

3.25

Marchand, an economist, has found that the amount T a family spends on entertainment is related to family income F by the following relationship:

$$T = .10F$$

If the mean family income is $10,000 and the standard deviation of F is $4,000.
(a) what is $E(T)$?
(b) at least 75 percent of the families spend between what two amounts on entertainment? (Hint: Use Chebyshev's Theorem.)

3.26

The number of refrigerators X an appliance dealer will sell in a week has a probability distribution given by

$$P(X) = \frac{10 - X}{40}$$

where X may equal 0, 1, 2, 3, or 4 refrigerators. For example, the probability of selling exactly 3 refrigerators next week is $P(X = 3)$ = $(10 - 3)/40 = 7/40$.
(a) Write out the distribution of X.
(b) What is the probability that the dealer will sell less than 3 refrigerators next week?
(c) Find the mean of X.
(d) Determine the standard deviation.
(e) If the dealer makes a profit of $50 per refrigerator sold, what is the dealer's expected profit for next week?

3.27

General Sherman's Georgia Fried Chicken is a new chain of restaurants with annual overhead expenses of $60,000. Each chicken restaurant the General can have opened by next year will generate a net income of $20,000 per year. (If only two were opened, the chain would experience a profit of $40,000 − $60,000 or −$20,000.) The General is unsure as to how many restaurants will be open next year. If X equals the number of restaurants open next year, the General sees X as having the following probability distribution:

X	2	3	4	5
$P(X)$	.2	.3	.4	.1

(a) Find $E(X)$.
(b) Write an equation which expresses profits for the chain in terms of X.
(c) Find the expected profit.
(d) Find the standard deviation of profits.

3.28

The number of daily inspections performed at a certain state auto inspection station has the following distribution:

N	100	110	120	130
$P(N)$	.2	.3	.3	.2

(a) Find $E(N)$.
(b) Find the standard deviation of N.
(c) If a fee of $4 is collected per inspection, what is the probability that the station will collect more than $425 in a day?
(d) What is the expected amount of fee money collected?

3.29

The cost to construct a new deep water drilling rig is given by the equation:

$$C = M + L + V$$

where M refers to the materials cost, L refers to labor costs, and V represents overhead costs. If the means of these three costs are $180,000, $110,000, and $40,000, what is the expected value of C?

3.30

The VPI agricultural extension service has found that the yield Y of tomatoes is related to rainfall R and bug infestation B by the following equation:

$$Y = 10R - B$$

If R and B have the following distributions, find the expected yield for tomatoes.

R	$P(R)$		B	$P(B)$
30	.2		100	.3
40	.6		200	.4
50	.2		400	.3

The extension service has also found that the yield M for melons is related to rainfall according to

$$M = R^2 + 100R$$

Find the expected yield for melons.

3.31

The Chapman Office Supply Company is a wholesaler of Writeright typewriters, which has two customers (retailers) who order type-writers in varying quantities each week. The number the first customer orders in a week is denoted by X, and the number ordered by the second is denoted by Y. The probability distributions of X and Y are given below.

X	$P(X)$		Y	$P(Y)$
0	.1		3	.2
1	.3		4	.3
2	.4		5	.3
3	.2		6	.1
			7	.1

(a) Find $E(X)$ and $E(Y)$.
(b) What is the expected total number of typewriters ordered in a week?
(c) If the wholesaler stocks eight typewriters, what is the probability that demand will exceed this quantity?
(d) Construct the probability distribution of T where $T = X + Y$.

CHAPTER 4

SPECIAL PROBABILITY DISTRIBUTIONS

4.1
INTRODUCTION

The general characteristics of a probability distribution were discussed in Chapter 3. In this chapter, attention will center on several special distributions which are appropriate to certain frequently encountered situations.

Within the domain of discrete distributions, the binomial, hypergeometric, and Poisson distributions will be studied. Finally, two continuous distributions, the rectangular and the normal, will be presented.

4.2
BINOMIAL DISTRIBUTION

The binomial distribution is a probability distribution applicable to situations where a *Bernoulli process* exists. Therefore, it is necessary to consider the character of a Bernoulli process before the binomial distribution can be studied.

Bernoulli Process

A Bernoulli process may be described by means of three characteristics. The *first* characteristic is:

> There are n distinct trials where there are exactly two possible outcomes on each trial. (The two outcomes on any trial are typically called "success" and

"failure." Furthermore, the probability of obtaining
a success on a given trial is denoted by p and the
probability of a failure occurring is q; so, $q = 1 - p$.)

Before considering the next two characteristics of a Bernoulli process, this first characteristic will be illustrated. Think of a process which consists of five successive flips of a coin. With such an experiment, there are $n = 5$ distinct trials where a trial consists of flipping a coin once. Furthermore, there are exactly two possible outcomes for each trial (flip); these are heads and tails. If heads is arbitrarily regarded as success and tails as a failure, then the probability of a success in a flip is $p = .5$, and the probability of a failure on one trial is $q = .5$. Therefore, five successive flips of a coin is an experiment which satisfies the first requirement of a Bernoulli process.

The *second* characteristic of a Bernoulli process is:

> The outcomes from trial to trial are statistically independent.

Statistical independence was originally defined in Section 2.6 of Chapter 2. If two events are independent, then the occurrence of either of them gives absolutely no information as to the likelihood of the occurrence of the other. Think again of the experiment where a coin is to be flipped five times in succession. Does the outcome of one flip give any information as to what will occur on another flip? In other words, if heads (success) occurs on the first flip, does this give any information as to what will occur on any other flip? Obviously the answer is no. The outcomes from flip to flip or trial to trial are independent in such an experiment.

The *third* and final characteristic of a Bernoulli process is:

> The probability p of a success on a given trial remains constant from trial to trial. In other words, p does not change from trial to trial.

Returning to the experiment consisting of five successive flips of a coin, it is apparent that p remains at the constant value of .5 from flip to flip. The probability of getting heads on a trial is always .5 regardless of which trial is being considered.

Because the experiment consisting of five successive flips of a coin meets the three requirements outlined above, it can be asserted that this is a Bernoulli process. Several more processes will now be examined in order to determine if they are Bernoulli.

A die is to be rolled four times. Is this a Bernoulli Process? Immediately we notice that any of six outcomes or sides is possible on each roll or trial. The first requirement for a Bernoulli process states that there must be exactly two outcomes for each trial; hence, this is not a Bernoulli process. However, if we were to define success as getting an even number of spots and a failure as getting an odd number of spots, then exactly two outcomes exist for each of the four trials, and the first requirement is satisfied. With this experiment, the outcomes from trial to trial are independent and p remains constant, and so it is Bernoulli.

Suppose you are going to randomly select eight households in a city and make a phone call to each asking if they currently have any hotdogs in their home. In such an experiment, there are $n = 8$ trials where there are two outcomes for each trial: "We do have hotdogs on the premises" and "We don't have any hotdogs here." Furthermore, the answers would be independent from household to household, and the probability of having hotdogs (success) would be constant from call to call if the households are being selected randomly. This then is a Bernoulli process.

As a final example, suppose three prisoners have been placed side by side with their backs to a wall. The prison doctor is next going to check the eyes of the prisoners. Notice that there are six eyes to be checked. If the eye color of each eye is to be checked letting success mean having a blue eye and failure mean having anything but a blue eye, then this is a process with six trials where there are only two outcomes on each trial. However, the process is not Bernoulli since the outcomes from trial to trial are not independent. If the first eye checked is blue (success), then the second eye is very likely to be blue, since most people have both eyes the same color. Even if the physician were testing the vision from eye to eye where success means 20-40 vision or better and failure means worse than 20-40 vision in an eye, the outcomes in every case from trial to trial would not be statistically independent and therefore the process would not be Bernoulli.

Derivation of the Binomial Distribution

The *binomial distribution* is a probability distribution which has been developed in order to make certain probabilistic assertions about the outcomes of a Bernoulli process. To begin, let the random variable x be defined as

x = the total number of successes achieved in a
Bernoulli process which has n trials.

By reason of this definition, x may take on a value of $0, 1, 2, 3, \ldots,$ $n - 1$, or n. For example, if a coin is to be flipped $n = 5$ times and if x equals the total number of heads achieved in this experiment, then the possible values for x are 0 heads, 1 head, 2 heads, 3 heads, 4 heads, and 5 heads. It is impossible to get more than 5 heads in n = 5 trials or flips.

The binomial distribution is a list of the possible values for x and the corresponding probabilities. For example, for the experiment consisting of five flips of a coin, where x equals the total number of heads achieved, the probability distribution, which is a binomial distribution since it arose from a Bernoulli process, is given in Table 4.1. Our interest now is in finding how these probabilities are determined. To this end, the remainder of this section is addressed.

TABLE 4.1

Binomial Distribution arising from a Bernoulli Process consisting of Five Flips of a Coin

Total Number of Heads x	Probability $P(x)$
0	.0312
1	.1562
2	.3125
3	.3125
4	.1562
5	.0312

Kiblees, a large chain of department stores, has decided to open a number of automobile repair centers next to their retail stores in Mexico City. In addition to installing shocks and mufflers, Kiblees will sell and install their own batteries. A market survey, however, has found that the Die-Tough label on their batteries sold in the United States has not caught the fancy of the Mexican motorist. Furthermore, the ads where ten Die-Toughs are subjected to the rigors of the Alaskan winter leaves the south-of-the-border motorist cold. Hence, Kiblees has decided to market their Mexican batteries under the label Mucho Macho. For the sake of advertising the Mucho Macho, Kiblees has arranged a test to be overseen by the Mexico Consumer Protection Agency. In this test, five batteries will be tried by the following ordeal. Each of the five batteries will be dropped from an altitude of 30,000 feet out of an Aeronauves Mexico jet while flying over the Square of Zócalo. The remains of the batteries will then be scraped up and simmered in a vat of chili for seven months, at which time they will be placed in five Chevys. Then five bull fighters will enter the Chevys and turn the keys to see what happens.

Before going through with this test of five Mucho Machos, Kiblees tested dozens of their batteries in this way and found that 30 percent of the batteries have enough juice after the fall and chili to start a Chevy. In view of this, what is the probability that exactly two batteries, for example, will work in the live nationally televised advertisement which is to be proctored by the Mexico Consumer Protection Agency?

We must first check to see if this is a Bernoulli process. There are $n = 5$ trials (batteries) where there are two outcomes on each trial: success refers to the Chevy starting, and failure refers to the Chevy not starting. What happens with one battery is independent of how any of the other batteries work, and $p = .30$ is constant from battery to battery. Hence, this is a Bernoulli process.

The random variable in this experiment is x, where x refers to the total number of batteries which work. The possible values for x are 0, 1, 2, 3, 4, and 5, since there is a total of 5 batteries being tested. Of these possible values, Kiblees particularly wants to know the probability of exactly two batteries working; that is, Kiblees is seeking $P(x = 2)$. The binomial distribution will now be developed in order to find this probability.

It should first be noticed that the probability of exactly two out of the five batteries working is not the same as $P(S, S, F, F, F)$, where S refers to the outcome of the Chevy starting and F refers to the Chevy not starting. The probability $P(S, S, F, F, F)$ is the probabilty that the first starts, the second starts, the third doesn't start, the fourth doesn't start, and the fifth doesn't start. This is not the same as exactly two starting since exactly two could start but yet the order be different from $SSFFF$. For example, if the first didn't start, the second did, the third didn't, the fourth didn't, and the fifth Chevy did start, this also would amount to having exactly two start, yet the order is different from $SSFFF$. In order to determine the probability of exactly two starting, we must determine how many distinct arrangements there are where two S's are mixed with three F's. Each one of these arrangements is called a *permutation* where two items are similar (the two S's) and where the remaining three items (the three F's) are similar. A list of all the permutations or arrangements of two working batteries and three nonworking batteries or dead batteries is given in Table 4.2. It is apparent from this listing that there are ten different permutations or arrangements.

It is now necessary to find the probability of each of these arrangements. Then when these ten probabilities are added we will have the probability of exactly two successes in five trials; that is, $P(x = 2)$. For the first permutation which is $SSFFF$ the probability is

$$P(S, S, F, F, F) = P(S) P(S) P(F) P(F) P(F)$$

This is true because of the multiplication law for independent events (see Section 2.6 of Chapter 2). Remember that the outcomes from trial to trial are independent in a Bernoulli process. In Bernoulli situations the probability of a success, $P(S)$, is denoted by p and the probability of a failure is denoted by q. Therefore,

$$\begin{aligned} P(S, S, F, F, F) &= P(S) P(S) P(F) P(F) P(F) \\ &= ppqqq = p^2 q^3 \end{aligned}$$

Finally, in the Mucho Macho case the probability of success (the Chevy starts) is $p = .3$ and the probability of failure is $q = .7$. This implies

$$\begin{aligned} P(S, S, F, F, F) &= ppqqq = p^2 q^3 \\ &= (.3)(.3)(.7)(.7)(.7) = (.3)^2(.7)^3 \\ &= .03087 \end{aligned}$$

Therefore the probability is .03087 that the first two Chevys will start and the third, fourth, and fifth will not start.

Next we seek the probability of $SFSFF$, which is another permutation of two successes and three failures. By the same logic,

$$\begin{aligned} P(S, F, S, F, F) &= P(S) P(F) P(S) P(F) P(F) \\ &= pqpqq \\ &= p^2 q^3 \\ &= (.3)^2(.7)^3 \\ &= .03087 \end{aligned}$$

TABLE 4.2
Permutations or Arrangements of Two S's and Three F's

$$SSFFF$$
$$SFSFF$$
$$SFFSF$$
$$SFFFS$$
$$FSSFF$$
$$FSFSF$$
$$FSFFS$$
$$FFSSF$$
$$FFSFS$$
$$FFFSS$$

This shows that the probability of $SFSFF$ is the same as the probability of $SSFFF$. In like manner, it turns out that the probability of each permutation in Table 4.2 is .03087. Knowing this, Kiblees can determine the desired probability, namely,

$$P\binom{\text{exactly 2 Chevys}}{\text{start out of 5}} = (2 \text{ successes in 5 trials})$$
$$= P(x = 2)$$
$$= \overbrace{P(S,S,F,F,F) + \ldots + P(F,F,F,S,S)}^{\text{ten}}$$
$$= \overbrace{.03087 + \ldots + .03087}^{\text{ten}}$$
$$= (10)(.03087)$$
$$= .3087$$

Several important ideas can be gleaned from the foregoing analysis. First, the probability of any given arrangement or permutation of two S's and three F's is the same as the probability of any other arrangement of the same number of S's and F's. Second, the probability of getting exactly two successes and hence three failures in five trials is equal to (10)(.03087), where ten is the total number of permutations of two S's and three F's and .03087 is the probability of any particular permutation. In other words,

$$P\binom{x = 2 \text{ successes}}{\text{in } n = 5 \text{ trials}} = \binom{\text{number of}}{\text{permutations of 2}}\binom{\text{probability of}}{\text{any particular}}$$
$$\text{successes in 5 trials} \quad \text{permutation}$$
$$= (10)(.03087)$$

By means of the foregoing logic, Kiblees could find the probability of exactly three Chevys starting by

$$P(x = 3 \text{ successes}) = \binom{\text{number of}}{\text{permutations of 3}}\left(\begin{array}{c}\text{probability of}\\ \text{any particular}\\ \text{permutation}\\ \text{of 3 successes}\\ \text{and 2 failures}\end{array}\right)$$
$$\text{successes in 5 trials}$$

Then, if there are ten different arrangments or permutations of three S's and two F's, and since the probability of a particular permutation like $SSSFF$ is p^3q^2 or $(.3)^3(.7)^2 = .01323$, it may be concluded that

$$P(x = 3 \text{ successes in 5 trials}) = (10)(.01323)$$
$$= .1323$$

Now a generalization can be made in the case where there are n trials and where p is the probability of success on any given trial. Letting x equal the total number of successes in n trials,

$$P\left(\begin{array}{c} x \text{ successes in} \\ n \text{ trials} \end{array}\right) = \left(\begin{array}{c} \text{number of} \\ \text{permutation of } x \\ \text{successes in } n \text{ trials} \end{array}\right)\left(\begin{array}{c} \text{probability of} \\ \text{any particular} \\ \text{permutation of} \\ x \text{ successes and} \\ n - x \text{ failures} \end{array}\right)$$

Instead of having to list all of the arrangements or permutations, mathematicians have developed a formula which quickly determines how many permutations there are. For the case where there are x successes and hence $n - x$ failures in a series of n trials, the total number of permutations or distinct arrangements is given by

$$\frac{n!}{x! \, (n - x)!}$$

(See Section 1.4 of Chapter 1 if you have forgotten what ! means.) Next, the probability of any particular arrangement of x successes and $n - x$ failures is

$$P(\overbrace{S, S, \ldots, S,}^{x} \overbrace{F, F, \ldots, F}^{n - x}) = \overbrace{pp \ldots p}^{x} \overbrace{qq \ldots q}^{n - x}$$
$$= p^x \, q^{n-x}$$

It then follows in the general case that

$$P\left(\begin{array}{c} x \text{ successes in} \\ n \text{ trials} \end{array}\right) = \left[\frac{n!}{x! \, (n - x)!}\right]\left[p^x \, q^{n-x}\right] \quad \begin{array}{c} \text{BINOMIAL} \\ \text{FORMULA} \end{array}$$

Number of Permutations   Probability of a Permutation

This expression shows how the probability of x successes may be determined, where x may range from 0 successes to n successes. Hence, this is the binomial distribution.

The rest of the distribution in the Kiblees case may be determined directly using the binomial formula. It has already been shown that $P(x = 2) = .3087$ and $P(x = 3) = .1323$; now the probabilities of the remaining values of x may be found:

$$P(x \text{ successes in } n \text{ trials}) = \frac{n!}{x! \, (n - x)!} p^x \, q^{n-x}$$

$$P(x = 0 \text{ successes in 5 trials}) = \frac{5!}{0!5!}(.3)^0(.7)^5$$

$$= \frac{5 \cdot 4 \cdot 3 \cdot 2 \cdot 1}{1 \cdot 5 \cdot 4 \cdot 3 \cdot 2 \cdot 1}(.3)^0(.7)^5$$

$$= (1)(.1681)$$

$$= .1681$$

$$P(x = 1 \text{ success}) = \frac{5!}{1!4!}(.3)^1(.7)^4$$

$$= \frac{5 \cdot 4 \cdot 3 \cdot 2 \cdot 1}{1 \cdot 4 \cdot 3 \cdot 2 \cdot 1}(.3)^1(.7)^4$$

$$= (5)(.07202)$$

$$= .3601$$

$$P(x = 4) = \frac{5!}{4!1!}(.3)^4(.7)^1$$

$$= .0284$$

$$P(x = 5) = \frac{5!}{5!1!}(.3)^5(.7)^0$$

$$= .0024$$

The complete binomial distribution for the Kiblees case is shown in Table 4.3.

TABLE 4.3_____

Binomial Distribution for Kiblees when $n = 5$, $p = .3$, and x equals the Number of Chevys that Start

x	$P(x)$
0	.1681
1	.3601
2	.3087
3	.1323
4	.0284
5	.0024
	1.0000

The binomial formula will now be used to determine probabilities in other examples. A film manufacturer produces rolls of film which undergo inspection before being shipped. In the past, about 10 percent of the rolls have had some sort of defect, and thus were rejected. If an inspector samples four rolls of film, what is the probability that exactly one of them will be defective? This situation is a Bernoulli process with $n = 4$ trials and where $p = .1$ if success refers to the film being defective. The probability of getting $x = 1$ defective is, therefore,

$$P(x = 1 \text{ in } n = 4 \text{ trials}) = \frac{4!}{1!3!}(.1)^1(.9)^3$$

$$= .2916$$

As a final example, an automobile dealership has found that about 80 percent of their new car purchasers buy on credit. Considering the next ten purchasers, what is the probability that exactly six will buy on credit? This situation is represented by a Bernoulli process, where $n = 10$ purchasers, $p = .80$, and $q = .20$. The probability of six successes is

$$P(x = 6) = \frac{10!}{6!4!}(.8)^6(.2)^4$$

$$= .0881$$

Characteristics of the Binomial Distribution

The binomial formula which has just been derived forms the basis of the binomial distribution. This formula was used, for example, in the Kiblees case for the sake of deriving the distribution of x, where x equals the number of Chevys which start in a test involving $n = 5$ batteries. This particular binomial distribution is given in Table 4.3. The expected value of x can be determined according to the definition set forth in Section 3.4 of Chapter 3. In particular,

$$E(x) = \Sigma x \, P(x)$$
$$= (0)(.1681) + (1)(.3601) + \ldots + (5)(.0024)$$
$$= 1.5 \text{ Chevys that start}$$

Likewise the variance and standard deviation could be determined according to the procedure of Section 3.5 of Chapter 3.

Because of the special nature of the binomial distribution, the mean, variance, and standard deviation may be determined according to an alternate shortcut procedure. For a Bernoulli process with n trials and where p is the probability of success in a given trial, the mean or expected value of x is

$$E(x) = np$$

and the variance and standard deviation are

$$\sigma^2 = npq$$

$$\sigma = \sqrt{npq}$$

The number of trials n and the probability of success p are called the *parameters* of the binomial distribution. The parameters identify the particular binomial distribution that is being considered from among the entire family of binomial distributions with varying n's and p's. Thus, the mean and standard deviation may be easily found, once the parameters are specified.

Recalling the Kiblees case, the mean of the binomial distribution of Table 4.3 may be found as

$$E(x) = np$$
$$= (5)(.3)$$
$$= 1.5$$

and the standard deviation is

$$\sigma = \sqrt{npq}$$
$$= \sqrt{(5)(.3)(.7)}$$
$$= 1.02$$

Binomial Table

Rather than using the binomial formula to compute binomial probabilities, Appendix B may be used to find these probabilities directly. In order to use Appendix B, the two parameters n and p must first be specified, and then the particular value for x must be identified. In the situation where there are $n = 10$ trials and $p = .20$, the probability of $x = 3$ successes may be found by first finding the n of 10 in the table and then moving horizontally to the column which is under $p = .20$. Finally the entry across from $x = 3$ is read; this is the desired probability, namely, $P(x = 3) = .2013$. Table 4.4 gives the appropriate part of Appendix B and shows where $P(x = 3)$ is found. Notice that the column of Appendix B which is reproduced in Table 4.4 is the complete binomial distribution whose parameters are $n = 10$ and $p = .20$. Several more examples will now be given to illustrate the use of Appendix B.

TABLE 4.4_____

Partial Binomial Table

n	x	.05	.10	.15	.20	.25	p .30	.35	.40	.45	.50
.	.				.						
.	.				.						
.	.				.						
.	.				.						
.	.				.						
10	0	.	.	.	.1074	.	.	.	.	.	.
	1				.2684						
	2				.3020						
	3	.	.	.	.2013	←$P(x = 3)$					
	4				.0881						
	5				.0264						
	6				.0055						
	7				.0008						
	8				.0001						
	9				.0000						
	10				.0000						
.	.										
.	.										
.	.										

In an electronic device that was originally designed to operate at room temperature, there are four components which are connected in series. The device is to be subjected to subzero temperatures for an extended period of time. Under these conditions there is a 40 percent chance that a component will work. What is the probability that the electronic device will work? In this case there are $n = 4$ trials (components), where success on a given trial refers to the proper functioning of the component. The parameter p is .40. The probability that the device works properly is equivalent to getting four successes in four trials. From Appendix B where $n = 4$ and $p = .40$,

$$P(\text{device works}) = P(x = 4 \text{ successes})$$
$$= .0256$$

At the Alphie Manufacturing plant there is a probability of .15 that there will be at least one accident in a day. Over a period of 20 days, what is the probability that there will be no more than three days with accidents? This is a Bernoulli process where $n = 20$ days and where $p = .15$ if a success refers to the occurrence of an accident(s). Letting the random variable x equal the total number of days in which there are accidents, the probability that x is less than or equal to three is desired. This may be found by breaking down the expression for $P(x \leq 3)$, and then using Appendix B:

$$P(x \leq 3) = P(x = 0) + P(x = 1) + P(x = 2) + P(x = 3)$$
$$= .0388 + .1368 + .2293 + .2428$$
$$= .6477$$

In the city of Dallas, ten thousand people have been approved for jury duty. Six thousand of the ten thousand people are women. If a jury of nine persons is to be randomly selected from the pool of ten thousand, what is the probability that women will be in the majority on the jury? In order to solve this problem, we first note that there are nine trials (persons selected), and that each person may be a woman (success) or a man (failure). The probability of a success on a trial equals .6, since 60 percent of the pool are women. Using Appendix B where $n = 9$ and $p = .6$, and letting x equal the total number of women on the jury,

$$P(\text{women in the majority}) = P(x \geq 5)$$
$$= P(5) + P(6) + P(7) + P(8) + P(9)$$
$$= .2508 + .2508 + .1612 + .0605$$
$$+ .0101$$
$$= .7334$$

Hence, the probability is .7334 that women will constitute a majority of the jury.

4.3

HYPERGEOMETRIC DISTRIBUTION

Van Gogh spent the summer painting in his cottage in Arles, which is in southern France. As a result of his efforts, six paintings have been produced. Unfortunately Van Gogh spilled catsup on two of the paintings before they were completely dry, thereby marring them. Instead of exhibiting each of the paintings and then seeking the best offer for each from the art dealers who have gathered at Arles to purchase his works, Van Gogh decided to sell his paintings sight unseen in sets of three to the two highest bidders. In doing this Van Gogh has said that he will randomly choose the three paintings which will go together to make a set.

Now suppose that the art dealer, Joyce Elaine, has submitted the highest bid, thereby entitling her to receive three paintings which will be randomly chosen from Van Gogh's six summer paintings. What, for example, is the probability that Joyce Elaine will end up with the two catsup paintings? with exactly one catsup painting? with no catsup painting?

One might be tempted to view the above situation as a Bernoulli process with three trials (paintings) and where a success refers to a catsup painting and a failure refers to a noncatsup painting. It should be remembered that with a Bernoulli process, the probability of success p must remain constant from trial to trial. In this case p, which would be the probability of a catsup painting, is not constant from trial to trial. For the first trial or painting, p would be 2/6. For the second painting, p would be either 1/5 or 2/5 depending on whether the first painting was or was not a catsup painting. Therefore, p does not remain constant from trial to trial. Since this is not a Bernoulli process, the binomial distribution cannot be used.

A distribution known as the *hypergeometric distribution* is appropriate for situations similar to that outlined above. If there is a collection or population of N items (like $N = 6$ paintings), of which A of them are successes (like $A = 2$ are catsup paintings) and B of them are failures (like $B = 4$ are noncatsup paintings), then the probability of getting exactly x successes and y failures in a sample of n items from the population is:

$$P\binom{x \text{ success and}}{y \text{ failures}} = \frac{\left(\dfrac{A!}{x!\,(A-x)!}\right)\left(\dfrac{B!}{y!\,(B-y)!}\right)}{\left(\dfrac{N!}{n!\,(N-n)!}\right)} \quad \begin{array}{l} \text{HYPERGEOMETRIC} \\ \text{FORMULA} \end{array}$$

This is the hypergeometric formula by which the hypergeometric distribution is computed. In hypergeometric situations, notice that $A + B = N$ and $x + y = n$.

Let us now use the hypergeometric formula to find the probabilities which Joyce Elaine is seeking. There is a collection or population of $N = 6$ paintings in Van Gogh's cottage. Of these, $A = 2$ are catsup paintings and $B = 4$ are noncatsup paintings. Van Gogh is going to randomly select $n = 3$ paintings from among the six and give them to Joyce Elaine, who was the highest bidder. The probability that Joyce Elaine will get $x = 2$ catsup paintings and $y = 1$ noncatsup painting is

$$P(x = 2, y = 1) = \frac{\left(\dfrac{2!}{2!\,(2-2)!}\right)\left(\dfrac{4!}{1!\,(4-1)!}\right)}{\left(\dfrac{6!}{3!\,(6-3)!}\right)}$$

$$= 4/20$$

Next, the probability that Joyce Elaine will get one catsup painting is

$$P(x = 1, y = 2) = \frac{\left(\dfrac{2!}{1!\,(2-1)!}\right)\left(\dfrac{4!}{2!\,(4-2)!}\right)}{\left(\dfrac{6!}{3!\,(6-3)!}\right)}$$

$$= 12/20$$

Finally, the probability of getting zero catsup paintings is

$$P(x = 0, y = 3) = \frac{\left(\dfrac{2!}{0!\,2!}\right)\left(\dfrac{4!}{3!\,1!}\right)}{\left(\dfrac{6!}{3!\,3!}\right)}$$

$$= 4/20$$

These three probabilities corresponding to x of 0, 1, and 2 form the hypergeometric distribution for this particular application.

Before leaving the hypergeometric distribution, a couple of comments might be made concerning the types of applications where this distribution is appropriate. Typically, the hypergeometric distribution is used where there is a relatively small population or collection consisting of two types of items (successes and failures), and where a sample of a considerable proportion of these items is drawn without replacement. The distribution will then give the probability of a specific number of successes occurring in this sample. All of the hypergeometric problems at the end of this chapter will fit this type of situation.

4.4

POISSON DISTRIBUTION

The third special purpose distribution to be studied is the Poisson distribution. The Poisson distribution is appropriate to situations where a Poisson process exists. In a *Poisson process*, some type of event occurs randomly along a continuum. For example, the continuum might be time and the event which occurs might be a telephone call. Starting at 8 a.m., telephone calls arrive at the catalog desk at Pennypinch department store. These calls typically arrive according to a random pattern along the continuum of time which stretches from 8 a.m. to 10 p.m. For instance, one call comes at 8:02, the next at 8:17, the next at 8:18, the next at 8:36, etc.

Another continuum encountered in Poisson processes is length. For example, a machine produces long strands of a fiber. Along the length of these strands, little imperfections occur at random points. Starting at the beginning of a strand there might be an imperfection 6 inches from the beginning, and then another imperfection at 94.3 inches from the beginning, and then another at 132.9 inches, another at 134.5 inches, another at 276.5 inches, and so on. Here, the imperfections (occurrences) occur randomly along a continuum of length.

The character of a Poisson process should now be more specifically stated. In a Poisson process,

1. Occurrences are random and independent along a continuum.

2. The probability of an occurrence from point to point along the continuum is constant.

3. The average or mean number of occurrences per unit of continuum is represented by λ (lambda). Lambda is the parameter of the Poisson distribution.

The Poisson distribution gives the probability of exactly x occurrences per unit of continuum. Letting λ equal the mean number of occurrences per unit of continuum,

$$P(x \text{ occurrences}) = \frac{e^{-\lambda}\lambda^x}{x!} \qquad \text{POISSON FORMULA}$$

In the expression above, the value of e is approximately 2.71828. Applications of the Poisson distribution will now be considered.

The computer at the auditing firm of Broda & Broda breaks down at random times, according to a Poisson process. The mean number of breakdowns per 80 hours of operation is λ = 2. In the next 80 hours of operation, what is the probability of no breakdowns? of exactly three breakdowns? Letting x equal the number of breakdowns in an 80 hour period of operation, the probability of $x = 0$ breakdowns is

$$P(x = 0) = \frac{e^{-2}\,2^0}{0!}$$
$$= 2.71828^{-2}$$
$$= .1353$$

The probability of exactly three breakdowns in the next 80 hours of operation is

$$P(x = 3) = \frac{e^{-2}\,2^3}{3!}$$

$$= .1804$$

Simplifying the expression on the right side in order to determine the desired probability is somewhat time consuming. Appendix P has been developed to permit the direct reading of such probabilities. For the case at hand, find the value of $\lambda = 2$ in Appendix P; then read below this lambda to the place across from $x = 3$. You will find the entry .1804, which is the probability of getting three occurrences or breakdowns in the 80 hour period of operation.

Let us now ask the question: what is the probability of 0 breakdowns in the next 80 hours, if in the previous few hours there have been a rash of breakdowns all of which have now been fixed? The probability of $x = 0$ breakdowns in the next 80 hours is still .1353 as found previously. This is because in a Poisson process the occurrences (breakdowns) are independent. In other words, what has gone on in the past has no influence on what will happen in the future; there is no memory to a Poisson process.

Suppose that Broda & Broda wishes to know the probability of breakdown-free operation in the next 20 hour period. In order to find this probability, the lambda must be adjusted to a 20 hour period. If there are an average of 2 breakdowns per 80 hours, then there will be an average of .5 breakdowns in a 20 hour period. This is because 20 hours is one fourth of 80 hours, and hence a lambda of .5 is appropriate which is one fourth of 2. Turning to Appendix P, when $\lambda = .5$,

$$P(x = 0) = .6065$$

Freighters arrive randomly and independently according to a Poisson process at the Port of New York. The average rate of arrivals is three per 24 hour period. What is the probability of the port having a busy day, where a busy day is one in which eight or more freighters arrive? From Appendix P, where $\lambda = 3$,

$$P(x \geq 8) = P(x = 8) + P(x = 9) + P(x = 10) + P(x = 11) + \ldots$$
$$= .0081 + .0027 + .0008 + .0002 + .0001 + .0000 + \ldots$$
$$= .0119$$

What is the probability that exactly two freighters will arrive in the next eight hours? Here, lambda must be adjusted to an eight hour period. This means that $\lambda = 1$ freighter per eight hours. From Appendix P, the desired probability is

$$P(x = 2) = .1839$$

While roaming around in the vicinity of Sweetwater, Texas in the spring, a hiker is apt to meet up with an average of 1.5 rattlesnakes per four miles traversed. What is the chance that a hiker taking an eight mile walk will meet up with less than two rattlers? By first adjusting the lambda we get $\lambda = 3$ rattlers per 8 miles. Then,

$$
\begin{aligned}
P(x < 2) &= P(0) + P(1) \\
&= .0498 + .1494 \\
&= .1992
\end{aligned}
$$

Before leaving this last example, it might be noted that one might question whether finding rattlers follows a Poisson process. If rattlers stay reasonably close to their dens, it follows that if you find one rattler at some location there is a better than average chance that you will stumble across another one from the same den within a very short distance. This in turn implies that such a process is not independent, since the occurrence of one rattler makes the occurrence of another within a short distance more likely than otherwise.

In concluding this discussion on the Poisson distribution, it might be noted that the mean of the distribution is

$$E(x) = \lambda$$

and the variance is

$$\sigma^2 = \lambda$$

The mean and the variance of the Poisson distribution are always the same as each other.

4.5

CONTINUOUS PROBABILITY DISTRIBUTIONS

The discussion of Chapter 3 and of Chapter 4 up to this point has been limited to discrete probability distributions. However, many times continuous variables (see Section 3.1 of Chapter 3) are encountered. It is now necessary to study probability distributions where the corresponding random variable is continuous.

In Section 3.2 of Chapter 3, it was shown that a discrete distribution may be represented by a graph such as is found in Figure 4.1. In this example the random variable X refers to the number of ping-pong tables that are sold in a day at a large department store. In this graph, the height of the block represents

FIGURE 4.1

Discrete Probability Distribution (X = Number of Ping-Pong Tables Sold)

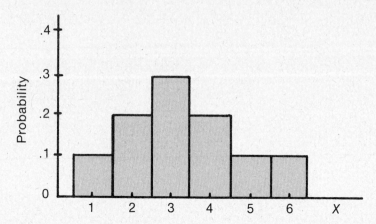

the probability. The probability of selling three tables is .3 since the block above $X = 3$ has a height of .3. This approach cannot be used when the random variable is continuous.

The Vice President of Personnel at Besnette Ltd. has just been approached by an employee group asking what pay raises will be next year. The Vice President then stated that raises will be anywhere from 4 percent to 8 percent (It is assumed that every employee will get the same percentage increase). The employee group then asked if the raise is more likely to be at the bottom or the top end of the 4–8 percent interval. The Vice President responded that every possible percentage raise between 4 percent and 8 percent was equally likely.

If the random variable R represents the pay raise, it is apparent that R may vary anywhere between 4 percent and 8 percent. Furthermore, R may be considered to be a continuous random variable since it can take on any value, such as 5.287 percent, along the continuum from 4 percent to 8 percent. Being a continuous random variable implies that there are actually an infinite number of possible values for R. It is therefore impossible to list all of these values. If a graph similar to that of Figure 4.1 were attempted for the distribution of R, it is apparent that there would have to be an infinite number of blocks squeezed in between 4 percent and 8 percent since there are an infinite number of R values between these two figures. Since this cannot be done, another way of graphing is needed if the distribution is continuous.

Figure 4.2 presents a graph of the continuous distribution of R. The first thing to notice is that although the height of the "curve" is .25, this does not imply that every value of R between 4 and 8

FIGURE 4.2

Continuous Distribution of Pay Raises

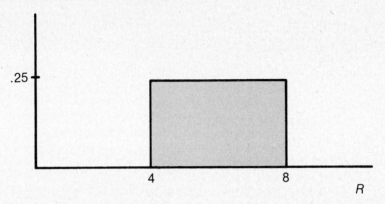

has a probability of .25. If each R value did have a probability of .25, they would add up to more than 1, since there are an infinite number of possible R values. Therefore, height cannot represent probability in the case of a continuous distribution. Rather, *area* represents probability. Notice that the total area under the curve in Figure 4.2 is 1. The height of the rectangle is .25 and the width of the rectangle is 4 (from 4 to 8), thus giving a total area of (.25)(4) = 1. It has previously been stated that the sum of the probabilities in any probability distribution must equal unity. Therefore, by letting area equal probability in this case, there is a total probability of 1, since the total area under the curve is 1. Thus, the probability of getting a raise between 4 percent and 8 percent is

$$P(4 \leq R \leq 8) = \text{area under the curve between } R \text{ values of 4 and 8}$$
$$= 1$$

Using the fact that area represents probability in a continuous distribution, the following probabilities may be determined:

$$P(4 \leq R \leq 6) = \text{area between 4 and 6}$$
$$= \text{shaded area in Figure 4.3a}$$
$$= (\text{height})(\text{width})$$
$$= (.25)(2)$$
$$= .50$$

and, $$P(5.5 \leq R \leq 6.25) = \text{area between 5.5 and 6.25}$$
$$= \text{shaded area in Figure 4.3b}$$
$$= (.25)(6.25 - 5.5)$$
$$= (.25)(.75)$$
$$= .1875$$

and, $P(R \geq 7.8)$ = shaded area in Figure 4.3c
                        = $(.25)(.20)$
                        = $.05$

FIGURE 4.3

Areas for the Rectangular Distribution of Pay Raises

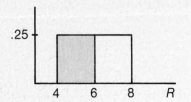
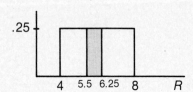

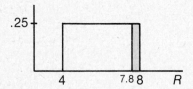

Finally, note that $P(4 < R < 6)$ is identical to $P(4 \leq R \leq 6)$ in the case of a continuous distribution. This is because the corresponding area above the $4 < R < 6$ interval is identical to the area above the $4 \leq R \leq 6$ interval; both have a width of four units. In dealing with continuous random variables, the "$\leq$" sign may be interchanged with the "$<$" sign; this is not true in the case of discrete random variables.

The continuous distribution under discussion is called a *rectangular distribution*. It is the simplest continuous distribution to work with, because finding areas (probabilities) is quite easy. The general form of the rectangular distribution, where X is the random variable which may take on any value between a and b, is

$$f(X) = \begin{cases} \dfrac{1}{b-a} & \text{for } a \leq X \leq b \\[2ex] 0 & \text{for other } X \end{cases}$$

The values of $f(X)$, when plotted, give a rectangular-shaped graph of the distribution. For example, if the Vice President had said that all raises between 2 percent and 9 percent are equally likely, then $a = 2$ and $b = 9$, which implies that the rectangle would have a height of $1/(9 - 2) = .143$ above all R values from 2 to 9. This distribution would have a total area of $(.143)(7) = 1$.

The mean and standard deviation of the rectangular distribution are

$$E(X) = \frac{a + b}{2}$$

$$\sigma = \sqrt{\frac{(b - a)^2}{12}}$$

4.6

NORMAL DISTRIBUTION

The most important distribution in probability and statistics is the normal distribution. The *normal distribution* is a continuous distribution having the familiar bell shape; it was mentioned briefly in Section 3.5 of Chapter 3. An example of the normal distribution is given in Figure 4.4

Since the normal distribution is a continuous distribution, the total area under the curve is unity. As indicated in Section 4.5, area represents probability. Finding areas under the normal

FIGURE 4.4

Daily Natural Gas Draw on the El Paseo Pipeline ($\mu = 200$, $\sigma = 10$)

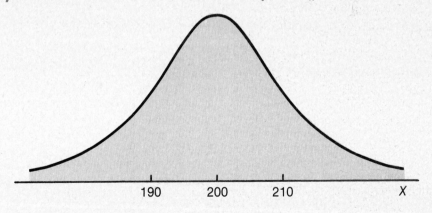

curve is more difficult than finding areas in the case of the rectangular distribution because of the irregular shape of the normal distribution. The method of finding areas (probabilities) for the normal distribution will now be considered. Applications giving rise to the normal distribution will be discussed later.

The El Paseo Natural Gas Company has a large pipeline which originates in the panhandle of Texas. The amount of natural gas which is drawn from this pipeline fluctuates daily. El Paseo has found that an average of $\mu = 200$ thousand cubic feet are drawn daily, and that the standard deviation of daily draws is ten thousand cubic feet. Furthermore, letting X be the random variable denoting the natural gas drawn in a day, X has a normal distribution. Figure 4.4 pictures this distribution of X.

Several probabilistic statements may immediately be made. For example, the probability that tomorrow's draw will exceed 200 thousand cubic feet is .5 since

$P(X > 200)$ = area under the curve from 200 to positive
             infinity
          = .5

This is true since the normal curve is symmetrical and the total area under the curve is 1. Likewise, $P(X < 200) = .5$. In Section 3.5 of Chapter 3 it was stated that if a probability distribution has the bell shape, then about 2/3 of the probability will fall within one standard deviation of the mean. In the El Paseo case, this means that there is a probability of about 2/3 that the draw on any given future day will be between 190 t.c.f. and 210 t.c.f., that is,

$P(X$ will be within 1 standard deviation of the mean)
$\qquad = P(X$ will be within 10 t.c.f. of 200)
$\qquad = P(190 \leq X \leq 210)$
$\qquad = 2/3$

In terms of the graph of Figure 4.4, this means that about 2/3 of the area under the curve lies between $X = 190$ and $X = 210$.

But what if El Paseo wishes to know the probability that the draw will fall between 200 and 215 t.c.f.? how can this probability be determined? Figure 4.5 has the area under the curve between 200 and 215 shaded; one might guess that this shaded area constitutes about 40 percent of the total area under the curve. This would lead us to estimate the probability to be about .40. Instead of relying on a visual estimate of the area between two points such as 200 and 215, a method has been derived to precisely measure this area (probability). This method will now be considered.

In the first place, if a probability like $P(200 \leq X \leq 215)$ is desired, the 200 and 215 must be converted to standard deviation units. The standard deviation units corresponding to any particular value of a random variable is merely the number of standard deviations that that particular value is from the mean. For instance, in the El Paseo case where the mean is $\mu = 200$ t.c.f. and

FIGURE 4.5

P(200 ≤ X ≤ 215) = Shaded Area

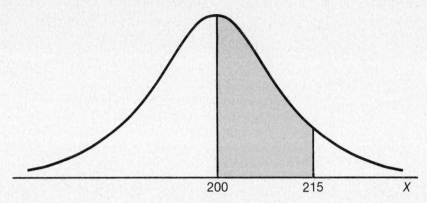

the standard deviation is $\sigma = 10$ t.c.f., a value of 220 is 2 standard deviations above the mean. A value of 190 is 1 standard deviation below the mean. A value of 215 is 1.5 standard deviations above the mean. Usually the standard deviation units are denoted by Z. Therefore, an X of 220 is equivalent to a Z of +2, an X of 190 is equivalent to a Z of -1, and a Z of 1.5 refers to an X of 215. The general relationship between Z and X is given by

$$Z = \frac{X - \mu}{\sigma}$$

For example, for $X = 200$

$$Z = \frac{200 - 200}{10}$$

$$= 0$$

and, for $X = 220$

$$Z = \frac{220 - 200}{10}$$

$$= 2$$

and, for $X = 197$

$$Z = \frac{197 - 200}{10}$$

$$= -.3$$

To repeat, the first step in finding normal areas or probabilities is to convert the values of the random variable to standard deviation units Z. In the case at hand the following conversion is made:

$$P(200 \le X \le 215) = P(0 \le Z \le 1.5)$$

The second and final step to finding normal probabilities is begun by turning to Appendix N in the back of the book. This appendix gives the areas under the normal curve from the center (mean) to some point which is Z standard deviation units above the mean. According to Appendix N, the area under *any* normal distribution from the mean ($Z = 0$) to a point which is 1.5 standard deviations above the mean ($Z = 1.5$) is .4332; that is, $P(0 \le Z \le 1.5)$ = .4332. This area is found by moving down the left margin to a Z of 1.5, and then moving horizontally to a position under the column labelled .00. The entry gives the area for a Z of 1.50. Hence the shaded region in Figure 4.5 has an area of .4332, which implies that

$$P(200 \le X \le 215) = .4332$$

Using Appendix N, many areas under the normal curve may be determined. For example, the area from $Z = 0$ to $Z = 2.11$ is .4826. This means that there is a probability of .4826 that the value of a random variable will fall between 0 and 2.11 standard deviations above the mean. Some other probabilities which may be directly read from Appendix N include $P(0 \le Z \le .34) = .1331$ and $P(0 \le Z \le 1.99) = .4767$.

Using Appendix N, each of the areas under the normal curve, as illustrated by the shaded areas in Figure 4.6, may be found. In Figure 4.6a the area between $Z = 0$ and $Z = -1.48$ is desired. According to Appendix N, the area from 0 to +1.48 standard deviations is .4306. Since the normal distribution is symmetrical about the mean, it may be concluded that the shaded area in Figure 4.6a is also .4306. In Figure 4.6b the area or probability beyond $Z = 2.13$ is desired. From Appendix N, it is seen that the area from 0 to 2.13 is .4834. Since the entire right half of the distribution has an area of .5000, the area beyond $Z = 2.13$ must be .5000 − .4834 = .0166. In Figure 4.6c the area from $Z = -.71$ to $Z = 1.82$ is desired. From Appendix N, the area from $Z = 0$ to $Z = -.71$ is .2611, and the area from $Z = 0$ to $Z = 1.82$ is .4656. Combining these two areas gives the total shaded area of .2611 + .4656 = .7267. Finally, in Figure 4.6d the area from $Z = .81$ to $Z = 1.35$ is sought. This area may be found by first finding the area from $Z = 0$ to 1.35 which is .4115.

FIGURE 4.6

Areas (Probabilities) under the Normal Curve

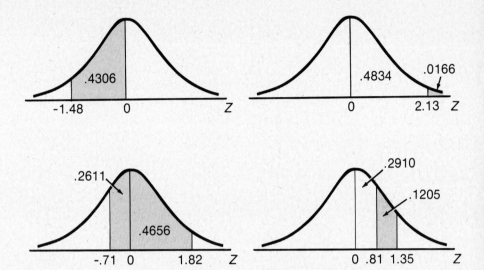

This means that .4115 is the entire area from the center out to Z = 1.35. But all of this area is not desired. Therefore, we must subtract from this the area from the center (Z = 0) out to Z = .81, which is an area of .2910 according to Appendix N. Thus the shaded area is .4115 − .2910 = .1205.

Because it is possible to find any area under the normal curve between or beyond various Z values, any normal distribution probability may be determined. Returning to El Paseo Natural Gas, where the daily gas draw X is normally distributed with a mean of 200 t.c.f. and a standard deviation of 10 t.c.f., the following probabilities may be found:

$$P(X \le 178.2) = P(Z \le -2.18) \quad \text{since } -2.18 = (178.2 - 200)/10$$
$$= .5000 - .4854$$
$$= .0146$$

$$P(190 \le X \le 214) = P(-1 \le Z \le 1.4)$$
$$= .3413 + .4192$$
$$= .7605$$

$$P(115 \le X \le 125) = P(1.5 \le Z \le 2.5)$$
$$= .4938 - .4332$$
$$= .0606$$

The areas or probabilities just found are analogous to those of Figure 4.6b, 4.6c, and 4.6d, respectively.

One topic yet remains in mastering the determination of probabilities from a normal distribution. El Paseo wants to answer the question: "The daily gas draw from the pipeline will exceed how many t.c.f. on 10 percent of the days?" In other words, "Find the value K such that $P(X > K) = .10$." Figure 4.7 shows the value K such that 10 percent of the area under the normal curve lies beyond it. In order to find K, we must first realize that the area must be .40 under the normal curve from $X = 200$ to $X = K$ if the area to the right of K is to be .10. We next turn to Appendix N and

FIGURE 4.7_____

Finding K such that $P(X > K) = .10$

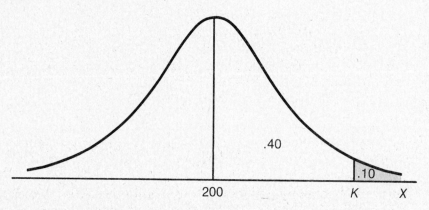

look in the heart of the table (where areas are given) for a value as close to .40 as possible. The closest areas to .40 in this table are .3997 and .4015. Since .3997 is closer to .40, we will discard .4015 from further consideration. Now we ask ourselves how many standard deviation units is associated with the area of .3997. By reading out to the margins, it appears that .3997 is the area for 1.28 standard deviation units. This implies that by going $Z = 1.28$ standard deviation units above the mean, an area of about .40 (actually .3997) is covered. Since the K of Figure 4.7 has an area of .40 between it and the mean, it follows that K must be 1.28 standard deviations above the mean. Therefore,

$K =$ a value which is 1.28 standard deviations above the
     mean
  = mean + (1.28) (standard deviation)
  = 200 + (1.28)(10)
  = 212.8 t.c.f.

The probability that the daily draw will exceed 212.8 t.c.f. is therefore .10, that is, $P(X > 212.8) = .10$.

As one more example of this process, suppose El Paseo wants to know what value of X separates the lowest 30 percent of the days from the top 70 percent of the days. Let this value of X be denoted by B as shown in Figure 4.8. The area between B and the mean is .20. Scanning the areas in the heart of Appendix N for an area as close as possible to .20, we find .1985. According to Appendix N, the area from $Z = 0$ to $Z = -.52$ is .1985 (which is about .20).

FIGURE 4.8

Finding B such that $P(X < B) = .30$

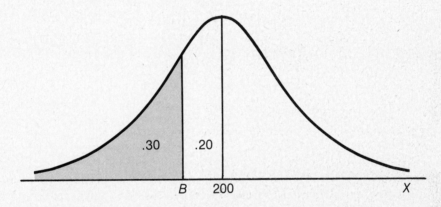

Thus by going .52 standard deviations below the mean, an area of about .20 is covered. Since B has an area of .20 between itself and the mean, it must be concluded that B is .52 standard deviations below the mean:

B = a value which is .52 standard deviations below the mean
$= 200 + (-.52)(10)$
$= 194.8$ t.c.f.

Therefore, $P(X < 194.8) = .30$ and $P(X \geq 194.8) = .70$.

4.7

APPLICATION OF THE NORMAL DISTRIBUTION

The normal distribution has many applications because many natural phenomena are normally distributed. For example, IQ scores are normally distributed for persons of age 10. The lives of many manufactured items, like tires, may be normally distributed. The annual amount of precipitation in certain locales is normally distributed. The reaction times of a driver may be normally distributed. And, if you were to measure the distance between two mountain peaks again and again, you would find that the measurements would tend to be normally distributed if organized in a frequency distribution. The normal distribution would be important if only for such reasons; however, in Chapter 6 an entirely new application of the normal distribution will be studied. This use of the normal distribution, which will be explained in Chapter 6, establishes the normal as the most important distribution in statistics. The applications to be presented in this section will not touch on this extremely important use of the normal distribution. Rather, a couple of applications similar to the El Paseo case will now be presented in order to complete the current discussion of the normal distribution.

One of the most severe problems in the southwestern United States is the scarcity of water. States like California have constructed huge aqueducts to transport water to the arid regions of southern California. One of the hotly contested water resources is the Colorado River, which begins in Colorado and flows through Utah and Arizona and then forms the border between Arizona and California. Arizona and California in particular have warred over the water of the Colorado. Although Arizona has been awarded an "equitable" amount of the flow, Arizona remains somewhat peeved at California with its big appetite for water. Now that Arizona has been awarded Colorado River water, a large project called the Central Arizona Project has been instituted by Arizonians. With the CAP, a large aqueduct is being constructed starting from the Colorado River at the Arizona-California border and ending in central Arizona. As might be suspected, various environmental groups have opposed the construction of such an aqueduct, and so Arizona has a pair of adversaries in California and the environmentalists.

At about this time Arizonians elected Maxwellus Smart as Director of Water Resources and Delivery Systems. As a campaign promise, Smart vowed to wage covert warfare against both California and the environmentalists. In fact, Smart promised that by the end of his four-year term as Director of WRDS he would have laid the groundwork for a major surprise for California and the environmentalists. It turns out that the normal distribution figured to be important in two aspects of Smart's plan.

Briefly stated, it was Smart's plan to drill a huge tunnel extending from Phoenix to the bottom of Lake Tahoe. The Mole Man of Alcatraz was retained as consulting engineer for this undercover operation. Smart first asked the mole man how many months the tunneling would take. The mole man had used a planning method known as PERT to schedule all the activities associated with the tunnel construction. One of the advantages of using PERT for planning projects such as this one is that a probabilistic estimate of the total project time can be made.[1] As a result, the mole man said that if the random variable T represents the total time for the tunneling, then T would be normally distributed with a mean of 40 months and a standard deviation of four months. This distribution will be used in a few moments.

Now it was Smart's plan that once the tunnel was finished, Arizona would drain off small amounts of Lake Tahoe water each year. In fact, Arizona would drain off the same amount of water each year as flowed into the lake. The California Water Resources Board has published information stating that the annual runoff, R, into Lake Tahoe is normally distributed with a mean of 100,000 acre feet and a standard deviation of 30,000 acre feet. Therefore, Arizona could expect to swipe an average of 100,000 acre feet each year and still leave the lake at the same water level. If Arizona took just the annual runoff, California would be none the wiser and the environmentalists would not suspect that the gem of lakes was being tampered with. However, if either California or the environmentalists got nasty about some other issue like the Colorado River water, it was Smart's grandiose plan to fix their wagons in one fell swoop. In particular, Smart would order the tunnel gate at the bottom of the lake opened all the way, thereby draining the entire lake in one night.

Let us now consider how the two normal distributions cited above figure into this scheme. First of all, the time T to construct the tunnel was said to be normally distributed with a mean of 40 weeks and a standard deviation of four weeks. Smart has just taken office on the heels of his promise to have his plan fulfilled by the time he leaves office in 48 months or four years. What is the probability that if the project starts immediately it will be completed in 48 months? Smart wishes to find $P(T \leq 48)$. First, the T of 48 must be converted into standard deviation units:

$$Z = \frac{T - \mu}{\sigma}$$

$$= \frac{48 - 40}{4}$$

$$= 2$$

This means that

$$P(T \leq 48) = P(Z \leq 2)$$

---

[1]PERT is an acronym for Program Evaluation and Review Technique. This planning technique is typically studied in a course on management science.

From Appendix N, the area between the center of the normal distribution to a point $Z = 2$ standard deviations above is .4772. Since the area of the entire left side of the normal is .5000, it follows that

$$
\begin{aligned}
P(T \leq 48) &= P(Z \leq 2) \\
&= P(Z \leq 0) + P(0 \leq Z \leq 2) \\
&= .5000 + .4772 \\
&= .9772
\end{aligned}
$$

Therefore, there is a probability of .9772 that Smart can keep his promise.

Once the tunnel is completed, Arizona will take only the annual runoff R, thus leaving the lake water level constant. R is normally distributed with a mean of 100,000 acre feet and a standard deviation of 30,000 acre feet. Under these circumstances what is the probability that the water taken in a year will fall below 50,000 acre feet? This may be found by

$$
\begin{aligned}
P(R < 50{,}000) &= P(Z < -1.67) \\
&= .5000 - .4525 \\
&= .0475
\end{aligned}
$$

There is therefore only a .0475 probability that Arizona will get less than 50,000 acre feet in a year. Finally, in the 15 percent of the years where the runoff is its greatest, how much water will Arizona get? Here we are seeking the value of W where $P(R \geq W)$ = .15. If an area of .15 lies above W on the normal distribution of runoff, then .35 is the area between the mean and the point W. Scanning the heart of Appendix N for a value as close to .35 as possible yields .3508. According to this, there is an area of .3508 between $Z = 0$ and $Z = 1.04$. Therefore, W must be 1.04 standard deviations above the mean, or

$$
\begin{aligned}
W &= 100{,}000 + (1.04)(30{,}000) \\
&= 131{,}200
\end{aligned}
$$

Smart may therefore conclude that in 15 percent of the years, Arizona will receive 131,200 acre feet or more.

PROBLEMS

4.1

Describe a Bernoulli process and give two examples of a Bernoulli process which are not given in the text.

4.2

An urn contains ten marbles of which four are purple. If three marbles are to be drawn in succession, does this constitute a Bernoulli process where a success is equivalent to a purple marble?

4.3

Consider a process which consists of ten monthly purchases of a tube of toothpaste by a homemaker. Let the purchase of Coldent toothpaste represent a success and the purchase of any other brand represent a failure. Why might this process not be Bernoulli?

4.4

Use the binomial formula to find each of the following probabilities:
(a) $P(x = 1)$ if $n = 4$ and $p = .3$
(b) $P(x = 0)$ if $n = 5$ and $p = .8$
(c) $P(x \leq 1)$ if $n = 3$ and $p = .2$

4.5

Use the binomial table of Appendix B in order to find the following probabilities:
(a) $P(x = 4)$ and $P(x = 5)$ if $n = 10$ and $p = .2$
(b) $P(x = 0)$ and $P(x = 2)$ if $n = 20$ and $p = .1$
(c) $P(x \leq 3)$ and $P(x > 3)$ if $n = 15$ and $p = .3$
(d) $P(x \leq 1)$ and $P(x \geq 2)$ if $n = 8$ and $p = .15$
(e) $P(x \geq 4)$ and $P(x \geq 1)$ if $n = 6$ and $p = .20$
(f) $P(1 \leq x \leq 5)$ and $P(0 < x < 6)$ if $n = 12$ and $p = .25$
(g) $P(4 \leq x \leq 7)$ and $P(4 < x < 7)$ if $n = 10$ and $p = .4$
(h) If there are 10 trials and the probability of success on a trial is .7, find the probability of getting 4 successes.
(i) If there are eight trials and the probability of success is .8, find $P(2$ successes$)$.
(j) $P(x = 3)$ if $n = 20$ and $q = .95$

4.6

How many permutations are there of two successes and four failures in six trials?

4.7

Empty Dr. Soda bottles are checked one by one before they are washed and refilled. About 10 percent of the incoming bottles are chipped and hence discarded. In the next batch of 20 bottles, what is the probability that none will be chipped? that two or fewer will be chipped? that three or more will be chipped? What is the expected number of chipped bottles in a batch of 20?

4.8

The United States Air Force has found that the Minuteman missile misses its target 10 percent of the time and the Secondwoman missile misses only 5 percent of the time. If eight Minuteman missiles are launched, what is the probability that none of the missiles will miss the target? If eight Secondwoman missiles are launched, what is the probability than none will miss their targets?

4.9

If it is given that 20 percent of the families in America own a Koduck camera, what is the probability that exactly three have a Koduck camera in a sample of 15 families? What is the probability that more than half of the families in a sample of 15 own a Koduck camera?

4.10

A television dealer has found that 5 percent of the televisions installed need some kind of service within a month. If 18 televisions have been installed recently, what is the probability that two or more will need to be serviced within a month? What is the expected number of televisions that will need service within a month?

4.11

In a 20 question multiple-choice test with five answers for each question, what is the probability of getting six or more correct answers by pure guessing?

4.12

Of the throat cultures taken at a certain clinic, 30 percent proved to be strep. If five cultures are taken today, what is the probability that none are strep? that more than one is strep?

4.13

Of the packages shipped by Greypooch, 85 percent arrive at their appointed destination within two days. If ten packages are shipped at various times, what is the probability that all of them will arrive within two days? that exactly eight will arrive within two days? Why was it important to state that the ten packages were shipped at "various times"?

4.14

A stockbroker for E. F. Hutton claims that 90 percent of the purchase orders placed by their customers are executed and confirmed within 15 minutes. What is the probability that six or more of the next seven purchase orders are confirmed within 15 minutes?

4.15

Of the oil wells in a certain field in east Texas, 60 percent prove to have more oil than anticipated. If you buy three wells from this field, what is the probability that at least one of the wells will have more oil than anticipated?

4.16

Using the binomial table of Appendix B, write out the binomial distribution for $n = 5$ and $p = .2$. Then compute the mean and variance of this distribution. Finally, compute the mean and variance by the shortcut formulas.

4.17

The random variables Y and X are related by $Y = 100X - 10$. If X has a binomial distribution with parameters of 18 and .4, find the expected value of Y.

4.18

Ramo Manufacturing has purchased 20 electronic components from a supplier which states that 15 percent of the components they sell are defective. Ramo has to repair a defective component at a cost of $300 per component. What is the expected number of defective components, and what is the expected repair cost?

4.19

The probability that a vital link in an assembly line at a sewing machine factory will break down in a day is .05. If it breaks down, the entire line is shut down for that day — this costs the manufacturer $10,000 in lost revenues. What is the expected lost revenues over a period of 20 days? What is the probability that the link will not break down in a 20-day period?

4.20

Seven persons have been qualified for the next space flight to Jupiter. One of the seven is a woman. The space agency has decided

to randomly choose the crew of three from among the seven qualified astronauts. What is the probability that the woman will not be
one of the three crew members?

4.21

Wells-Fargo is sending five stages from Denver to various locations. On two of the stages, an agent is hiding that is an expert
shotgun sharpshooter. The James Brothers have decided to attack
three of the stages. What is the probability that the Brothers will
meet zero agents? exactly one agent? exactly two agents? exactly
three 3 agents?

4.22

There are eight circuits in a system. From tests of the system, the
analyst has determined that three of the circuits are malfunctioning. If the analyst, who does not know which are the malfunctioning circuits, proceeds to check six of the circuits, what is the probability that the three malfunctioning circuits will be among the
six that are checked?

4.23

Describe the Poisson process and give two examples of a Poisson
process that are not mentioned in the text.

4.24

Find the following probabilities using the Poisson formula:
(a) $P(x = 0)$ and $P(x = 2)$ if $\lambda = 1$
(b) $P(x = 3)$ if $\lambda = 2$
(c) Estimate $P(x = 0)$ if $\lambda = 100$

4.25

Find the following probabilities using the Poisson table of Appendix P:
(a) $P(x = 1)$ if $\lambda = 2$
(b) $P(x = 3)$ if $\lambda = 2$
(c) $P(x = 0)$ if $\lambda = 1.5$
(d) $P(x \leq 2)$ and $P(x > 2)$ if $\lambda = 4$
(e) $P(x \geq 5)$ and $P(x \leq 4)$ if $\lambda = .5$
(f) $P(1 \leq x \leq 3)$ if $\lambda = 1$
(g) $P(4 \leq x < 7)$ if $\lambda = 3$

4.26

Cars arrive at a tollbooth on the Turner Turnpike according to a
Poisson process at an average of six per ten minutes. What is the

probability of exactly two cars in the next ten minutes? of exactly one car in the next five minutes?

4.27

Accidents occur randomly at a steel mill at the rate of 1.5 per month. What is the probability of no accidents next month? What is the probability of less than two accidents in the next two-month period? What is the expected number of accidents in a year?

4.28

Imperfections occur randomly in a certain fabric at a rate of three per 100 yards of fabric. What is the probability that the next 100 yards will have no imperfections? What is the probability of more than six imperfections in the next 100 yards? What is the probability of no imperfections in a 50 yard piece? What is the expected number of imperfections in a 50 yard piece?

4.29

In a large office building the plumbing crews get calls for service according to a Poisson process at the rate of five calls per hour. The crews are "extremely busy" if ten or more calls are received in an hour. What is the probability that the crews will be extremely busy during the next hour? What is the probability of no calls in the next hour? What is the expected number of calls in an eight hour day?

4.30

Workers for the S & F Railroad have found that an average of three ties must be replaced per mile of track. What is the probability that no ties will need replacing in the next mile? that three or fewer will need replacing? If it costs $30 to replace a tie, what is the expected cost to replace the ties over the next ten-mile stretch of track? What is the standard deviation of the cost?

4.31

Professor Helmuth states that the rate of inflation, r, for next year has the following probability distribution:

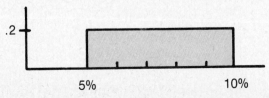

Find the following probabilities for this continuous distribution.

(a) $P(r \geq 6)$ and $P(r > 6)$
(b) $P(r \leq 7)$ and $P(r < 7)$
(c) $P(8 < r < 9.5)$ and $P(8 \leq r \leq 9.5)$

4.32

The time t that a mercury vapor lamp will last under subzero temperatures is given by the following continuous probability distribution. What is the probability that the lamp will last more than one year?

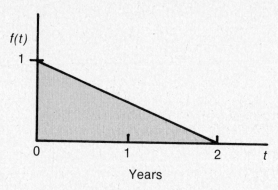

4.33

The n-ach ratios for the employees of Alphy-Gro Corporation have the rectangular distribution given by

$$f(y) = \begin{cases} .1 & \text{for } 30 \leq y \leq 40 \\ 0 & \text{for other } y \end{cases}$$

where y represents the n-ach ratio. Draw the graph of this distribution. What is the probability that an employee chosen at random has an n-ach ratio of 33.5 or more? What is the expected value of y and the standard deviation?

4.34

Convert each of the following values of X to standard deviation units, assuming that the expected value of X is 140 and the standard deviation is 20.
(a) $X = 140$
(b) $X = 145$
(c) $X = 157$
(d) $X = 130$
(e) $X = 95$
(f) $X = 106.4$

4.35

If Y is normally distributed with a mean of 24 and a standard deviation of six, find the following probabilities:

(a) $P(Y > 24)$ (e) $P(20 \leq Y \leq 30)$
(b) $P(Y \geq 24)$ (f) $P(16 < Y < 22)$
(c) $P(Y > 29)$ (g) $P(30 \leq Y < 36.5)$
(d) $P(Y \geq 18)$ (h) $P(Y > 42)$

4.36

The normal distribution of V has a mean of 800 and a standard deviation of 50. Find the value of K (which is a specific value of V) which makes each of the following true:
(a) $P(V \geq K) = .10$
(b) $P(V < K) = .30$
(c) $P(V > K) = .02$

4.37

A box of "Little Donuts" cereal contains, as printed on the box, 425 grams of tasty little rings. In packing the cereal, machines are set to put an average of 428 grams into each box. Of course, it's impossible to get exactly 428 grams in each box. The grams, g, that go into the boxes are normally distributed with a mean of 428 and a standard deviation of 1.5 grams. With such a packaging process what is the probability that the box of cereal you purchase will have less than 425 grams?

4.38

A lightbulb manufacturer claims that the average life of its EKM projector bulbs is 20 hours with a standard deviation of three hours. What is the probability that the EKM you purchase will last less than 15 hours? more than 24 hours? Assume that the bulb lives are normally distributed.

4.39

Dayspring Electric states that the time it will take to complete an electrical job at Fort Huachuca is normally distributed with a mean of 14 months and a standard deviation of 2 months. What is the probability that the job can be completed in 13 months or less? What is the probability that it will be completed within 1 month of 14 months? There is a 10 percent chance that the job will take how many months or more?

4.40

New MBA students at Northern Arizona University must take the GMAT examination. The scores achieved by the incoming students are normally distributed with a mean of 500 and a standard deviation of 50. What proportion of the students score below 425?

If NAU gives a scholarship to the top 15 percent of the students, what score must be achieved in order to get a scholarship?

4.41

A truck in transit during the winter from Cameron, Arizona to Denver can take either of two routes. The first is the shorter, taking the truck through the Rockies over Wolf Creek Pass. Depending on road conditions, this route could be very slow or very fast. The time for this route is normally distributed with a mean of 12 hours and a standard deviation of 5 hours. The longer route goes south via Flagstaff and Albuquerque. The time for this route is normally distributed with a mean of 15 hours and a standard deviation of 1 hour. Which route offers the higher probability of arriving in Denver in less than 16 hours?

4.42

The annual toll revenues for the Pennsylvania Turnpike are normally distributed with a mean of $800,000 and a standard deviation of $60,000. What is the probability that the turnpike will be able to cover its operating expenses which are $750,000 per year? In the best 20 percent of the years, the toll revenue exceeds what figure? Using the multiplication law of probability for independent events, what is the probability that the turnpike would make less than $750,000 in two successive years?

4.43

The monthly demand for a company's product is normally distributed with a mean of 4,000 units and a variance of 250,000. The company can produce the product at a maximum rate of 5,000 units per month. What is the probability that production cannot keep up with demand next month?

4.44

A company produces resistors with a mean resistance of 2,000 ohms and a standard deviation of 12 ohms. Each resistor is tested. What proportion of the resistors will have a resistance of more than 2.5 standard deviations away from the mean?

4.45

The accounts receivable held by Kaibab Industries have a mean value of $1,450 and a standard deviation of $80. If an auditor samples one account, what is the probability that it is under $1,400? If two are sampled, what is the probability that both are under $1,400?

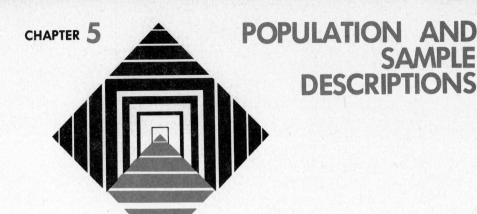

CHAPTER 5

POPULATION AND SAMPLE DESCRIPTIONS

5.1

TRANSITION

This chapter marks a major transition from the subject of probability to that of statistics. Probability is concerned with answering questions like "What is the probability of getting a stock which pays a dividend?" or "What is the probability of getting two defective transistors in a sample of ten transistors from this shipment?" It is very important to notice that probability questions like these always make reference, either implicitly or explicitly, to two distinct entities, namely,

1. a population
2. a sample.

For example, in the first question above, the population might consist of all the stocks traded on the New York Stock Exchange. From this population of over a thousand stocks, a sample of one stock is to be randomly selected. Probability theory tells how likely a particular sample result is. Likewise, in the second question dealing with transistors, there is a population or shipment of transistors, some of which are defective and the rest of which are good. From this population a random sample of ten is taken. Through probability theory (the binomial distribution), the likelihood of getting a particular result like two defective transistors can be determined. As in the first case with the stocks, the probability of the sample result is determined on the basis of the nature or make-up of the population.

In summary, probability theory as presented in Chapters 2 through 4 deals with determining the probability of getting some

particular sample result when the sample is drawn from a population whose make-up is given. This concept bears repeating. First, a
population is given. Once this population is described, probability
theory can tell us what the chances are of getting some particular
sample result.

If probability theory deals with finding the probability of some
sample result when the sample is taken from a known population,
what is statistics all about? Statistics might be thought of as being
something of the reverse. In statistics, we are presented with a
sample result and then asked to infer something about the population from which that sample was drawn. Here is a huge batch or
population of thousands of projector bulbs. Someone has randomly
sampled 30 of the bulbs and found that the average life of these 30
bulbs is 22.4 hours. What can be inferred about the entire population of bulbs from which the sample of 30 was taken? This is the
kind of question that statistics deals with. More precisely, this is
what *analytic* or *inferential statistics* is all about.

In order to be able to make inferences about a population (like
the entire batch of projector bulbs) on the basis of a sample, two
prerequisites must be satisfied. First, the analyst must have an
understanding of probability theory. We shall see that probability
is constantly being used in inferential statistics. Most of the probability that will be needed has already been presented in Chapters
2 through 4. However, a little more probability which is very
closely tied to inferential statistics is needed and will be presented
in Chapter 6. The second prerequisite to a full-scale study of inferential statistics is descriptive statistics. *Descriptive statistics* simply deals with describing a population or a sample. Descriptive
statistics has already been implicitly encountered in our discussion of probability theory; this will become evident in Chapter 5,
which is devoted to a full treatment of descriptive statistics. With
the ensuing discussion of descriptive statistics and probability
theory, we will be in a good position to study inferential statistics.

5.2

DESCRIPTIVE STATISTICS PRELIMINARIES

Descriptive statistics has just been defined as being that
branch of statistics which is concerned with the description of a
sample or a population. Through descriptive statistics, the data in
a sample or population is organized, summarized, and presented.
Since a sample is taken from a population, it would be accurate to
conclude that a sample is usually described in much the same way
as the population from which the sample is derived. We shall see,

for example, that one way of describing a sample is by averaging all of the values in the sample; this average will be denoted symbolically by $\overline{X}$. Similarly, all the values in the entire population from which the sample is drawn may be averaged; the average of the population will be denoted by the Greek letter μ. An important convention should now be emphasized:

1. Characteristics of a population are usually denoted by Greek letters. These characteristics are called *parameters*.

2. Characteristics of a sample will be denoted by English letters. These characteristics are called *statistics*.

Before embarking upon a consideration of how a sample and how a population can be described, make sure that you have a clear idea as to the difference between a sample and a population. For example, the ten people gathered at the Rocky Mountain Fur Company rendezvous (in Section 2.4 of Chapter 2) constitute a population. From this population one person was selected for the door prize; this person is the sample. As another example, a population might consist of all the flounders in Chesapeake Bay. From this population of thousands of flounders, a sample of five flounders may be taken. As yet another example, a population might consist of all the students enrolled in a statistics course in the United States. From this population a sample of 25 students might be selected. Finally, the cook's big kettle of soup might be the population from which a sample of the size of a tablespoon is taken. In each of these examples, the sample is a randomly selected part of the entire population. Descriptive statistics deals with describing the characteristics of the sample and/or the population. The remainder of this chapter will be devoted to a consideration of descriptive statistics.

5.3

DESCRIBING DATA

Suppose you were taking a friend from Oregon around New York City. Your friend becomes particularly interested in a certain skyscraper and asks you, "How big is that building?" This question can be answered in many ways since the term "big" may refer to many different characteristics of a building. You might answer "The building is 80 stories tall," or "It is 986 feet tall," or "It has 3.2 million square feet of floor space," or "Ten thousand people work in the building," and so on. With these various answers you are attempting to describe the "bigness" or size of the building. One could go on forever giving measurements which continue to describe the size of the building. Nevertheless, most of us would be content with a description in terms of one dimension like the number of stories. The number of stories, therefore, becomes a *descriptive measure* of the size of the building.

The sports page in a local newspaper will often list the starting players for an upcoming football game. How many things could be said about Bruno Burp, the starting fullback? The paper could list how many teeth Bruno has, how many sore throats he has had in the past five years, how much sleep he gets each night, what his serum cholesterol level is, and so forth. But instead of printing the aforementioned data, the paper is more inclined to describe Bruno by a very few descriptive measures like height, weight, and speed. These three descriptive measures would satisfy most fans.

Suppose that instead of having a building or a football player, there is a set of numbers such as

$$\{45, 96.7, 3.22, 8, 23, 100\}$$

Now assume that you are called upon to say a word of general description concerning this set of numbers. There might be many things that could be said about these six numbers, just as there were many things which could be said about the size of the building or about the football player. However, just as a few measurements seemed to suffice in describing an otherwise complex object like a building or football player, so there might be a few measurements regarding this set of numbers which would provide an adequate description. We shall now consider the matter of presenting or organizing sets of data, and then we will study methods of briefly, but adequately, describing the data.

5.4

UNGROUPED AND GROUPED DATA

The number of checks that a bank must clear in a day varies. For example, over the past five Tuesdays the Bank of Megatown has cleared 10,000, 14,000, 12,000, 12,000, and 11,000 checks. The set of these five Tuesday clearings

$$\{10,000, 14,000, 12,000, 12,000, 11,000\}$$

constitutes a set of *ungrouped data*. Each actual value appears in the set; there is no attempt to lump together any of the data.

The Bank of Megatown also keeps daily records on how many people seek service from one of their automatic tellers. Over the past 100 operating days, for example, there were 10 days when from 50 to 99 customers used the automatic teller, 17 days when from 100 to 149 used the automatic teller, and so on. This information is presented in Table 5.1. Here the data is presented in *grouped* form. In particular, the table is known as a *frequency distribution*. In a frequency distribution, various classes (like 50–99, 100–149, 150–199, etc.) are listed along with the frequency of observations in each class. If on the right the percentage of days is recorded instead of the actual number or frequency of days for each class, then this table would be called a *relative frequency distribution*. The relative frequency distribution corresponding to Table 5.1 would indicate that on 10 percent of the days, from 50–99 customers used the automatic teller; on 17 percent of the days, from 100–149 used the teller; and so on. Regardless of the form of the frequency distribution, it is obviously much easier to present a large amount of data by using a frequency distribution than by stringing out each individual value as when the data is presented in an ungrouped format.

In constructing a frequency distribution for the sake of presenting data, a few principles should be kept in mind. *First*, the classes should be mutually exclusive. To say that the classes must be mutually exclusive means that they must not overlap. If the first class is 50–99, the second must not, for example, be something like 95–149. *Second*, the classes must be collectively exhaustive. This means that there should be no gaps between the classes and that the highest and lowest classes must encompass the highest and lowest observations. If the first class is 50–99 and the second is 105–149, for example, then this requirement of exhaustive classes would not be satisfied, since there would be no way to record an observation of 102. *Third*, it is usual practice to make each class the same width. Each class in the Bank of Megatown example is 50 units wide. Occasionally the first and last classes are

TABLE 5.1_____

Frequency Distribution for the Daily Number of Customers Using the Automatic Teller

Classes (Customers)	Frequencies (Days)
50–99	10
100–149	17
150–199	43
200–249	19
250–299	11
	100

open-ended, as would be the case if the last class were 250–above. Open-ended classes are appropriate when there are a relatively few observations which are especially high or low. In the *fourth* place, the number of classes must be considered. Typically, from 5 to 15 classes are used in a frequency distribution. The purpose for which the data are being assembled will guide in determining how many classes should be used. If only a very general overview is needed, then a relatively few classes will suffice.

In concluding this section on the form of data, it should be noted that data in a sample or data in a population may be presented either in an ungrouped or grouped form.

5.5

HISTOGRAMS

It is often helpful to graphically display the data from a frequency distribution. A graphical presentation enables the analyst to quickly get a feel for the data. The most common method of graphing a frequency distribution is by means of a *histogram*. In a histogram, a block is drawn above each class such that the height of the block corresponds to the class frequency. For example, Figure 5.1 portrays a histogram based on the Bank of Megatown frequency distribution of Table 5.1. The reader should note that a histogram is very similar to the graph of a discrete probability distribution, as was presented in Section 3.2 of Chapter 3.

FIGURE 5.1

Histogram for Frequency Distribution of Table 5.1

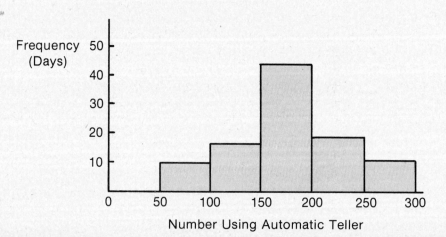

5.6

CUMULATIVE DISTRIBUTIONS AND OGIVES

It has already been shown that a frequency distribution is a convenient way to present data. A special type of frequency distribution is occasionally used instead of the noncumulative type which was introduced in Section 5.4. This special type is called a *cumulative frequency distribution*. An example will be used to introduce the cumulative distribution.

The amount of gasoline demanded on weekdays by motorists using the Navajo Turnpike varies. Table 5.2a gives a frequency distribution for daily gasoline demand based on a sample of 100 days. From this distribution it is seen, for example, that on 14 of the 100 days the demand fell from 5,000.1 to 10,000 gallons. Using such information from this noncumulative frequency distribution, several questions can be answered. In how many days was demand less than or equal to 10,000 gallons? The answer is 15, since on 1 day the demand was from 0.1 to 5,000 gallons and on 14 days the demand was from 5,000.1 to 10,000 gallons. Another question — On how many days was demand less than or equal to 15,000 gallons? The answer here is 41, which equals 1 + 14 + 26. Finally, on how many days was demand less than or equal to 30,000 gallons? The answer is 100, since Table 5.2a shows that in no case did demand exceed 30,000 gallons.

TABLE 5.2

Daily Gasoline Demand on the Navajo Turnpike

(a) Noncumulative Frequency Distribution		(b) Cumulative Distribution "less than or equal to"	
Gallons of Gasoline	*Frequency*	*Gallons of Gasoline*	*Cumulative Frequency*
.1– 5,000	1	0	0
5,000.1–10,000	14	5,000	1
10,000.1–15,000	26	10,000	15
15,000.1–20,000	39	15,000	41
20,000.1–25,000	17	20,000	80
25,000.1–30,000	3	25,000	97
	100	30,000	100

A cumulative frequency distribution of the "less than or equal to" variety may be constructed by answering the type of questions just considered. The cumulative distribution is given in Table 5.2b.

Across from each value of demand (in gallons) is given the number of days in the sample where demand was less than or equal to that figure. For example, there were 0 days with demand less than or equal to 0 gallons, there was 1 day with demand less than or equal to 5,000 gallons, there were 15 days with demand less than or equal to 10,000 gallons, there were 41 days with demand less than or equal to 15,000 gallons, and so on. It should be emphasized that the cumulative distribution of Table 5.2b gives exactly the same information as the noncumulative distribution of Table 5.2a. This means that a cumulative distribution can always be constructed if a noncumulative distribution is given, and a noncumulative distribution can be determined if a cumulative distribution is given. Consider now how a noncumulative distribution might be constructed when a cumulative frequency distribution is given. The process is analogous to that involving cumulative and noncumulative probability distributions as explained in Section 3.3 of Chapter 3.

Table 5.3 gives a cumulative frequency distribution based on the past 100 Pan World Airline flights arriving at Stapleton Airport in Denver. From this cumulative distribution it is seen that 15 of the planes arrived less than or equal to 2.00 minutes late, 45 of the planes arrived less than or equal to 4.00 minutes late, and so on. From this cumulative distribution, a noncumulative frequency

TABLE 5.3

Cumulative Distribution of Arriving Flights "less than or equal to"

Minutes Late	Cumulative Frequency
0	0
2.00	15
4.00	45
6.00	70
8.00	70
10.00	95
12.00	100

distribution can easily be constructed. The first class in the noncumulative distribution will be from .01 to 2.00 minutes late. How many planes fall into this class? Since 15 planes arrived less than or equal to 2.00 minutes late, and since none arrived on time or ahead of time, all 15 must have arrived between .01 and 2.00 minutes late. The second class is from 2.01 to 4.00 minutes late. Since 45 planes arrived 4.00 minutes late or less, and since 15 planes arrived 2.00 minutes late or less, it follows that 45 − 15 or 30 planes must have arrived from 2.01 to 4.00 minutes late. The third class which is 4.01 − 6.00 would have a frequency of 25, the fourth class which is 6.01 − 8.00 would have a frequency of 0, the fifth class which is 8.01 − 10.00 would have a frequency of 25, and the last class which is 10.01 − 12.00 would have a frequency of 5 planes or flights. In this manner, the noncumulative distribution is derived from the given cumulative distribution.

The graph of a cumulative frequency distribution is called an *ogive* (which is not pronounced like the first two words of "Home on the Range" but rather as "ōjīve"). Figure 5.2 gives the ogive corresponding to the cumulative distribution of Pan World Airline arrival times as shown in Table 5.3. To construct the ogive, a point corresponding to the appropriate cumulative frequency is placed above each of the "minutes late" values which are taken from Table 5.3 and listed on the horizontal axis. For example, a point is placed at a height (cumulative frequency) of 15 above the value of 2.00 minutes late. After each of the seven points have been plotted, they are connected with straight lines, thus forming the ogive.

FIGURE 5.2

Ogive of the Cumulative Frequency Distribution of Table 5.3

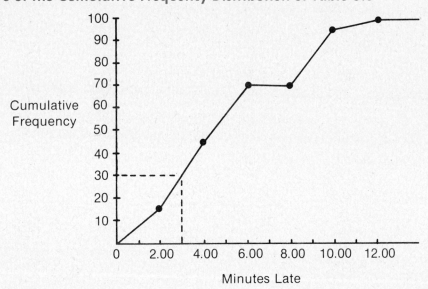

Several conclusions can be drawn from an ogive. For example, if an estimate of the number of planes arriving less than or equal to 3.00 minutes late is desired, a vertical line (dotted in Figure 5.2)

is drawn above 3.00 until it intercepts the ogive; then the line is extended horizontally to the left until it intercepts the vertical axis. The frequency of 30 at that point indicates that approximately 30 planes arrived no more than 3.00 minutes late. The term "approximately" is used since there is no way to accurately determine exactly when the planes arriving between 2.01 and 4.00 minutes late arrived. Therefore, it is assumed that the planes arrived uniformly throughout this two-minute interval.

The cumulative distributions discussed thus far have been of the "less than or equal to" variety. Cumulative distributions of the "more than or equal to," "more than," and "less than" varieties can also be constructed similarly. For example, the "more than" cumulative distribution associated with the noncumulative distribution of Table 5.2a is given in Table 5.4. From this distribution, it is seen, for instance, that the demand was more than 15,000 gallons on 59 days. An ogive for such a distribution can be drawn in much the same way as just demonstrated.

TABLE 5.4
_____

"More than" Cumulative Frequency Distribution Corresponding to Table 5.2a

Gallons	Cumulative Frequency
0	100
5,000	99
10,000	85
15,000	59
20,000	20
25,000	3
30,000	0

5.7

THE CENTER OF THE DATA

To this point attention has been directed to presenting data, whether it be from a sample or a population, in ungrouped or grouped forms. Ungrouped data consists of an exhaustive listing of each individual datum; grouped data refers to data which is organized by a frequency distribution, whether it be cumulative or noncumulative. In Section 5.3 it was noted that the size of a building can be measured in many different ways. One can give the height, the square feet, the number of stories, and so on in an attempt to describe the size of the building. In looking at a set of data rather than a building, one characteristic of considerable importance is the *center* of the data.

Finding the center of a set of data is not an easy matter in that not everyone will agree where the center really is. In like manner, not everyone will readily agree on what size means in talking about a building. The difficulty in finding a center may be illustrated geographically. Everyone would agree on the location of the geographical center of a rectangular state like Kansas. However, finding the geographical center of a state like Virginia is not so obvious and in fact is open to differing opinions. Likewise, finding the center of the ungrouped data

$$\{2, 4, 6\}$$

is not difficult; everyone would agree that 4 is the center. But what about this set of data:

$$\{2, 3, 7\}$$

What is its center? Some might argue that 3 is the center; others might maintain that a value like 4 is the real center. Since it is useless to argue over what is the true center, several types of centers will be defined for the purpose of describing the data of a sample or population. Then the analyst can use that type of center which best suits the situation at hand.

There are three types of centers or averages which are commonly used in statistics: the mean, the median, and the mode. Each will now be considered in the context of both ungrouped and grouped data.

Mean

The *mean* is the center or average which is most often used in inferential statistics and in management science. For ungrouped sample data, the mean is denoted by $\overline{X}$ and defined by

$$\overline{X} = \frac{\Sigma X}{n} \qquad \text{SAMPLE MEAN}$$

where X is an individual value in the set of sample data and n is the number of values in the sample. For example, if a sample of $n = 3$ items were taken from a population, and the three sampled values were 2, 3, and 7, then the mean of this sample data is

$$\overline{X} = \frac{2 + 3 + 7}{3}$$
$$= 4$$

For ungrouped population data, the mean is instead denoted by μ (the Greek letter mu) where

$$\mu = \frac{\Sigma X}{N} \qquad \text{POPULATION MEAN}$$

Here N refers to the total number of items or values in the entire population. Remember that since $\overline{X}$ is a characteristic of the sample, it is called a statistic. μ is called a parameter of the population since it is based solely on population data.

If sample data is presented in grouped form by a frequency distribution, then the mean is

$$\overline{X} = \frac{\Sigma(f)(X)}{n}$$

where X represents the class midpoint, f is the class frequency, and n is the total number of observations in the frequency distribution. For example, look at Table 5.5 which again gives the daily gasoline consumption on the Navajo Turnpike for a sample of $n = 100$ days. The mean of this sample data is

frequency of first class　　frequency of last class
midpoint of first class　　midpoint of last class

$$\overline{X} = \frac{(1)(2,500) + (14)(7,500) + (26)(12,500) + \ldots + (3)(27,500)}{100}$$

total number of observations

$$= 15,800 \text{ gallons}$$

In essence, the mean here is based on the assumption that the 1 day in the .1 – 5,000 gallons category had a demand of 2,500 gallons, the 14 days in the 5,000.1 – 10,000 gallons category had a

TABLE 5.5

Daily Gasoline Demand on the Navajo Turnpike

Gallons	Frequency
.1– 5,000	1
5,000.1–10,000	14
10,000.1–15,000	26
15,000.1–20,000	39
20,000.1–25,000	17
25,000.1–30,000	3
	100

demand at the 7,500 level, etc. The mean of the data which constitutes a population is analogously defined by

$$\mu = \frac{\Sigma(f)(X)}{N}$$

where N is the total number of items in the population. Notice
that the Greek letter is used for the population mean.

Median

The median is the second type of center or average. The *median* of a set of data is the middle value. That is, the median is the
value such that an equal number of observations are above and
below it. For the ungrouped data $\{7, 2, 3\}$, the median can be found
by arranging the observations according to size and then picking
the middle value. For example, 3 is the median since it is the middle value of the data 2, 3, and 7 which is ordered according to increasing size. When there are an even number of observations
such as in $\{5, 6, 6.2, 65\}$, the median is the value halfway between
the two center values after all the values have been arranged by
size. Thus, the median in this case would be 6.1.

When sample or population data appear in the form of a frequency distribution, the median may be estimated by the formula

$$\text{MEDIAN} = L + \left(\frac{n/2 - p}{f} \right)(W)$$

where L is the lower limit of the median class (the *median class* is
the class in which the median falls), n is the total number of observations in the frequency distribution, p is the total number of observations preceding the median class, f is the number of observations in the median class, and W is the width of the median class.

Consider now the frequency distribution of Table 5.5 in order
to estimate the median. A word must be said initially with regard
to the limits of the classes in this distribution. There seems to be a
very small gap of width .1 between each of the classes. Suppose
exactly 5,000.05 gallons were demanded on a given day. Would this
day be counted in the first or second class? It could be argued that
because gasoline is sold only by the tenth of a gallon, a value of
5,000.05 is impossible. Instead of taking this way out, let us inter-
pret the classes given in Table 5.5 as follows. The class 5,000.1 –
10,000 will include all observations which are just over 5,000, up to
and including 10,000 gallons. Similarly, the .1 – 5,000 class would
include all values which exceed 0 but are not over 5,000 gallons.

Following this interpretation, a day where 5,000.05 gallons are demanded would be counted in the 5,000.1 − 10,000 class. This would also imply that there are no gaps in the frequency distribution, and that each class would have a width of 5,000 gallons. With the class limits clarified, we may now compute the median.

Since there are $n = 100$ observations (days), the median or middle value will come between the 50th and 51st observation if the data are arranged by increasing size. The 50.5th observation would come somewhere in the class from 15,000.1 to 20,000 gallons, since there are 41 observations preceding this class and 39 observations in this class. Because the median or 50.5th value will be in the 15,000.1 − 20,000 class, this class is designated as the *median class*. It is now easy to apply the formula for the median given above. L, the lower limit of the median class, in view of the discussion of the previous paragraph is equal to 15,000; n has already been seen to equal 100; the total number of observations in all classes preceding the median class is $p = 1 + 14 + 26$ or 41; f, which is the frequency of the median class, is 39; and W, which is the width of the median class, is 5,000. Therefore, the median daily demand for gasoline along the Navajo Turnpike is

$$\text{MEDIAN} = 15,000 + \left(\frac{100/2 - 41}{39} \right) (5,000)$$

$$= 16,154 \text{ gallons}$$

This implies that on half the days in the past, the daily demand for gasoline was below 16,154 gallons and on half the days it was above 16,154 gallons.

It has been stated that the mean is the center or average which is commonly used in inferential statistics, in economic or management science models, and in decision-making. The median is apt to be the more appropriate average or center in cases where no economic decisions are to be made but where a person is trying to get a feel for a typical value in a set of data. In other words, if the center of some data is being sought for purely informational purposes, the median might be the more appropriate measure. An example will now be given in an attempt to clarify the relative merits of the mean and median.

The realtors of Rochester publish a real estate guide which describes the bedroom communities of Irondequoit, Webster, Penfield, Pittsford, Henrietta, Gates, and Greece which surround the city of Rochester, New York. One of the items of interest is the family incomes of the residents in each of these seven communities. Which average or center would be used to describe the family incomes, the mean family income, or the median family income? If it were reported that the median family income for Webster is

$25,000, this would mean that half the families residing in Webster make more than $25,000 and half make less. Hence, it could be argued that the median would represent a typical Webster family. If the mean income were given instead, it might not give an adequate picture of a typical family. For example, suppose that the mean family income for the community of Pittsford is $36,500; this figure might be very misleading if one's desire is to get a picture of a typical Pittsford family. The statement "The families in Pittsford are a lot wealthier than those in Webster" might be incorrect. Suppose that of the 400 families in Pittsford, 100 make $15,000, 100 make $20,000, 100 make $30,000, 90 make $34,444, and 10 families make $500,000 per year. With this composition, the mean income is

$$\text{MEAN} = \frac{(100)(\$15,000) + (100)(\$20,000) + \ldots + (10)(\$500,000)}{400}$$

$$= \$36,500$$

But since only 10 of the 400 families make an income which exceeds the mean, it would be inappropriate to use the mean income for the purpose of describing a typical Pittsford family. The median would be the appropriate measure; it is $25,000, which is the same as in Webster.

The above example demonstrates that the mean is affected by extreme values (like the 10 families with annual incomes of $500,000), whereas the median is unaffected by these extremes. Another brief example might be presented here to further show that using the mean may be a very poor method of describing a typical observation because of the influence of extreme values. Suppose there are five students in a graduate seminar in management science at Northern Arizona University. The ages of these five students are 22, 25, 22, 23, and 78. The mean age is therefore 34. However, this mean of 34 years does not give an adequate picture of a typical seminar student. The median, 23, gives a better picture of a typical seminar student. Thus, the mean may be inappropriate for describing a typical value in a population.

Return now to the example of the families in the Rochester area. It has been indicated that the mean family income would not be too useful for the sake of picturing a typical family in a community like Pittsford. But when might the mean be a useful measure? Suppose that the communities around Rochester have decided to enact an income tax of 2 percent of gross family income. In this case, the mean would be the measure the community officers should consider. If every family in Webster had an income of $25,000, then the mean (as well as the median) would be $25,000. Therefore, the community would collect (.02)($25,000) or $500 from each family, yielding a total revenue of $200,000 since there are

400 families. On the other hand, the 400 families of Pittsford whose mean income is $36,500 (and whose median income is $25,000) would collect an average of (.02)($36,500) or $730 per family. This would result in a total revenue of (400)($730) or $292,000 to Pittsford. Notice that it would be incorrect to use the median figure of $25,000 in order to project total revenue to Pittsford; this would underestimate revenues. Thus, the mean is the appropriate center to use in such an application.

As another example to demonstrate the applicability of the mean versus the median, suppose that you are purchasing 100 projector bulbs. Company A says their bulbs have a mean life of 25 hours and a median life of 21 hours. Company B says their bulbs have a mean life of 22 hours and a median of 27 hours. Whose bulbs should be purchased? In this case Company A's bulbs should be purchased because the expected total hours of performance for the 100 bulbs will be (100)(25) or 2,500 as compared to 2,200 hours for the Company B bulbs. The median is not a particularly useful measure upon which to base such a purchase; the mean should be used. As stated earlier, the mean is often the better center to use when economic decisions are to be made.

In conclusion, we have seen that one average is appropriate at times and another average is appropriate at other times. Neither is uniformly the best in describing the center of population or sample data.

Mode

The mode is the last type of average or center which is commonly encountered. The *mode* is that value or observation which occurs most frequently. The mode of the ungrouped data

$$\{2.5, 4, 5.7, 9, 9\}$$

is 9. The set of data consisting of

$$\{2, 6, 6.1, 7.8\}$$

has no mode since no value appears more frequently than any other.

When data is presented in the form of a frequency distribution, the mode cannot be isolated. Rather, the *modal class* is identified. The modal class is that class which has the greatest number of observations. For the frequency distribution of Table 5.5, the modal class is 15,000.1–20,000 since the 39 observations in this class is not surpassed by any other class. In dealing with ungrouped or grouped data, there may be two modes or modal classes. In these cases the data is said to be *bimodal*. The set of data

$$\{3, 4.1, 4.1, 5, 6.3, 7.4, 7.4\}$$

for example, is bimodal.

The mode is the least used of the three measures of the center of data. However, where a person is particularly interested in the most common characteristic of the item under study, the mode is useful. For example, it might be of interest to know that the modal family size in Germany is four or the modal number of bikes owned by American families is zero. In the last instance, this means that more families own zero bikes than own one bike, or two bikes, etc. Modes are also useful in dealing with qualitative variables. For example, the modal color for recently purchased refrigerators is white, and the modal cause of deaths in the United States is heart disease. It would be impossible to use a mean or median in such cases.

In concluding this section on averages, the reader should remember that the concept of a mean or expected value which was presented in Chapter 3 is analogous to the mean of data which has been presented here. The expected value of Chapter 3 served to identify the center of a probability distribution just as $\overline{X}$ and μ serve to identify a center of sample and population data. Often a probability distribution is used to portray a population, as in the case where the lives of a batch of radial tires are normally distributed with an expected value of 40,000 miles and a standard deviation of 5,000 miles. In such a case, the population is the batch of tires; therefore, the expected value is identical to the mean μ.

5.8

THE DISPERSION OF THE DATA

In Section 5.7, several measures of the center of a set of data were introduced. Determining the center of a set of data is typically the most useful way to describe or summarize the data. However in many situations, more needs to be known about the data. For example, Green & Sons is developing a new kind of tie for use on railroad tracks. Two designs, A and B, for the new tie have been tested by a simulation technique with the following results. The six ties of design A which were tested lasted 18, 20, 19, 19, 18, and 20 years, respectively. The six ties of design B which were tested lasted 19, 12, 9, 29, 19, and 26 years, respectively. In both cases, the mean and median equal 19 years. Nevertheless, Green & Sons is not likely to be indifferent between the two types of ties.

The variability in the lives of the ties would be a very important factor in determining which is the preferable design. Judging from the sample evidence Green & Sons has obtained, design A has less variability in the lives of the ties and would undoubtedly be the optimal design, assuming it did not cost too much more than design B. Here then was a case where the variability or dispersion of the data was of considerable importance. Therefore it would be useful to be able to simply measure the dispersion of a set of data. This will be accomplished in this section. A very simple method of measuring dispersion will first be considered with its shortcomings; then good methods for measuring the variability inherent in a set of data will be presented.

Range

The first type of measurement of the variability of a set of data is called the range. The *range* of a set of data is defined by

$$\text{RANGE} = \text{greatest value} - \text{smallest value}$$

Let us see how the range is computed and also see its weakness.

You have been called upon to assess the dividend performance of two mutual funds sponsored by the Jabberwock Fund. The dividend yields for last year for the eight stocks in the Jabberwock Utilities Fund were

$$\{8.4\%, 8.8\%, 8.5\%, 8.9\%, 4.3\%, 8.4\%, 8.8\%, 8.1\%\}$$

The yields for the eight stocks in the Jabberwock Chemicals Fund were

$$\{2.3\%, 6.1\%, 3.9\%, 5.8\%, 2.4\%, 6.0\%, 2.5\%, 6.3\%\}$$

In which fund is there more variability with respect to dividend yields? Most analysts would agree that the yields among the stocks in the Chemicals Fund are the more variable or dispersed. But notice that the range of yields for the Utilities Fund is

$$\begin{aligned}\text{RANGE} &= 8.9\% - 4.3\% \\ &= 4.6\%\end{aligned}$$

whereas the range for the Chemicals Fund is

$$\begin{aligned}\text{RANGE} &= 6.3\% - 2.3\% \\ &= 4.0\%\end{aligned}$$

Here is a case where the range for the fund, which would generally be considered as less variable, is greater than the range for the more variable fund in terms of yields. This implies that the range, which is easily computed, may not be a desirable method of measuring the dispersion or variability of a set of data. The problem with the range is that it ignores all of the data except the greatest and least values.

Despite its limitations, the range is often useful in cases where there is a whole continuum of observations from the greatest to the least; that is, where one of the extreme values does not stand alone. For example, it might be reported that the range of temperatures today in Flagstaff, Arizona was 35 degrees. In this case every temperature in the continuum from 40 degrees to 75 degrees was experienced. As another example, the range of the Dow Jones Industrials Index is often reported in order to quickly picture the variability of the stock market over the day.

Since in most cases the range is not a particularly good measure of dispersion in that it only considers extreme values, we will now present a measure of dispersion which considers each value in a set of data.

Variance and Standard Deviation

Generally speaking, one would say that a set of data is quite dispersed or variable if many of the values are at a considerable distance from the center of the data. On the other hand, if the values were all quite close to the center, we would say that there is very little variability or dispersion to the data. The *variance* of a set of data is a widely used measure of the dispersion of the data. In computing the variance, the distance from each value in the set of data to the center of the data is considered. The center which is used is the mean. In particular, the variance of a set of *sample* data is given by

$$s^2 = \frac{\Sigma(\text{distance from value to center})^2}{\text{number of values minus one}}$$

$$s^2 = \frac{\Sigma(X - \overline{X})^2}{n - 1} \qquad \text{SAMPLE VARIANCE}$$

In this definition, the center is represented by the sample mean $\overline{X}$; individual values of the data are denoted by X; and the number of values or observations in the sample is given by n.

To illustrate the computation of the sample variance, a new factory employee is asked to perform a task three times. The times it takes the employee to complete the task on the three occasions are 6, 8, and 10 minutes. To compute the variance, the sample mean $\overline{X}$ must first be calculated. In this case $\overline{X}$ equals 8 minutes. Therefore, the sample variance is

$$s^2 = \frac{(6 - 8)^2 + (8 - 8)^2 + (10 - 8)^2}{3 - 1}$$

$$= \frac{(-2)^2 + (0)^2 + (2)^2}{2}$$

$$= 4$$

In an analogous manner, the variance of the data in a *population* is denoted by sigma squared and is defined by

$$\sigma^2 = \frac{\Sigma(X - \mu)^2}{N} \qquad \text{POPULATION VARIANCE}$$

Notice that μ is used rather than $\overline{X}$, and that N is used rather than n; this is because we are here dealing with the variance of the population rather than the sample.

In comparing the statistic s^2 and the parameter σ^2, similarities are quite obvious — such would be expected, since both are variances. However, one difference is evident in that the denominator of the sample variance has $n - 1$, whereas the denominator of the population variance has N. The reason that $n - 1$ is used in the sample variance is that it can be shown through complicated mathematics that if n were instead used, the sample variance would tend to be too small. Later we shall see that s^2 is used to estimate the value of the population variance; it is under these conditions that s^2 proves to be too small if n is used in its denominator. With $n - 1$ in its denominator, the sample variance becomes an accurate estimate of the population variance when the sample is drawn from the population. This will be considered in detail in a later chapter.

As was explained in Section 3.5 of Chapter 3 where the variance of a probability distribution was introduced, the variance is expressed in meaningless units such as square minutes or square dollars. In order to get a measure of dispersion which is expressed in the original units such as minutes or dollars, the square root of the variance is taken. The standard deviation is defined to be the square root of the variance. Since s^2 is the symbol representing the variance of a set of sample data, s is the symbol which represents the standard deviation of sample data. Also, since σ^2 is the population variance, σ denotes the standard deviation of the population.

The variance computed above for the performance of the new factory employee was $s^2 = 4$ square minutes. It follows that the standard deviation in this case is

$$s = \sqrt{s^2}$$

$$= \sqrt{4} \text{ square minutes}$$
$$= 2 \text{ minutes}$$

As with the variance and standard deviation of a probability distribution, the greater the value of the variance and standard deviation, the greater the variability. For example, if the times to perform the task were 4, 8, and 12 minutes instead of 6, 8, and 10, then the variance and standard deviation would be

$$s^2 = \frac{(4 - 8)^2 + (8 - 8)^2 + (12 - 8)^2}{3 - 1}$$

$$= 16$$

and, $s = 4$ minutes

Likewise, when the values are more compact around the mean, the variance and standard deviation decrease. If the employee's times were 8, 8, and 8 minutes, then $s^2 = s = 0$.

As the mean was also computed for grouped data, so the variance and standard deviation may be computed if the data is given in the form of a frequency distribution. The mean, $\overline{X}$, of the sample data in Table 5.5 has already been found to equal 15,800 gallons. Now the variance and standard deviation may be computed according to

$$s^2 = \frac{\Sigma (f)(X - \overline{X})^2}{n - 1}$$

$$s = \sqrt{\frac{\Sigma (f)(X - \overline{X})^2}{n - 1}}$$

where f denotes the class frequency, X denotes the class midpoint, $\overline{X}$ represents the mean, and n is the number of observations in the frequency distribution. Therefore, for the Navajo Turnpike gasoline data of Table 5.5,

$$s^2 = \frac{(1)(2,500 - 15,800)^2 + (14)(7,500 - 15,800)^2 + \ldots + (3)(27,500 - 15,800)^2}{100 - 1}$$

$$= 27,383,838$$

and,

$$s = \sqrt{27,383,838}$$
$$= 5,233 \text{ gallons}$$

Analogously, the variance and standard deviation of a population which is presented in the form of a frequency distribution are

$$\sigma^2 = \frac{\Sigma(f)(X - \mu)^2}{N}$$

$$\sigma = \sqrt{\frac{\Sigma(f)(X - \mu)^2}{N}}$$

where f denotes the class frequency, X denotes the class midpoint, μ represents the population mean, and N is the number of items or values in the population.

As was discussed in Section 3.5 of Chapter 3, once the mean and standard deviation have been found, it is possible to express any datum in standard deviation units. The standard deviation units for some value X is given, as in Chapter 3, by

$$Z = \frac{X - \text{mean}}{\text{standard deviation}}$$

The meaning and relevance of such a measure were adequately discussed in Section 3.5 and therefore will not be repeated here.

Coefficient of Dispersion

You have just entered the physician's office and have begun chatting with the other two patients already waiting for the doctor. As the conversation progresses it turns out that both the other two patients have been struck with the same symptoms. Marfa claims that her weights as measured on the past four Fridays have been 220, 200, 240, and 220, and Pinta says her past four Friday weights have been 100, 80, 120, and 100 pounds. Just as the two women have told you of their wildly fluctuating weights, the doctor bursts into the waiting room advising the three of you that there is only time to see one of you. Since you were the last to arrive and since Marfa and Pinta arrived together, the doctor asks you to make the decision as to who should be examined. Whom would you recommend?

It might seem reasonable to compute the standard deviation of the Friday weights for both women in order to determine whose weight is the more variable. Unfortunately, if this were done you would find that the standard deviation based on the four observations for each patient would be the same. Both women would have a sample standard deviation of $s = 16.3$ pounds. Of course you would already have determined that Pinta is in poorer shape since her loss of 20 pounds, then gain of 40 pounds, then loss of 20 pounds took place relative to a smaller body than with Marfa. This means that the standard deviation is not too useful in determining variability in certain cases where a comparison is being made. Since we would argue that the mean weight for Marfa (220 pounds) and the mean for Pinta (100 pounds) should be considered in judging which has the more variable weight change, another measure of dispersion has been devised which is based on the mean as well as the standard deviation. This measure is called the *coefficient of dispersion* (or sometimes the *coefficient of variation*) and is defined as

$$D = \frac{s}{\bar{X}} \qquad \text{for a sample}$$

$$\delta = \frac{\sigma}{\mu} \qquad \text{for a population}$$

The coefficient of dispersion for Marfa is, therefore,

$$D = \frac{16.3}{220}$$

$$= .074 \text{ or } 7.4\%$$

and for Pinta is

$$D = \frac{16.3}{100}$$

$$= .163 \text{ or } 16.3\%$$

Since D is greater for Pinta, we would conclude that on a relative basis her weight variability is the greater.

There are many instances in management where the coefficient of dispersion is a useful measure of variability. The investment analyst should use D in measuring the variability of the price of various stocks. For example, suppose the closing price of Stock A for the past three Thursdays was $30, $31, and $29, and the closing price for Stock B on successive Thursdays was $200, $201, and $199. Both stocks would have a standard deviation of $1, however, the analyst would state that Stock A is a relatively more volatile stock. This is shown by the coefficient of dispersion which is $D = 1/30$ or 3.3% for Stock A and $D = 1/200$ or 0.5% for Stock B.

With the coefficient of dispersion, we conclude this section dealing with the description of the dispersion or variability of data. Other measures of dispersion exist, but the range, variance, standard deviation, and coefficient of dispersion are the measures most commonly used.

5.9

SKEWNESS AND KURTOSIS OF THE DATA

When sample or population data is grouped in the form of a frequency distribution, the distribution may be graphed by means of a histogram as was demonstrated in Section 5.5. It was pointed out that a histogram is very similar to the graph of a discrete probability distribution. In Section 3.6 of Chapter 3, the concepts of skewness and kurtosis were introduced as they relate to a probability distribution. Recall that a skewed distribution has a predominant tail to one side or the other, and kurtosis refers to the peakedness of the distribution (see Figure 3.7 in Chapter 3). In an analogous fashion, the data of a frequency distribution or histogram may be described. Section 3.6 should be reviewed if you have forgotten what skewness and kurtosis mean in relationship to a probability distribution or histogram. A quick way to judge the skewness of data analytically is to compare the mean to the median. If the mean is to the right of the median, then the data is skewed to the right (positively skewed). If the mean is less than the median, then the data is skewed to the left.

Before leaving this brief discussion of skewness, notice how the mean, median, and mode are related in the case of a skewed distribution. Figure 5.3 presents a histogram which has been smoothed so that it looks like the graph of a continuous probability distribution. The position of the three centers or averages are

FIGURE 5.3

Relative Positions of the Mean, Median, and Mode in a Positively Skewed Distribution

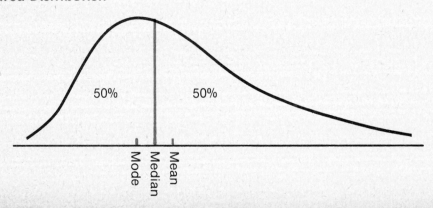

indicated in this graph. The mode, being the most often observed value, falls directly below the peak of the distribution. The median marks the value such that half the observations are below and half are above. This implies that half the area under the curve must be to the left and half to the right of the median. Finally, the mean is pulled toward the right tail by the extremely high-valued observations. The mean represents the center of gravity of the distribution.

5.10

PROPORTIONS

Some populations are composed of items which are qualitative in nature. For example, the population consisting of all the accountants residing in North Dakota could be viewed as being composed solely of males and females. It makes no sense in such a case to speak of a population mean because being male and being female can not be averaged like ages or incomes or weights. In situations where a population is broken into qualitatively defined categories (e.g. males and females, residents and nonresidents, defective and good components, watching and not watching television), the method of describing the population is by means of a proportion. Thus the population consisting of all the accountants in North Dakota might be described by saying that of the N accountants in the state, 83 percent are males. The letter p is used to represent the proportion of items in a population which fall into the qualitative category under consideration. Hence the parameter p in the North Dakota case equals .83 and $1 - p = .17$ which is the proportion of female accountants. Here is an example where an English rather than a Greek letter represents a parameter of the population.

When a sample is drawn from a population of qualitative categories, the sample is described by the statistic $\bar{p}$ which represents the sample proportion. For example, if 20 accountants in North Dakota were randomly selected and 18 of them proved to be male, then the sample proportion is $\bar{p} = X/n = 18/20 = .90$, where $\bar{p}$ represents the proportion of the sample which is male, X is the actual number of males in the sample, and n is the total number of accountants in the sample.

5.11

SUMMARY OF DESCRIPTIVE MEASURES

Descriptive statistics is concerned with describing a population and/or sample. In this chapter, we have seen that population data and sample data may be organized for presentation by using a frequency distribution, or the data may be simply listed. A number of descriptive measures were defined which serve to describe the data in a population or sample. The most important of these measures or characteristics are:

1. Measuring the center of ungrouped quantitative data

$$\text{sample mean} = \overline{X} = \frac{\Sigma X}{n}$$

$$\text{population mean} = \mu = \frac{\Sigma X}{N}$$

2. Measuring the center of grouped quantitative data

$$\text{sample mean} = \overline{X} = \frac{\Sigma (f)(X)}{n}$$

$$\text{population mean} = \mu = \frac{\Sigma (f)(X)}{N}$$

3. Measuring the dispersion of ungrouped quantitative data

$$\text{sample standard deviation} = s = \sqrt{\frac{\Sigma (X - \overline{X})^2}{n - 1}}$$

$$\text{population standard deviation} = \sigma = \sqrt{\frac{\Sigma (X - \mu)^2}{N}}$$

4. Measuring the dispersion of grouped quantitative data

$$\text{sample standard deviation} = s = \sqrt{\frac{\Sigma (f)(X - \overline{X})^2}{n - 1}}$$

$$\text{population standard deviation} = \sigma = \sqrt{\frac{\Sigma (f)(X - \mu)^2}{N}}$$

5. Measuring the composition of qualitative data

$$\text{sample proportion} = \bar{p} = X/n$$

where X equals the number of items in the sample of size n which fall into the qualitative category in question,

$$\text{population proportion} = p = X/N$$

where X equals the number of items in the population of size N which fall into the qualitative category in question.

These are the statistics and parameters which will primarily be used in the study of inferential statistics.

PROBLEMS

5.1

Explain the differences between probability theory, inferential statistics, and descriptive statistics.

5.2

Explain the difference between a population and a sample. List five populations and samples therefrom which are not mentioned in the text.

5.3

What is a parameter? What is a statistic? Through symbols, how is a statistic usually distinguished from a parameter?

5.4

Someone asks you, "What is the climate like in Chicago?" Give five descriptive measures which might be used to describe the climate of Chicago.

5.5

A friend asks you, "How big is the University of Kentucky?" Give five descriptive measures which might be used to describe the size of this university.

5.6

Explain the difference between ungrouped and grouped data.

5.7

Four principles were given in the text to guide in the construction of a frequency distribution. State each of these principles.

5.8

The monthly prices of a bushel of corn at the Omaha grain market for the past 30 months were:

$2.40, 2.18, 2.26, 2.42, 2.35, 2.34,
2.30, 2.41, 2.18, 2.19, 2.25, 2.37,
2.51, 2.47, 2.15, 2.18, 2.43, 2.36,
2.29, 2.35, 2.25, 2.41, 2.30, 2.31,
2.48, 2.19, 2.20, 2.50, 2.46, 2.32

(a) Construct a frequency distribution with six classes and draw the corresponding histogram.
(b) Construct a frequency distribution with eight classes and draw the corresponding histogram.
(c) Construct a relative frequency distribution for parts (a) and (b) above.

5.9

Construct a frequency distribution for the prices of the first 50 stocks listed alphabetically in the New York Stock Exchange section of your newspaper. Justify the number of classes you used. Draw a histogram.

5.10

The number of persons admitted each day to the Good Samaritan hospitals over the past 40 days were:

18, 42, 60, 19, 11, 41, 60, 46, 30, 18,
27, 38, 54, 24, 50, 42, 59, 38, 22, 14,
39, 54, 45, 46, 41, 38, 55, 17, 40, 36,
25, 49, 38, 57, 19, 44, 25, 34, 46, 44

(a) Construct a frequency distribution with six classes and draw a histogram.
(b) Construct a frequency distribution with ten classes and draw a histogram.
(c) Construct a relative frequency distribution for (a) and (b).

5.11

If a frequency distribution were to be constructed on the basis of a very few observations, should there typically be just a few or many classes? Why?

5.12

The hourly wages of workers for Alpheno Chemical Corporation, which has many plants scattered over the United States, are typically values like $4.60, $5.30, and $8.50 rather than $4.63, $5.38, and \$8.51. Alpheno wishes to construct a frequency distribution where there are 10,000 observations representing Alpheno's 10,000 hourly wage employees. Alpheno has already decided that the width of each class will be .10. Which of the two classification systems given below would be preferable? Why?

Frequency Distribution A	*Frequency Distribution B*
.	.
.	.
.	.
.	.
\$2.50–2.59	\$2.45–2.54
2.60–2.69	2.55–2.64
2.70–2.79	2.65–2.74
.	.
.	.
.	.

5.13

Get five coins and simultaneously toss them in the air. Repeat this 20 times counting the total number of heads achieved each time. Based on your results, construct a frequency distribution for the number of heads.

5.14

Two frequency distributions are given below.

X	Frequency		Y	Frequency
0–19.99	10		200.1–300	4
20–39.99	18		300.1–400	26
40–59.99	20		400.1–500	78
60–79.99	30		500.1–600	30
80–99.99	22		600.1–700	22
			700.1–800	20

(a) Construct a "more than or equal to" cumulative distribution for X and then graph the ogive.
(b) Construct a "less than or equal to" cumulative distribution for Y and graph the ogive.
(c) Construct a "less than" cumulative distribution for X and then graph the ogive.

5.15

Two cumulative distributions are given on the following page.

W	"Less Than or Equal to" Cumulative Frequency
100	0
150	16
200	25
250	49
300	49
350	70

R	"More Than or Equal to" Cumulative Frequency
6.2	80
6.4	50
6.6	40
6.8	40
7.0	12
7.2	3
7.4	0

(a) For W, how many observations fall between 200.01 and 300?
(b) Construct an ogive for W and use it to estimate the number of observations that are less than or equal to 325.
(c) Construct a noncumulative frequency distribution for W.
(d) Construct an ogive for R and use it to estimate the number of observations greater than or equal to 6.9.
(e) Construct a noncumulative distribution for R.

5.16

Fifty automobiles were sampled and checked to see how many miles each had been driven. The following frequency distribution describes the results:

Miles	Frequency
0–19,999	12
20,000–39,999	14
40,000–59,999	10
60,000–79,999	8
80,000–99,999	6

(a) Construct a relative frequency distribution.
(b) Draw a histogram for (a).
(c) Construct a "less than" cumulative relative distribution.
(d) Draw an ogive for (c).

5.17

The Diamond Tooth Drilling Company has drilled for water in a number of places in the panhandle of Oklahoma. The depths of the wells are given by the following "less than or equal to" cumulative distribution:

Depth	Cumulative Frequency
40 feet	0 wells
60	8
80	24
100	24
120	49
140	60
160	68
180	70

(a) Construct a noncumulative frequency distribution.
(b) Construct a relative frequency distribution.
(c) Draw an ogive and from it estimate the number of wells that are less than or equal to 115 feet deep.
(d) From the ogive of (c), the 30 wells that are most shallow do not exceed what depth?

5.18

The anticipated research and development budgets for five manufacturers of small engines in the United States are $60,000, $140,000, $10,000, $20,000, and $50,000.

(a) Why is this population data?
(b) Compute the mean.
(c) Find the median.
(d) Find the mode.
(e) Find the range.
(f) Compute the variance.
(g) Compute the standard deviation.
(h) Compute the coefficient of dispersion.
(i) Express the $10,000 budget in terms of standard deviation units.

5.19

A random sample of six pharmacies in Philadelphia quoted the following prices for a prescription of tetracycline: $9.00, $5.00, $3.00, $5.00, $4.00, and $5.00.

(a) Compute the mean, median, and mode.
(b) Which is preferable, the mean or the median, in order to describe what tetracycline prices are like in Philadelphia?
(c) Find the range.
(d) Compute the standard deviation.
(e) Compute the coefficient of dispersion.
(f) Express the $9.00 price in standard deviation units.

5.20

The annual budget deficits during the four year reign of King Franklin were $200, $800, $40, and $50.

(a) Why is this population data?
(b) Compute the mean, median, and mode.
(c) Why is the mean inadequate as a measure of a typical deficit?
(d) Find the range.
(e) Compute the standard deviation.
(f) Compute the coefficient of dispersion.
(g) Express the $200 deficit in terms of standard deviation units.

5.21

An ornithologist has raided six nests of the yellow-bellied nuthatch, finding 2, 1, 2, 1, 1, and 3 eggs, respectively.

(a) Why is this sample data?
(b) Find the mean, median, and mode.
(c) Compute the standard deviation.
(d) Find the coefficient of variation.
(e) The mean number of eggs in the lark bunting's nest is 2.8 with a standard deviation of 2.1 eggs. Is there more variability with the nuthatch or the bunting? Justify.

5.22

You, as proprietor of a small business, are going to purchase ten floodlight replacement bulbs for your single outdoor floodlight which illuminates your sign. Notice that you only use one bulb at a time, replacing it when it burns out. Two dealers offer to sell you the ten bulbs. Dealer A says their bulbs have a mean life of 3,000 hours and a median life of 2,000 hours. Dealer B says their bulbs have a mean life of 2,000 hours and a median of 3,000 hours. Which brand should you purchase?

5.23

Why is the range often a poor measure of dispersion?

5.24

Why is the standard deviation often preferred over the variance?

5.25

Over the past 20 years the state of Arizona has produced a mean of 800 million pounds of copper per year with a standard deviation of 70 million pounds. Comparable figures for Montana show a mean of 100 million pounds with a standard deviation of 30 million pounds. Discuss how it could be argued that either state has the more variability in copper production. Which is the better argument?

5.26

A large department store has recorded daily gross sales for the past 20 days by the following distribution:

Gross Sales	Frequency
$10,000–19,999	5
20,000–29,999	9
30,000–39,999	6

(a) Determine the corresponding relative frequency distribution.
(b) Why can this be considered sample data?
(c) Find the mean, median, and modal class.
(d) Find the variance, standard deviation, and coefficient of dispersion.

5.27

Alexander has 20 forts scattered over the far reaches of his empire. The following frequency distribution discloses the level of staffing at these forts:

Soldiers	Frequency
8	3
9	5
10	7
11	5

(a) Why is this population data?
(b) Find the mean, median, and mode.
(c) Find the variance and standard deviation.
(d) Find the coefficient of dispersion.
(e) Discuss the skewness of the distribution.

5.28

The amount of wheat, in metric tons, currently being held in 50 elevators in a county in Kansas is given by the following frequency distribution.

Metric Tons of Wheat	Frequency
10–14.99	30
15–19.99	10
20–24.99	10

(a) Why is this population data?
(b) Compute the mean, median, and modal class.
(c) Estimate the total amount of wheat held in the county.
(d) Compute the standard deviation.
(e) Discuss the skewness of the distribution.

5.29

A company produces x-ray film at a plant in New Jersey. The daily production in square meters of the film over the past 11 days has varied as shown by the following distribution:

Square Meters of Film	Frequency
500–549.9	4
550–599.9	5
600–649.9	2

(a) Treating the data as sample data, find the three averages.
(b) Find the standard deviation and coefficient of dispersion.
(c) Estimate total production for the past 11 days.

5.30

The assessed property values for the homes in Sedona have the following frequency distribution where the assessed value is .01 of the market value:

Assessed Value	Frequency
$100–199.9	0
200–299.9	10
300–399.9	50
400–499.9	30
500–999.9	10

(a) Why is this population data?
(b) Find the mean, median, and modal class.
(c) Estimate the total assessed value of the hundred homes in Sedona. If the tax rate is $2 tax per dollar of assessed value, estimate the total property tax revenue.
(d) Find the standard deviation and coefficient of dispersion.
(e) Discuss the skewness of the distribution.
(f) What proportion of the homes are assessed below $400? Is this $\bar{p}$ or p?

5.31

A sample of 11 supermarkets in Salt Lake City show that the inside temperature during operating hours in the winter are

Temperature	Frequency
66–67.99	1
68–69.99	0
70–71.99	5
72–73.99	3
74–75.99	0
76–77.99	2

(a) Find the mean, median, and modal class.
(b) Find the standard deviation and coefficient of dispersion.
(c) If a supermarket keeps its thermostat set at 78°, how many standard deviations is this from the mean?
(d) What proportions have a temperature of 72° or more? Is this $\bar{p}$ or p?

5.32

The telephone bills for the month of November for the 1000 residential phones of Las Cruces have the following distribution:

Telephone Bill	Frequency
$ 5.00– 9.99	300
10.00–14.99	500
15.00–19.99	100
20.00–49.99	100

A random sample of ten residential phone bills was taken, yielding $\overline{X} = \$16.75$ and $s = \$8.43$.

(a) Are the sample mean and population mean the same? Do they have to be the same? Why or why not?

(b) Are the sample standard deviation and population standard deviation the same?

(c) Are the population data bimodal?

(d) Estimate how much the phone company collected in November.

5.33

A television station randomly calls 100 homes in the Seattle area and finds that 23 of them are watching the documentary entitled "Love Song — General Custer and his Indian Friends." By means of which parameter or statistic should the station describe this data?

5.34

If a sample of size n is drawn from a population with the parameter p, does the statistic $\bar{p}$ have to equal p? Explain why or why not.

5.35

The five principal Mexican states bordering the United States have per capita incomes (in pesos) and populations as shown below.

State	Mean Per Capita Income	Population
Baja	10,000	200
Sonora	11,000	500
Chihuahua	12,000	800
Coahuila	13,000	900
Tamaulipas	14,000	900

What is the mean per capita income for all the Mexicans living in the five border states? The answer is not 12,000 pesos.

CHAPTER 6

SAMPLING AND SAMPLING DISTRIBUTIONS

INTRODUCTION

In the last chapter, the distinction between a population and a sample was emphasized. It was seen that a population might consist of every national bank in the United States. If we were generally interested in the number of branches these banks have, we might proceed to compute the mean number of branches per bank (μ) and the standard deviation (σ) in an attempt to briefly describe the extent of branch banking among national banks. Instead, a sample could be taken from this large population of national banks. Perhaps $n = 25$ banks might be sampled. This sample data could also be summarized or described by a mean and a standard deviation. However, since it is sample data, the mean and standard deviation would be designated by the statistics $\overline{X}$ and s rather than by μ and σ which are the parameters of the population. This was the subject matter considered in the last chapter.

This chapter is concerned with two further areas of study which have to do with populations and samples. First, we will consider methods of drawing a sample from a population. How, for example, should the analyst choose the 25 banks which are to constitute the sample from the population of all U.S. national banks? Methods of selecting a sample from a population will be considered in Section 6.2, which is entitled "Sampling Methods." The second concern of this chapter is to determine how close the value of a statistic will be to the value of the parameter. For example, assume that the true mean number of branches per national bank is $\mu = 4.2$. If a sample of 25 of these banks were randomly selected and $\overline{X}$ computed, how close would the $\overline{X}$ be to $\mu = 4.2$? Is it very likely that it would be very close to μ, or might $\overline{X}$ be a long way from μ? This is the sort of thing that will be investigated through a study of sampling distributions. It is the last bit of probability needed to prepare for a full-scale study of inferential statistics.

6.2

SAMPLING METHODS

Suppose your instructor wishes to take a sample of five students from your class (the population consists of all the students in your class) in order to get an idea of the class's reaction to the text. How might these five students be selected? The instructor might ask the first five students from the class who visit him or her during office hours for their reactions. Such a sampling method is known as *convenience sampling*. It is most convenient to get the reactions of the students who go to visit the instructor. A pollster is convenience sampling when he or she stands in front of a grocery store asking people how they will vote. It should be obvious that the results derived from convenience sampling can be quite misleading.

Getting back to the selection of five students from your class, another method known as *judgment sampling* might be used. With judgment sampling, the instructor would look over the class and by using his or her judgment would choose the five students. In so doing, your instructor might purposely seek to get both men and women, older students and younger students, good and not-so-good students, and so forth in the sample. Such a method makes sense, however biases might creep in so that the sample is not as representative of the entire class as your instructor had envisioned. Though judgment sampling has merit, the primary defect in it and convenience sampling lies in the fact that probability theory and inferential statistics cannot be applied to sample data so derived. The powerful techniques of probability theory and inferential statistics are both based on *random sampling*. Since probability and inferential statistics are the subjects of this text, only random sampling will be used here. Consider now some methods of random sampling.

Simple Random Sampling

When most people think of random sampling, they are thinking of simple random sampling. Suppose the instructor wishes to randomly select $n = 5$ students from your class of $N = 30$ students. The instructor could get 30 computer cards and write each student's name on a separate card. Then the cards are shuffled and five cards are taken blindly. The five students so drawn would constitute a sample taken by simple random sampling.

In simple random sampling each item in the population has an equal chance of being drawn. No item in the population has a better chance of being selected than any other item. Thus, the concept of simple random sampling is not difficult to understand. What can be a bit more complicated is attempting to actually take a sample by means of simple random sampling. Suppose you wanted to take a simple random sample of 30 supermarkets in the United States. The first problem is in finding a list of all the supermarkets. Such a list probably does not exist, and therefore, simple random sampling would have to be abandoned and another sampling method tried. But let us assume that a list of all the supermarkets has been found. Also, assume that there are $N = 20,000$ supermarkets in this population or list. How can a simple random sample of 30 be taken? The computer-card approach loses its appeal if only because of the difficulty in shuffling a deck of 20,000 cards. Instead, a simple random sample of $n = 30$ supermarkets can be taken by using a table of random numbers. This will now be explained.

To begin, we might number all of the supermarkets on the list as follows:

00001	AAA Aardvark Supermarket
00002	AAA Supermarket
.	.
.	.
.	.
01492	Bashas' #12 Supermarket
.	.
.	.
.	.
17671	Serveway #296 Supermarket
.	.
.	.
20000	ZZ & Z Supermarket

In doing this, each supermarket has been assigned a unique five-digit number. Next we go to a table of random numbers as given in Appendix R. This table is composed of randomly generated numbers. There are essentially equal quantities of each digit from 0 through 9 in this table; and because they have been randomly generated, there are no patterns in the table. For example, odd numbers do not typically follow even numbers, or high numbers do not typically follow low numbers, and so forth. No matter how the table of random numbers is read, whether from top to bottom, bottom to top, diagonally, right to left, and so on, no patterns exist. From this table we begin to select five-digit numbers. Suppose we start at the upper left corner of the table with the intent to read down the left column. The first five-digit number is 73310 in Appendix R. Since no supermarket has this number, we abandon it and go to the next five-digit number immediately below it. The next number is 01847 which means that the supermarket identified by this number is the first supermarket in our sample. The second supermarket in the sample would be 11415, the third would be 04778, and so on. (Always skip five-digit numbers which exceed 20000 since they do not represent a supermarket on the list.) In such a manner, a simple random sample of $n = 30$ supermarkets can be taken. Once the 30 sample supermarkets are isolated, the statistician can go on to collect the required information from each of the markets in the sample.

Systematic Random Sampling

A few years ago, a railroad completed a 30-mile stretch of track where the ties were treated with a new substance different from creosote which is usually used to preserve the ties. The 30-mile stretch covers a variety of terrains from mountains to plateaus. Each year the railroad wants to sample 30 ties to ascertain how they are holding up. The $n = 30$ ties in the sample are actually removed from the roadbed and then analyzed at a laboratory. Because the railroad wishes to draw certain probabilistic conclusions concerning the performance of the ties, a random sample is required.

With a little thought, it is apparent that simple random sampling would be a cumbersome method of sampling in this case. Instead, the railroad employed systematic sampling. In *systematic sampling* every k^{th} item in the population is selected. For example, systematic sampling could be used to take the sample of 30 from the list of 20,000 supermarkets given earlier. This would involve taking every 666th (which is found by dividing 20,000 by 30) supermarket on the list starting with a randomly chosen market from among the first 666 markets on the list. If the first market were 00034, then the second market to be selected would be 00034 + 666 or the market identified by the number 00700, and the third market would be 01366. Continuing this process, a sample could be systematically drawn.

Returning to the railroad situation, the company certainly does not have the ties numbered, and so using systematic sampling in a way which is directly analogous to the systematic selection of supermarkets is out of the question. Instead, a simple adaption of systematic sampling can be utilized. In particular, the railroad could remove the first tie near the beginning of the 30-mile stretch. Then the crew removing the ties should travel one mile down the track to get another tie. Then another tie could be removed another mile further down the track. Since the track is 30 miles long, such a procedure would yield a sample of 30 ties. These 30 ties would then be sent to the laboratory for analysis.

When applying systematic sampling, the analyst should always be sure that bias is not inadvertantly introduced into the sample. For example, a community association wishes to know how the homeowners in the neighborhood feel about putting in sidewalks. If the sidewalks were constructed, each homeowner would be taxed according to the amount of sidewalk that borders the homeowner's property. If the community association used systematic sampling with $k = 6$ to determine the neighborhood's reaction, and if there were exactly six houses on each side of the block, an obvious bias would be introduced. If the community association began with a corner house and then counted six more houses to find the next house in the sample, the next house would also be a corner house. This would bias the sample since corner homeowners view sidewalks differently than the others on a block. On the other hand, if the first house were an "internal" house and $k = 6$ is used, then none of the sampled houses would be corner houses and again bias is present. Therefore, be careful in using systematic sampling.

Cluster Sampling

A certain brand of soup has conducted a publicity campaign where randomly selected persons across America are called on the phone and invited to sing the soup's advertisement jingle. Not to be outdone, another brand has decided to try the same sort of thing, except that personal visits would be made by a celebrity instead of phone calls. Here is the plan: it was decided that Dracula would visit randomly chosen homes in the United States and ask the homeowner if he or she could produce a can of Seedy's tomato soup. If the homeowner could bring out the tomato soup, Dracula would drink the soup instead. All that remained with this plan was to determine how a truly random sample of residences across the U.S.A. could be taken.

A sampling technique known as *cluster sampling* can be used in such a situation. In order to apply cluster sampling, the entire United States is first broken into geographical subdivisions like counties; these counties are called *clusters*. Then a random sample of counties (clusters) is taken. (Counties with a greater number of residences should get a better chance of being selected.) Suppose that through this process 20 counties were selected. These counties might in turn be broken into clusters such as districts. Then several districts would be randomly sampled from each of the 20 counties. Finally, from a list of all the residences in the selected districts, a simple random sample of residences could be chosen — these homes would be visited by the Drac.

In concluding this brief example of cluster sampling, a few things should be noted. First, no other method of random sampling may be possible since a list of the entire population of all the residences in the United States might not be available. Even if such a comprehensive list were available, a simple random sample would end up selecting residences in all sorts of remote areas as well as in populous regions. This would entail a lot of traveling to get to each residence. With cluster sampling, visits need only be made to a limited number of counties. Even if these counties were widely scattered, the travel necessitated would still not be nearly so extensive as with simple random sampling. Therefore, cluster sampling offers real economic advantages. Furthermore, all this is achieved in a manner such that every residence in the United States initially has an equal chance of being selected.

Stratified Random Sampling

Stratified sampling is one of the most efficient methods of random sampling. More information can typically be gained by stratified sampling from a sample of 100, for example, than by a method like simple random sampling. The essence of stratified sampling lies in segmenting the population into fairly homogeneous strata. Then items are randomly sampled from each of the strata according to some criterion. An example will clarify this brief description of stratified sampling.

The stock market brokerage firm of Lynch, Lynch, and Lynch is exploring the possibility of altering its commission schedule and expanding some of its custodial services which are provided free-of-charge to its customers. Lynch, Lynch, and Lynch is somewhat unsure as to how its customers (the population) will react to the proposed changes. Therefore, it has been decided that a random sample of customers should be taken, where each of the sampled customers would be presented with the proposed changes, and their reactions solicited. Lynch, Lynch, and Lynch does have a list of its 1,000 customers. Thus simple random sampling or systematic sampling could easily be used. However, Lynch, Lynch, and Lynch realizes that stratified sampling is more efficient than these other techniques and therefore prefers it as the sampling method to be employed.

A stratified sampling plan is begun by segmenting the entire set of customers (the population) into strata. Each stratum should be relatively homogeneous in that the customers in each stratum hopefully would react more or less alike to the proposed changes. In view of the homogeneity requirement, it would be wrong to stratify by geographical regions. For example, if the first stratum were western customers, the second southern customers, the third midwestern customers, and the fourth eastern customers, such a stratification would *not* be good since the geographical location of customers does not tie them together in homogeneous groups with regard to reactions to the proposed changes. Rather, Lynch, Lynch, and Lynch stratified according to the size and type of customers. The strata which were used are

> Stratum 1: Large Institutional Customers (50)
> Stratum 2: Small Institutional Customers (150)
> Stratum 3: Large Personal Customers (200)
> Stratum 4: Medium-Sized Personal Customers (300)
> Stratum 5: Small Personal Customers (300)

(The number of customers in each stratum is given in parentheses, yielding a total of $N = 1,000$ customers.) The customers in each of these strata might very well tend to think alike in regard to the proposed changes. In other words, the strata are homogeneous with respect to the subject under study.

Once the strata have been defined, a simple random sample of customers is taken from each stratum. There are several criteria which have been suggested to guide in determining how many customers should be selected from each stratum. One criterion says that if a total of $n = 100$ customers are to be sampled from the entire population of $N = 1,000$ customers, the sampled customers should be taken according to the proportion of customers in each of the strata. For example, since 50/1,000 or 5 percent of the customers are Large Institutional Customers, this criterion would dictate that 5 percent of $n = 100$ or 5 customers should be taken from Stratum 1. Likewise, 15 should be sampled from Stratum 2 since 15 percent of the population is in Stratum 2. Though this criterion for allocating the sample among the strata is simple, it is generally a poor method. For example, the Large Institutional Customers might account for 40 percent of Lynch, Lynch, and Lynch's business even though they constitute only 5 percent of the customers. Thus, it would make sense to sample more than five of these important customers. Another criterion states that more of the total sample should be taken from the most important strata. Such a plan has obvious advantages over the proportional plan.

A third criterion for the allocation of the total sample among the strata states that more of the total sample should be taken from the strata which are relatively heterogeneous and hence less from the strata which are more homogeneous. If persons who are small investors (Stratum 5) are known to think very much alike on commission and custodial matters, just a small sample of them is necessary. In other words, if they are like 300 peas in a pod, only a few peas need be selected in order to judge their reaction to the proposed changes. But if there is considerable diversity or heterogeneity among a stratum like Small Institutional Customers, Lynch, Lynch, and Lynch would do well to sample relatively more from such a stratum. Such an approach is obviously reasonable.

It should be noted in closing this discussion of stratified sampling that even though relatively more customers may be sampled from certain small strata like Stratum 1, the representativeness of the overall sample is not destroyed, because the sample results from the various strata are specially weighted to achieve an accurate estimate. These weighting procedures as well as the other methods of setting up a stratified sampling plan are beyond the scope of this text.

Since sampling methods like cluster sampling and stratified sampling involve considerable expertise in their use, simple random sampling will be used exclusively in this text, since it is the simplest to use. The reader interested in the more sophisticated sampling methods should study a text dealing with sample survey methods and analyses.

6.3

A SAMPLING DISTRIBUTION

You may have wondered what Hank Thoreau was up to during his years at Walden Pond. Legend has it that Thoreau was engaged in aquaculture. After years of tireless effort, Thoreau was able to populate the pond with 3 fish. The weights of the respective fish were 3, 5, and 7 pounds. These $N = 3$ fish constitute the population of fish in Walden Pond. The parameters of this population are

$$\mu = \frac{3 + 5 + 7}{3}$$
$$= 5 \text{ pounds}$$

$$\sigma = \sqrt{\frac{(3 - 5)^2 + (5 - 5)^2 + (7 - 5)^2}{3}}$$
$$= 1.63 \text{ pounds}$$

Though Thoreau attempted to keep his aquaculture successes a secret, rumor got out that the tight-lipped transcendentalist had a veritable gold mine in those scaly water-breathing swimmers.

One who happened to hear the rumors was none other than B. F. Skinert. B. F. was the highly successful proprietor of the Rat & Fish Company. B. F. was always looking for a reliable supply of fish, so she paid a visit to Thoreau in hopes of purchasing the contents of the pond. To B. F.'s surprise, Thoreau seemed willing to sell the fish in the pond. However, Thoreau was unwilling to say anything about either the number of fish in the pond or their sizes. B. F. was sure, because of the rumor, that the pond was teeming with fish; her only concern was the size of the fish. Still Thoreau would say nothing about the size of the fish. Ultimately, however, Thoreau agreed to permit B. F. to fish in the pond and let her make up her own mind as to how big the fish are.

The plan to which B. F. agreed was this. She would sample $n = 2$ fish *with replacement*. Sampling with replacement means that after a fish is caught and weighed it must be returned to the pond. Then the second fish can be caught, weighed, and returned. If on the other hand there were sampling *without replacement*, this would mean that once a fish is withdrawn it is not returned to the population. Using a sampling procedure with replacement where n equals 2, we wish to determine how well B. F. can estimate the size of the fish in the pond.

To begin, it is important to remember from the discussion of descriptive statistics that the sizes of the fish in the population can be summarized or described by μ, which is the population mean. B. F. would like to know the value of μ; however, only we and Thoreau know that the population mean is five pounds. The best that B. F. will be able to do is *estimate* μ on the basis of her random sample of two fish. For example, if the two fish that B. F. caught were the three and five pound fish, B. F. would proceed to compute the sample mean which would be $\overline{X} = 4$ pounds. It would then be reasonable for B. F. to conclude, in the absence of any other information, that the fish in the pond have a mean of about four pounds. In other words, $\overline{X}$ becomes B. F.'s estimate of μ. Thus $\overline{X}$ is called an *estimator* of μ. In like manner, if B. F. wanted an estimate of the standard deviation σ of the population, she could compute s from the two fish in her sample.

The supposition of the last paragraph was that B. F. would catch the three and five pound fish. It might be, however, that she would catch the seven pound fish twice, thereby getting an $\overline{X}$ of seven. The $\overline{X} = 7$ would then serve as her best estimate of μ. It is apparent that there are a number of combinations of fish that might be caught if two are sampled from the population with replacement. Table 6.1 presents all the possible sample results. There are nine distinct sample results that are possible if we are careful to record the size of the first fish first and then the size of the second fish.

The next thing to be considered is the probability of B. F. getting any particular arrangement of the fish as listed in Table 6.1. Each of the nine arrangements, which are mutually exclusive, is equally probable. Hence, the probability of each is 1/9. This may be confirmed by the multiplication law for independent events. For example, $P(3, 5) = P(3) P(5) = (1/3)(1/3) = 1/9$. The probability of each possible arrangement is given in the second column of Table 6.1

TABLE 6.1

Sampling Two Fish With Replacement

Possible Sample Results (First Fish, Second Fish)	Probability	Sample Mean $\overline{X}$
(3, 3)	1/9	3
(3, 5)	1/9	4
(3, 7)	1/9	5
(5, 3)	1/9	4
(5, 5)	1/9	5
(5, 7)	1/9	6
(7, 3)	1/9	5
(7, 5)	1/9	6
(7, 7)	1/9	7

In the third column of Table 6.1 the sample mean corresponding to each of the possible sample results is given. For example, if (3, 3) occurs, then $\overline{X} = 3$. If (7, 5) occurs, then $\overline{X} = 6$. If (5, 7) occurs, then $\overline{X} = 6$. A glance at this third column indicates that B. F. will end up with a sample mean of 3, 4, 5, 6, or 7. (Always keep in mind that $\overline{X}$ serves as B. F.'s estimate of μ). It is also apparent from the third column of Table 6.1 that an $\overline{X}$ of 6, for example, can result from either of two different sample results. This implies that the probability of B. F. getting an $\overline{X}$ equal to 6 is 2/9. That is,

$$P(\overline{X} = 6) = P(5, 7) + P(7, 5)$$
$$= 1/9 + 1/9$$
$$= 2/9$$

Similarly the probability that $\overline{X}$ will equal 5 is

$$P(\overline{X} = 5) = P(3, 7) + P(5, 5) + P(7, 3)$$
$$= 1/9 + 1/9 + 1/9$$
$$= 3/9$$

Following the same sort of analysis for the other sample means, the following set of probabilities results:

$$P(\overline{X} = 3) = 1/9$$
$$P(\overline{X} = 4) = 2/9$$
$$P(\overline{X} = 5) = 3/9$$
$$P(\overline{X} = 6) = 2/9$$
$$P(\overline{X} = 7) = 1/9$$

These probabilities are summarized in Table 6.2; they form a probability distribution where $\overline{X}$ is the random variable dependent on the particular sample result achieved.

TABLE 6.2_____

Sampling Distribution of $\overline{X}$

$\overline{X}$	$P(\overline{X})$
3	1/9
4	2/9
5	3/9
6	2/9
7	1/9

The probability distribution of Table 6.2 is extremely important. A person will never understand inferential statistics if the origin and meaning of this distribution remains a mystery. This distribution is called a *sampling distribution*. The particular type of sampling distribution as given in Table 6.2 is the sampling distribution of $\overline{X}$. Sometimes it is called the distribution of the sample mean. The sampling distribution of $\overline{X}$ as given in Table 6.2 shows all of the possible sample means which might occur if a sample of two fish are taken with replacement from Walden Pond. Furthermore, the probability of each value for $\overline{X}$ is also given.

It is the sampling distribution which enables us to predict how well B. F. will succeed at estimating the population mean which is $\mu = 5$ pounds. According to the sampling distribution of $\overline{X}$, the probability of B. F. getting an $\overline{X}$ of five pounds is 3/9. This implies that by sampling two fish with replacement, there is a .33 chance that B. F. will perfectly estimate μ. Thus, a sample of size $n = 2$ might serve quite well in B. F.'s quest to accurately estimate μ. Along the same line, what is the probability that $\overline{X}$ will be within a pound of the true value of μ? Since μ equals five pounds, B. F. would be within a pound of μ if $\overline{X} = 4$, $\overline{X} = 5$, or $\overline{X} = 6$ occurred. Hence, the probability of being within a pound of μ is 2/9 + 3/9 + 2/9 or 7/9. Thus, it is by means of the sampling distribution that the precision of some sampling plan (like sampling two fish with replacement) can be judged. To repeat, it is the sampling distribution which gives insight into how closely $\overline{X}$ comes to μ.

At this point, it should be noticed that there are three distinct, yet related, entities which have been considered in this section. They are

1. The population with $\mu = 5$ and $\sigma = 1.63$.

2. A sample of size $n = 2$. The mean of the sample is $\overline{X}$ and the standard deviation is s. (Since B. F. has not yet taken the sample, the actual $\overline{X}$ and s that she would have obtained are not given.)

3. The sampling distribution of $\overline{X}$.

The thrust of this section has been toward the development of the sampling distribution of $\overline{X}$. Now that it has been developed, it can be described. Back in Chapter 3, it was explained that a probability distribution may be described by its expected value or mean which measures its center and by its standard deviation which measures its variability or dispersion. Since the sampling distribution of $\overline{X}$ as shown in Table 6.2 is a probability distribution, it has a mean and standard deviation. Its mean will be denoted by $\mu_{\overline{X}}$ and its standard deviation, or *standard error* as it is usually called, will be denoted by $\sigma_{\overline{X}}$.

For the sampling distribution of Table 6.2, the mean and standard deviation (standard error) are

$$\mu_{\overline{X}} = E(\overline{X}) = (3)(1/9) + (4)(2/9) + (5)(3/9) + (6)(2/9) + (7)(1/9)$$
$$= 5 \text{ pounds}$$

$$\sigma_{\overline{X}} = \sqrt{(3-5)^2(1/9) + (4-5)^2(2/9) + \ldots + (7-5)^2(1/9)}$$
$$= 1.15 \text{ pounds}$$

There is, however, an easier method of finding the mean and standard error of the sampling distribution. It is based on the fact that the sampling distribution is derived, through sampling, from the population. The following important theorem shows the relationship of the sampling distribution of $\overline{X}$ to the population and in so doing provides a quick way to determine the mean and standard error of the sampling distribution.

The mean $\mu_{\overline{X}}$ and standard error $\sigma_{\overline{X}}$ of the sampling distribution of $\overline{X}$ are given by

$$\mu_{\overline{X}} = \mu$$

$$\sigma_{\overline{X}} = \frac{\sigma}{\sqrt{n}} \quad \text{or} \quad \sigma_{\overline{X}} = \frac{\sigma}{\sqrt{n}}\sqrt{1 - \frac{n}{N}}$$

where μ and σ are the parameters of the population from which the sample of size n is drawn. The first expression for the standard error is appropriate in all cases where sampling is with replacement or where sampling is without replacement and n is less than 10 percent of N. If sampling is without replacement and n is 10 percent or more of the population size N, then the second expression for the standard error should be used.

Since B. F. is sampling with replacement from a population whose mean is μ = 5 and standard deviation is σ = 1.63, this theorem states that the mean of the sampling distribution of $\overline{X}$ will be

$$\mu_{\overline{X}} = \mu$$
$$= 5 \text{ pounds}$$

and the standard error is

$$\sigma_{\overline{X}} = \frac{\sigma}{\sqrt{n}}$$

$$= \frac{1.63}{\sqrt{2}}$$

$$= 1.15 \text{ pounds}$$

The theorem above gives an important insight into the relationship between the precision of the estimate and the sample size. The standard error is the standard deviation of the sampling distribution. When the standard error is large, there is considerable variability or dispersion among the $\overline{X}$'s in the sampling distribution. Since $\overline{X}$ serves as the estimate of μ, this implies that $\overline{X}$ could easily be quite a distance from μ if the standard error is large. On the other hand, if the standard error is very small, this implies that the $\overline{X}$'s of the sampling distribution are tightly packed near the center which is $\mu_{\overline{X}}$. Since the mean of the sampling distribution, $\mu_{\overline{X}}$, equals the population mean, it follows that the $\overline{X}$'s are very close to the population mean if the standard error is small. Hence, the estimating procedure (where $\overline{X}$ is taken as the estimate of the population mean μ) is very reliable if the standard error $\sigma_{\overline{X}}$ is small.

According to the theorem, the standard error is computed by

$$\sigma_{\overline{X}} = \frac{\sigma}{\sqrt{n}}$$

Notice that the standard error decreases when the sample size increases. For example, in the Walden Pond case where $n = 2$, the standard error is $\sigma_{\bar{x}} = 1.63/\sqrt{2} = 1.15$. If B. F. could sample $n = 16$ fish with replacement, the standard error would be reduced to $\sigma_{\bar{x}} = 1.63/\sqrt{16} = .41$. This implies that if a sample of size 16 is used, the sample means are a lot closer to μ than if $n = 2$. Thus, the sample would be much more reliable for the sake of estimating the population mean.

Several brief examples will now be given to illustrate the theorem. The beauty of this theorem lies in the fact that the actual sampling distribution of $\overline{X}$ does not have to be constructed, as was done in Tables 6.1 and 6.2, in order to find its mean and standard error. Only the mean and standard deviation of the population need to be known.

Suppose that the mean weight of a herd (population) of $N = 1,000$ cattle is $\mu = 600$ pounds and that the standard deviation is $\sigma = 200$ pounds. If a sample of $n = 4$ head of cattle were randomly selected without replacement from this herd, the sampling distribution of $\overline{X}$ would have a mean and standard error of

$$\mu_{\bar{x}} = \mu$$
$$= 600$$
$$\sigma_{\bar{x}} = \frac{\sigma}{\sqrt{n}}$$
$$= \frac{200}{\sqrt{4}}$$
$$= 100$$

Notice that since n is less than 10 percent of N, the first expression for the standard error as given in the theorem is appropriate.

As a second example, if a random sample without replacement of size 25 were selected from a population of $N = 100$ sheep whose mean is $\mu = 60$ pounds and standard deviation is $\sigma = 20$ pounds, then the sampling distribution of $\overline{X}$ would have a mean and standard error of

$$\mu_{\bar{x}} = \mu$$
$$= 60$$
$$\sigma_{\bar{x}} = \frac{\sigma}{\sqrt{n}}\sqrt{1 - \frac{n}{N}}$$
$$= \frac{20}{\sqrt{25}}\sqrt{1 - \frac{25}{100}}$$
$$= 3.47$$

Here the second form of the standard error is used since the sample size of 25 is not less than 10 percent of N.

In summary, it has been the purpose of this section to explain what a sampling distribution is, how it might be derived, and how its mean and standard deviation (standard error) are related to the mean and standard deviation of the population from which the sample is drawn. Furthermore, the importance of the standard error in determining the accuracy of using $\overline{X}$ as an estimate of μ was noted. The remainder of the chapter will be based on the concepts developed in this section.

6.4

SAMPLING FROM A NORMAL POPULATION

Though the discussion of the last section was quite challenging because of the introduction of various theoretical concepts, the application of these concepts is actually quite straightforward. In this section and the section to follow, a couple of applications will be given along with a little more theory.

Suppose Consolidated Power & Light has stated that the April electric bills for the 1,100 families in a high-rise apartment building in New York City are normally distributed with a mean of $30 and a standard deviation of $6. If a random sample of $n = 9$ families were taken, what is the probability that the sample mean would fall within $1 of the population mean? In other words, what is the probability that $\overline{X}$ will fall between $29 and $31?

This question can be answered once the sampling distribution of $\overline{X}$ is determined. A similar type of question was asked in the Walden Pond illustration, namely, what is the probability that B. F.'s estimate $\overline{X}$ will be within one pound of the population mean of five pounds? This was answered by referring to the sampling distribution of $\overline{X}$ as found in Table 6.2. From this distribution it was seen that the probability that $\overline{X}$ will fall between four and six pounds is 7/9. Thus, the sampling distribution is the key to determining how close $\overline{X}$ will come to μ.

Returning to the Consolidated Power & Light case, the probability that $\overline{X}$ will fall between $29 and $31 could easily be found once the sampling distribution of $\overline{X}$ is determined. From the theorem given in Section 6.3, several characteristics of the sampling distribution of $\overline{X}$ can be determined quite readily. The mean of the sampling distribution is always equal to the population mean. Therefore,

$$\mu_{\overline{X}} = \mu$$
$$= \$30$$

since it was given that the mean bill of the 1,100 families in the population is \$30. Furthermore, the standard error (standard deviation of the $\overline{X}$ distribution) is

$$\sigma_{\overline{X}} = \frac{\sigma}{\sqrt{n}}$$

$$= \frac{\$6}{\sqrt{9}}$$

$$= \$2$$

since the standard deviation of the population was given as $\sigma = \$6$ and the sample size is $n = 9$ families. Also notice that the factor $\sqrt{1 - n/N}$ was not used to compute the standard error, since the n of 9 is less than 10 percent of the N of 1,100. Thus, the sampling distribution of $\overline{X}$ is a probability distribution which has a mean of \$30 and a standard deviation (standard error) of \$2.

Though $\mu_{\overline{X}}$ and $\sigma_{\overline{X}}$ are known, we still do not know what type of distribution the sampling distribution is. That is, is it skewed? is it leptokurtic? is it normal? etc. The following theorem helps us here:

> The sampling distribution of $\overline{X}$ will be a normal distribution if the population from which the sample of size n is drawn is normal.

At the outset, Consolidated Power & Light reported that the population of April electric bills was normally distributed. Therefore, because of this theorem we may conclude that the sampling distribution of $\overline{X}$ is normal. Knowing this wraps up our investigation of the sampling distribution of $\overline{X}$ because it is known to be normal with a mean of \$30 and a standard deviation (standard error) of \$2. Nothing more need be said to identify this distribution.

All that remains is to find the probability that $\overline{X}$ will fall between \$29 and \$31 where $\overline{X}$ is normally distributed with a mean of $\mu_{\overline{X}} = 30$ and a standard error of $\sigma_{\overline{X}} = 2$. In Section 4.6 of Chapter 4, considerable attention was devoted to finding probabilities (areas) for normal distributions. Figure 6.1 depicts the area (probability) being sought. In order to find the probability that $\overline{X}$ falls between 29 and 31, the 29 and 31 must be converted to standard deviation units:

$$Z = \frac{29 - 30}{2}$$

$$= -.5$$

FIGURE 6.1_____

Sampling Distribution of $\overline{X}$ ($\mu_{\overline{X}} = 30$, $\sigma_{\overline{X}} = 2$)

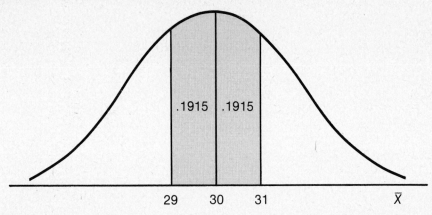

and,

$$Z = \frac{31 - 30}{2}$$
$$= .5$$

Therefore, the probability being sought may be found as follows:

$$P(29 \le \overline{X} \le 31) = P(-.5 \le Z \le .5)$$
$$= .1915 + .1915 \qquad \text{(from Appendix N)}$$
$$= .3830$$

Thus, it may be concluded that the probability is .3830, and that the estimate $\overline{X}$ will fall within \$1 of the population mean which is \$30.

In summary, whenever the sample is taken from a normal population, then the sampling distribution of $\overline{X}$ is also normal. Since the mean and standard error of the sampling distribution can easily be computed by the theorem of Section 6.3, the sampling distribution can be completely described. Being a normal distribution, any probability involving $\overline{X}$ (which is the random variable of the sampling distribution) can be found using Appendix N.

6.5_____

SAMPLING FROM A NONNORMAL POPULATION

In the last section, it was stated that the sampling distribution of $\overline{X}$ will always be normal if the sample is being drawn from a normal population. In this section, we consider the far more common situation where a sample is drawn from a population which is not normal. In such a case we might wonder what the form or shape of the sampling distribution of $\overline{X}$ would be. One of the most important theorems in statistics, the *central limit theorem*, deals with the form of the sampling distribution of $\overline{X}$ when the sample is taken from *any kind* of population. The central limit theorem states:

> Regardless of the form of the population from which the random sample is drawn, the sampling distribution of $\overline{X}$ will be approximately normal if the sample size n is at least 25.

This is an exceedingly important statement. The shape of the population (whether it be highly skewed, symmetrical, bimodal, platykurtic, etc.) is immaterial in so far as its influence on the shape of the sampling distribution of $\overline{X}$ is concerned. The sampling distribution will always be normal (have the bell shape) as long as the sample size is 25 or more. Because of the central limit theorem, we need not care what the shape or form of the population is. Consider an example where the El Cajon restaurant made use of the central limit theorem.

The Old Ranger was a hunter without equal in the wild west. His specialty was dealing in elk. However, the Old Ranger did not consider himself to be a hunter; rather, he thought of himself as something of a self-styled animal doctor. It seemed that the Old Ranger heard that the elk population of California was suffering from a mineral deficiency. Because of the Old Ranger's interest in his four-footed friends, he took it upon himself to head into the hills where he would administer a copper-coated lead pill to each elk that was suspected to be suffering from a mineral deficiency. It was during these times that the El Cajon restaurant signed a contract with the Old Ranger which called for the Old Ranger to supply the restaurant with 25 elk who had received the Ranger's mineral supplement. As time was a pressing issue, the contract stated that the Old Ranger need not specifically supply large elk. The Old Ranger merely had to bring in the first 25 full-grown elk that came his way whether they be small or large.

As the Old Ranger sauntered off to accomplish the task, the El Cajon restaurant began to wonder how much elk the Old Ranger would procure. There was no question that the Old Ranger would get 25 of them; the only question was how big they would be. Upon checking with the California Game and Fish Commission, the El Cajon found that the population of thousands of full-grown elk in California had a mean weight of about 400 pounds and a standard deviation of 60 pounds. In view of this information, the restaurant wished to determine the probability that the Old Ranger would bring back 25 elk which averaged more than 420 pounds each. The amount of elk on hand would determine the extent to which the El Cajon would advertise this specialty.

In condensed form, the El Cajon's desire is to find the probability that $\overline{X}$ will exceed 420 pounds in a situation where a sample of 25 is being randomly drawn from a population which has a mean of 400 pounds and a standard deviation of 60 pounds. Let us state this symbolically:

> Population of elk —
>
> > N = thousands of elk
> > μ = 400 pounds
> > σ = 60 pounds
>
> Sample —
>
> > $\overline{X}$ to be computed on the basis of a sample of $n =$ 25 elk.

Under these conditions the restaurant wants to find the following probability:

> $P(\overline{X} > 420 \text{ pounds})$

In order to find the desired probability, the probability distribution of $\overline{X}$ (which is the sampling distribution of $\overline{X}$) must be determined. According to the theorem of Section 6.3, the mean and standard error of the sampling distribution of $\overline{X}$ are

$$\mu_{\overline{X}} = \mu$$
$$= 400 \text{ pounds}$$
$$\sigma_{\overline{X}} = \frac{\sigma}{\sqrt{n}}$$
$$= \frac{60}{\sqrt{25}}$$
$$= 12 \text{ pounds}$$

According to the central limit theorem, the $\overline{X}$ distribution is normal since the sample size n was at least 25. It might be noted that the population of elk is probably bimodal since there are both male, which are larger, and female elk comprising the population. Nevertheless, the sampling distribution of $\overline{X}$ is normal.

Since the sampling distribution of $\overline{X}$ is normal with $\mu_{\bar{x}} = 400$ and $\sigma_{\bar{x}} = 12$, it is now easy to determine the probability that $\overline{X}$ will exceed 420 pounds. Converting to standard deviation units (see Section 4.6 of Chapter 4) yields:

$$P(\overline{X} > 420) = P\left(Z > \frac{420-400}{12}\right)$$
$$= P(Z > 1.67)$$
$$= .5000 - .4525 \qquad \text{(from Appendix N)}$$
$$= .0475$$

Hence, there is a probability of .0475 that the Old Ranger's catch will average more than 420 pounds per elk.

6.6

SUMMARY OF SAMPLING DISTRIBUTIONS

Generally speaking, this last half of the chapter has shown what the values of the statistic $\overline{X}$ might be when $\overline{X}$ is based on a random sample from a population which is at least partially known.

In the Walden Pond example the population was completely described, in that every item (fish) in the population (pond) was identified by its weight. From this population a sample of size $n = 2$ could be drawn. The sampling distribution of $\overline{X}$, as given in Table 6.2, displayed all of the possible values that $\overline{X}$ might take on with their respective probabilities. By studying this distribution, the analyst could judge how good $\overline{X}$ was at estimating the population mean. On the basis of this distribution, probabilities involving $\overline{X}$ could also be readily determined.

In the Consolidated Power & Light example, the population was completely described in that it was given as normal with a known mean and standard deviation. From this population a sample of any size could be drawn. The sampling distribution of $\overline{X}$ is normal and its mean and standard error can be computed. On the basis of this sampling distribution, probabilities involving $\overline{X}$ can easily be computed.

In the Old Ranger example, the population, in contrast to the two previous examples, was only partially described. Only its mean and standard deviation were given; its shape or form was unknown. According to the central limit theorem, if a sample of at least 25 is randomly selected from the population, then the sampling distribution of $\overline{X}$ will be normal. (If a sample of less than 25 were taken, there is no way to determine the shape or form of the sampling distribution.) Since the mean and standard error of the sampling distribution can be computed, any probability involving $\overline{X}$ can be easily determined since $\overline{X}$ is normally distributed.

In each of the three cases just mentioned, probabilities involving $\overline{X}$ can be determined. In other words, probabilistic statements can be made concerning the value of the sample mean. This is one of the primary reasons for constructing the sampling distribution. Another reason for the importance of the sampling distribution resides in what can be deduced from it concerning the accuracy of $\overline{X}$ as an estimator of μ. Whenever the sample size n increases, the standard error decreases. When the standard error decreases, this in turn implies that the $\overline{X}$'s lie closer to μ which is the mean of the population and the sampling distribution. Thus, $\overline{X}$ becomes a better and better estimator of μ as the sample size increases. This means that if the mean of some population is unknown, but a very large sample has been taken from that population, you can be sure that the $\overline{X}$ you get from that sample will be very close to μ. This is because the standard error in such a case would be very small. Hence, the value of $\overline{X}$ gives the statistician a good idea as to what the mean of the population is.

With this chapter, the door to inferential statistics has been opened. Inferential statistics rests on the foundation of the sampling distribution. The study of inferential statistics commences in the next chapter.

PROBLEMS

6.1

The purpose of sampling is to estimate a population parameter such as the population mean. What is the statistic that is typically used to estimate the population mean?

6.2

Describe convenience sampling. Give an example of convenience sampling that was not mentioned in the text.

6.3

Describe judgment sampling. Give an example of judgment sampling that was not mentioned in the text.

6.4

Why are convenience sampling and judgment sampling not used in this text?

6.5

Identify and briefly describe the four methods of random sampling that were explained in the text.

6.6

Describe how a union official could use simple random sampling to sample union members from the Teamsters Union.

6.7

Describe how a quality control engineer might use systematic sampling to sample binoculars coming off a production assembly line.

6.8

Describe how a researcher might use cluster sampling in order to determine the average age of the residents of Little Rock.

6.9

Describe how an economist could use stratified sampling in order to estimate the average salary of the thousands of persons employed on a large military base.

6.10

You are a border patrol agent responsible for inspecting vehicles entering the United States from Juarez, Mexico. There is no way in which you can inspect every vehicle, thus only a sample of the vehicles crossing can be inspected for contraband. What type of random sampling would be useful? Why? Would judgment sampling be advisable? Why or why not?

6.11

What kind of sampling method is the customer employing who picks out the avocados from a big bin at the grocery market?

6.12

An interviewer for a local radio station approaches people on the street in downtown Omaha asking them about the government's farm policies. What type of sampling method is being used?

6.13

An actuary wishes to determine certain characteristics of all the employees of computer software firms who are members of CSFA.

There are about 400 member firms in CSFA. The actuary proceeds to sample 10 of the 400 firms in CSFA; then each employee of the 10 sampled firms is interviewed. What type of sampling method is the actuary using?

6.14

An economist wishes to determine the capital spending plans of the 500 largest U.S. companies as listed in Fortune magazine. The intent of the study is to predict future unemployment rates, which are related to the amount of capital spending that is going on. The economist has decided to use stratified sampling to select a sample of about 30 companies from the 500. Suggest two different stratification schemes that the economist might use.

6.15

Assume that B. F. Skinert of the Walden Pond example is going to sample $n = 2$ fish *without* replacement.
(a) Construct a table similar to Table 6.1.
(b) Construct the sampling distribution of $\overline{X}$.
(c) What is the probability that B. F.'s sample mean will perfectly estimate μ?
(d) What is the probability that $\overline{X}$ will be within one pound of μ?

6.16

There are three light bulbs in a carton. The lives of the bulbs are 2,000, 2,200, and 2,700 hours. A sample of two bulbs is taken with replacement.
(a) Find μ.
(b) Construct the sampling distribution of $\overline{X}$.
(c) What is the probability that the sample mean will be within 100 hours of the population mean?
(d) Find the mean and standard error of the sampling distribution.

6.17

Let all of the digits in Appendix R constitute a population.
(a) What is N?
(b) Based on your knowledge of what a table of random numbers is, what is the value of μ?
(c) Now reach into Appendix R and sample a group of five digits. Compute $\overline{X}$.
(d) Repeat (c) 20 times. Therefore you now have a set of 20 $\overline{X}$ values. Construct a frequency distribution for these $\overline{X}$ values as follows (you merely supply the frequencies):

$\overline{X}$	Frequency
0–0.99	
1–1.99	
2–2.99	
3–3.99	
4–4.99	
5–5.99	
6–6.99	
7–7.99	
8–8.99	
9–9.99	

(e) Draw a histogram based on your frequency distribution. Does it have an appearance remotely resembling a normal distribution?

(f) What percentage of the sample means had a value from 4 to 5.99?

6.18

If a population has a mean of 500 and a standard deviation of 80, what are the mean and standard error of the sampling distribution of $\overline{X}$ if $n = 4$? if $n = 16$? if $n = 100$? (Assume that N is infinite.) Based on your answers, what happens to the standard error as n increases? What does this imply about the closeness of the sample means to the population mean?

6.19

Is it possible for μ to equal 10 and $\mu_{\overline{x}}$ to equal 12?

6.20

Can the standard error ever be greater than the standard deviation of the population? Why or why not?

6.21

The factor $\sqrt{1 - n/N}$ is known as the *finite population correction factor*. It is used to diminish the size of the standard error if n becomes a considerable proportion of N. Determine the value of the finite population correction factor if $n = 10$ and $N = 100$, if $n = 10$ and $N = 1,000$, and if $n = 10$ and $N = 20$. In view of your findings, why is the finite population correction factor of little consequence in computing the standard error when n is no more than 10 percent of N?

6.22

It has been stated that the standard error gives us a feel for how accurately the sample mean estimates the population mean. Explain why this is true.

6.23

A population of 50 boxes has a mean weight of 30 pounds and a standard deviation of 15 pounds. If a random sample of nine boxes were selected, what would the mean and standard error of the sampling distribution of $\overline{X}$ be?

6.24

If a sample of any size is drawn from a normal population, the sampling distribution of $\overline{X}$ will have what shape?

6.25

If a sample of size 36 is drawn from a nonnormal population, the sampling distribution of $\overline{X}$ will have what shape?

6.26

If a sample of size 10 is drawn from a nonnormal population, what will be the shape of the sampling distribution of $\overline{X}$?

6.27

The annual net incomes of the restaurants in a chain of 200 are normally distributed with a mean of $40,000 and a standard deviation of $16,000.
(a) If four of these restaurants are randomly sampled, what is the probability that their sample mean will fall within $5,000 of the population mean?
(b) Answer (a) if n were 100.

6.28

The breaking strengths of 100 strands of a new fiber are normally distributed with a mean of 80 pounds and a standard deviation of five pounds. If nine strands are randomly sampled, what is the probability that their mean breaking strength is less than 78 pounds? more than 83 pounds?

6.29

The annual rainfall in Flagstaff is normally distributed with a mean of 19″ and a standard deviation of 7″. What is the probability that the mean annual rainfall over the next four years will exceed 22″?

6.30

The net weights of a shipment of 100 bags of fertilizer are normally distributed with a mean of 50 pounds and a standard deviation of two pounds. If you purchase four bags, what is the probability that they will, in total, weigh 204 or more pounds? If instead you purchased 20 bags, what is the probability that their mean weight would fall below 49.5 pounds?

6.31

The mean life insurance in force on adult, male Texans is $26,000 with a standard deviation of $15,000. If 25 adult, male Texans were randomly sampled, what is the probability that their mean life insurance is between $24,000 and $28,000?

6.32

The mean diameter of the Douglas firs near Mount Hood is 48". The standard deviation of the diameters is 12". If 36 firs are randomly cut, what is the probability that their mean diameter will exceed 50"? will exceed 54"?

6.33

A computer service engineer in Knoxville receives an average of eight calls for service per day. The standard deviation is four calls per day. What is the probability that over the next 25 days the engineer will receive an average of seven or more calls per day? an average of more than nine calls per day? an average of more than 12 calls per day?

6.34

For the 1,000 stocks traded on the Hong Kong Stock Exchange, the mean dividend yield is 4 percent with a standard deviation of 3 percent. If 25 stocks are randomly chosen, what is the probability that their mean yield will exceed 5 percent?

6.35

The mean grocery bill of the customers shopping at a particular supermarket is $36. The standard deviation of the bills is $14. If 49 customers are randomly selected, what is $P(35 \leq \overline{X} \leq 37)$?

6.36

A quality control engineer has just received a shipment of 20,000 mercury vapor lamps. The engineer knows that the standard deviation of the lives of these lamps is 1,000 hours, however the mean life of them is unknown. If a sample of 100 lamps were tested yielding an $\overline{X}$, what is the probability that the $\overline{X}$ so found will be within 200 hours of the true population mean?

CHAPTER 7

ESTIMATION

7.1

INFERENTIAL STATISTICS

Through inferential statistics, the statistician draws conclusions about a population on the basis of sample results. The value of the parameter of the population is unknown; therefore, the statistician takes a random sample from the population. From this sample the statistician computes a statistic which becomes an estimate of the population parameter. For example, the mean size μ of a finance company's 200 bad debts might be unknown. In order to estimate the value of μ, the statistician randomly samples 25 of the bad debts and computes the mean. Suppose the sample mean turns out to be $\overline{X}$ = \$143. The statistician would then infer, on the basis of $\overline{X}$, that the population mean is probably close to \$143. Notice that the $\overline{X}$ of \$143 would serve as an estimate of μ which is "probably close to μ." The statistician does not claim that this estimate is perfectly accurate. Therefore, probability enters into the estimation process. More fully defined, *inferential statistics* is the methodology by which probabilistic conclusions concerning a population are derived on the basis of sample evidence.

Inferential statistics has traditionally been broken into two branches: estimation and hypothesis testing. In *estimation*, there is no preconceived idea as to what the value of the unknown population parameter might be. The statistician moves directly to take a sample and then makes a probabilistic statement about the value of the parameter on the basis of the sample. In *hypothesis testing*, the analyst has a preconceived notion as to what the value of the population parameter is. This preconceived notion is the hypothesis. After formulating the hypothesis, a sample is taken and the analyst decides if the sample evidence supports or contradicts the hypothesis. In this way, the hypothesis is either accepted or rejected. This chapter will deal with estimation; the next chapter will deal with hypothesis testing.

7.2

ESTIMATION

Suppose the management of a large amusement park wants to know the average age μ of all the persons visiting the amusement park in a year. Just as management is beginning to think about how this average age might be estimated through random sampling, one of the managers says, "Why not forget all this business about sampling and estimation? Let's ask everyone their age and then we can accurately figure out the average age of our visitors." This manager is proposing a *census*. A census involves individually checking each of the N items in the population. It is true that a census could be used to accurately determine the value of a parameter such as μ or σ. In such a case, there would be no need to question whether the value obtained is accurate. Thus, it is legitimate to ask "Why bother with sampling and its probabilistic conclusions? Why not take a census and know for sure what we are after?" Before setting forth the methodology of inferential statistics with its probabilistic estimates, it is important that we deal with this question.

There are a number of reasons why a sample might be preferable to a census for the sake of determining some unknown population parameter. Four reasons will now be considered.

First, there is the matter of *cost*. It might be quite expensive to take a census of a large population. If the population being studied were the hundreds of thousands of people who frequently buy a popular soft drink, imagine the cost if we had to find every one of them and then ask some psychologically probing questions in order to see why they buy one soft drink rather than another. Obviously a sample is the only way to go.

Second, a sample may offer more *accuracy* than a census. This is because with the complexity and size of taking a large census, it is difficult to keep from making errors like overlooking part of the population or not properly instructing and controlling the census takers. A sample permits a more intensive, controlled study of the soft drink consumers, for example. This yields more accurate conclusions about the population.

Third, sampling may be necessary because of a shortage of *time*. There may not be enough time to take a census; thus, a sample must be taken. For example, if during the week before an election the candidates desire to know how the electorate is leaning, they do not have enough time to take a census of all the voters. If any information is to be gained, it must be by sampling.

Fourth, many items are destroyed in the process of being tested. For example, the mean life of a batch of flares could be accurately established by a census where each flare is burned to measure its life. Though the mean life would then be known, no flares remain to be used or sold. Thus, sampling is required in all *destructive* testing situations. So for a combination of reasons, a sample rather than a census may be the optimal way to gain information about an unknown population parameter.

It has been indicated in this chapter and the last that estimates based on a sample can be wrong. There are two types of reasons why a statistic like $\overline{X}$ can miss or be in error in estimating a parameter like μ. Because of pure chance, the statistic or estimator may differ from the parameter. Remember the Walden Pond example of the last chapter. It was demonstrated there that by chance, $\overline{X}$ could equal either 3, 4, 5, 6, or 7 pounds. Only if $\overline{X}$ equalled five pounds would it provide a perfect estimate of the true population mean which is five pounds. If $\overline{X}$ did equal some value like four pounds, then B. F.'s estimate of μ would be in error (by one pound). This kind of error is called a *sampling error*. It is the error which results by pure chance because the items in the sample do not happen to be a perfect representation of the items in the population. The only way that sampling error can be reduced is by increasing the size of the sample. Much ado was made in the last chapter concerning the principle that by increasing n the standard error is decreased. A decrease in the standard error implies that the statistic $\overline{X}$ becomes closer to μ. In other words, sampling error decreases as n increases. Nevertheless, as long as a sample rather than a census is taken, sampling error will exist, and therefore conclusions should be stated probabilistically.

The other reason why an estimate of a parameter might be wrong is because of *nonsampling error*. These errors can exist in taking a census as well as in sampling. A common type of nonsampling error is caused by a biased measuring device. For example, if you are seeking to determine the weight of the bales of cotton on a loading dock by using a scale which always weighs about five pounds too light, you will obviously be in error in estimating the mean weight of the bales. Consider another example where there is bias in a measuring device (a questionnaire) and where the sampling process itself is biased because it does not offer each item in the population an equal chance of being selected. Socrates is trying to get the reaction of the voters in his school district to a proposed bond issue. Socrates therefore decides to take a sample of 50 people who are shopping in the big shopping mall located in the center of the school district. His first question is, "Do you care

about the education of our children?" His second is, "Do you realize that the education of our children will seriously suffer if this
bond issue is not approved?" His third is, "Do you favor this bond
issue?" If you say no, he has a quick little follow-up question, "Are
you a Philistine?" Such a sampling endeavor, which is riddled with
nonsampling errors, is not uncommon. Whether it is a census or a
sample, the analyst must be careful to keep the analysis clean of
nonsampling errors.

7.3

POINT ESTIMATION

What will be the rate of inflation next year? A person could
answer this question in at least three ways. One answer might be,
"My best guess is 6 percent"; another might be, "I think it will be
somewhere between 4 percent and 8 percent"; and yet another
reply might be, "I'm about 90 percent sure that the inflation rate
will be between 5 percent and 7 percent." Each of these three
types of answers constitutes an estimate of next year's rate of inflation. They are estimates, since no one knows with certainty
what the rate of inflation will be. The first type of estimate which
is a single best guess estimate is called a *point estimate*. The last
two are called *interval estimates*. In this section, the process of
point estimation will be studied; interval estimation will be considered in a later section.

An *estimator* is a sample statistic, like $\overline{X}$, which is used to estimate a population parameter, like μ. When a population parameter is unknown, a random sample is taken from the population,
and on the basis of the sample data, an estimate is made of the
unknown population parameter. As indicated above, if the estimate is a single number or best guess, then the estimate is called
a point estimate.

In order for an estimator to be considered as good, it must be
unbiased and consistent. An estimator like $\overline{X}$, which is used to
estimate μ, is *unbiased* because its expected value equals the population mean. In other words, if $\overline{X}$ is used to estimate μ again and
again, the resulting estimates will not, on the average, be too high
or too low. The second criterion is that of *consistency*. $\overline{X}$, for example, is a consistent estimator of μ. This means that $\overline{X}$ tends to get
closer to μ as the sample size n increases. In other words, the standard error of the sampling distribution decreases as n increases.
This implies that the $\overline{X}$'s in the sampling distribution cluster
more closely around μ which is the mean of both the sampling distribution and the population. The analysis of the sampling distribution of $\overline{X}$ as given in the last chapter provides the basis for concluding that $\overline{X}$ is an unbiased and consistent estimator of μ.

Two other population parameters that have been mentioned in previous chapters are σ, the population standard deviation, and p, the population proportion. The estimators that are used in order to get a point estimate of these two parameters are s, the sample standard deviation, and $\bar{p}$, the sample proportion. Also, the sample variance s^2 is the best estimator of the population variance σ^2. Table 7.1 presents the estimators and the respective parameters they estimate.

TABLE 7.1

Parameters and Their Estimators

Parameter	Estimator
μ	$\overline{X} = \dfrac{\Sigma X}{n}$
σ	$s = \sqrt{\dfrac{\Sigma(X - \overline{X})^2}{n - 1}}$
σ^2	$s^2 = \dfrac{\Sigma(X - \overline{X})^2}{n - 1}$
p	$\bar{p} = \dfrac{X}{n}$

The disbursements journal for Daylight Electric contains thousands of entries recording the disbursements made over the past year. An auditor wishes to estimate three parameters of this population of thousands of disbursements. The three parameters are the mean size of the disbursements, the standard deviation of the disbursements, and the proportion of the disbursements made to manufacturers of electrical supplies. The auditor took a random sample of $n = 40$ disbursements. Here is a partial listing of the sample data:

$986.49   to Cobra Copper

   22.10   to Goose Electric

340.00   to Samuel Casey

   15.63   to Little Beaver Office Supply

149.12   to Arizona Public Service

.

.

.

The three unknown parameters which are to be estimated are

μ = mean size of the disbursements

σ = standard deviation

p = proportion of disbursements going to manufacturers

These three parameters are estimated by the following estimators: $\overline{X}$, s, and $\bar{p}$. The point estimates based on the sample of $n = 40$ disbursements are

$$\overline{X} = \frac{986.49 + 22.10 + 340.00 + 15.63 + 149.12 + \ldots}{40}$$

$$= \$76$$

$$s = \sqrt{\frac{(986.49 - 76)^2 + (22.10 - 76)^2 + (340.00 - 76)^2 + \ldots}{40 - 1}}$$

$$= \$104.68$$

$$\bar{p} = \frac{6}{40} \qquad \text{since 6 of the 40 sampled disbursements went to manufacturers like Cobra and Goose Electric}$$

$$= .15$$

These point estimates are the single numbers which are the best guesses or estimates for the respective parameters. Notice that being statistics they are based exclusively on sample data.

Though these are the best estimates available, the auditor realizes that they are undoubtedly not the precise values of μ, σ, and p. This, of course, is because of sampling error. In general, however, the auditor can expect that these point estimates are probably pretty close to the true values of the parameters; this is because a fairly large sample was taken. Since the three estimators are consistent, they do yield estimates which tend to be close to the parameter as n increases.

Point estimates are easy to compute. However, their weakness is that they carry no information concerning their accuracy. If n happens to be large, we can say that the resulting point estimate is "probably pretty close" to the population parameter. Though such a statement is of some help, it is still quite ambiguous and does not give us much usable information. Therefore, in an attempt to indicate something of the accuracy of an estimate, interval estimates have been developed. These will be considered in the next section.

7.4

INTERVAL ESTIMATES OF THE POPULATION MEAN

Winnie Estes was yearning to take an extended vacation to South America. Financing such a vacation was going to be a problem for Winnie, so she made a visit to the Little Big Horn Bank for the purpose of seeking a vacation loan. The bank loan officer was not eager to lend Winnie $900,000 on the security of her signature. This prompted the loan officer to ask for collateral. Winnie explained that this would be no problem since she owned a ranch covered with acres of tanks containing cottonseed oil. Furthermore, Winnie figured she had in excess of a million dollars worth of the oil. The loan officer immediately assured Winnie that liquid assets in such quantity would make fine collateral. However, the officer added that as a matter of procedure, the bank's auditor would have to visit Winnie's ranch to confirm the existence of the cottonseed oil.

Thus it was that the Little Big Horn Bank sent the fledgling auditor Poohmer von Schoohmer to Winnie's ranch. Pooh's task was to estimate how much cottonseed oil was at the ranch. Pooh began by counting the 500 tanks scattered around the ranch. As the hot Western sun beat down, Pooh decided that checking each of the tanks would be too much trouble. Thus, he decided to randomly sample 25 tanks. Sensing that this case was going to be a biggy in the annals of auditing, Pooh took each step quite deliberately, always being careful to understand what he was doing. Thus, he began by realizing that the 500 tanks constitute the population. The important parameter of the population which was unknown was μ, the mean amount of oil per tank.

Upon taking the sample of $n = 25$ tanks, Pooh decided he would compute $\overline{X}$, which would serve as an estimate of μ. Pooh was quick to realize, however, that he would get a different $\overline{X}$ depending on what 25 tanks happened to end up in the sample. Because there is variability in the estimate $\overline{X}$ depending on what tanks end up in the random sample, it stands to reason that some of the possible estimates will be more accurate than others. Furthermore, since there is no way to tell if the $\overline{X}$ computed from a particular sample is especially close to μ, Pooh was not prone to bring back to the bank a mere point estimate of μ. Pooh instead wanted to derive an interval estimate. He fancied that he would like to be able to conclude something like "I am 90 percent confident that μ is between 800 and 900 gallons."

Computationally speaking, it is quite easy to find an interval estimate of μ similar to the one just given. The theory behind the construction of such an interval is a bit more involved. Let us look

at this theory and then examine the mechanics of actually constructing an interval estimate.

In order to understand interval estimation, the reader must
feel comfortable with the sampling distribution of $\overline{X}$. All the details of the sampling distribution of $\overline{X}$ were set forth in Chapter 6
and will not be repeated here. The theory of interval estimation
rests on this foundation.

To begin, if a sample of size $n = 25$ is drawn from a population,
any of a variety of values of $\overline{X}$ may occur. The full range of potential values of $\overline{X}$ with their probabilities is given by the sampling
distribution of $\overline{X}$. The sampling distribution of $\overline{X}$ will have a mean
$\mu_{\bar{x}}$ which equals the mean μ of the population and a standard error
$\sigma_{\bar{x}}$ which equals $\sigma/\sqrt{n}$, where σ is the standard deviation of the
population. Furthermore, the $\overline{X}$ distribution will be normal because of the central limit theorem, since n is 25. Figure 7.1 pictures the sampling distribution of $\overline{X}$.

FIGURE 7.1_____

Sampling Distribution of $\overline{X}$

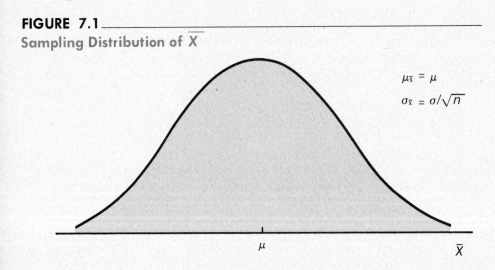

$$\mu_{\bar{x}} = \mu$$
$$\sigma_{\bar{x}} = \sigma/\sqrt{n}$$

μ $\overline{X}$

By using the techniques introduced in Section 4.6 of Chapter 4,
it is possible to show that 90 percent of the area (probability)
under any normal distribution lies within 1.65 standard deviations
of the mean. This is apparent from Appendix N, which shows that
the area between a Z of 0 and a Z of 1.65 is .4505. (Remember that
Z represents standard deviation units.) Thus, .4505 + .4505 or
about .90 lies between a Z of -1.65 and a Z of $+1.65$. Applying this
to the sampling distribution of $\overline{X}$, which is a normal distribution,
it can be concluded that there is a probability of .90 that $\overline{X}$ will fall
between a value which is 1.65 standard errors below the mean and
a value which is 1.65 standard errors above the mean. This is illustrated in Figure 7.2.

FIGURE 7.2

Sampling Distribution of $\overline{X}$

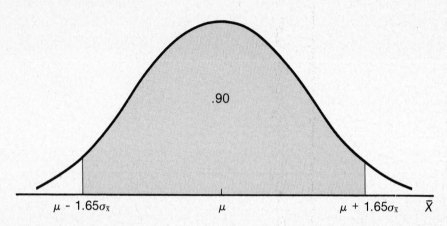

Now suppose that a sample is taken from the population and $\overline{X}$ is computed. If the number $1.65\sigma_{\bar{x}}$ were added to the particular value of $\overline{X}$ derived from the sample, the result would be $\overline{X}$ + $1.65\sigma_{\bar{x}}$. Similarly, if $1.65\sigma_{\bar{x}}$ were subtracted from $\overline{X}$ it would yield the number $\overline{X}$ − $1.65\sigma_{\bar{x}}$. These two values, when taken together, form an interval; the interval is from $\overline{X}$ − $1.65\sigma_{\bar{x}}$ to $\overline{X}$ + $1.65\sigma_{\bar{x}}$.

Let us compare this interval which centers on $\overline{X}$ to the sampling distribution of $\overline{X}$. Focus your attention on Figure 7.3. Suppose that the particular $\overline{X}$ that resulted from the sample is the one located across from (a) in Figure 7.3. (It is shown below because the graph is getting too congested. The $\overline{X}$ that we are talking about is a value slightly less than μ.) If the interval from $\overline{X}$ −. $1.65\sigma_{\bar{x}}$ to $\overline{X}$ + $1.65\sigma_{\bar{x}}$ is constructed about this $\overline{X}$, it yields the interval which is depicted in Figure 7.3 by ├──────┤. Notice that μ falls within this interval. Let us now look at the $\overline{X}$ across from (b). μ falls within the interval constructed about this $\overline{X}$ also. Next, consider the $\overline{X}$ across from (c); μ does not fall within its interval. It should be apparent that the interval about each $\overline{X}$ which is within the dotted lines will include μ, and the interval about each $\overline{X}$ outside the dotted lines will not include μ. This is because the dotted lines are the same distance apart as the extremes of the intervals about $\overline{X}$.

In the foregoing paragraphs, it was demonstrated that the interval around $\overline{X}$ which extends from $\overline{X}$ − $1.65\sigma_{\bar{x}}$ to $\overline{X}$ + $1.65\sigma_{\bar{x}}$ will encompass μ if and only if $\overline{X}$ lies between the dotted lines. It has also been shown that 90 percent of the $\overline{X}$'s fall between the dotted lines because 90 percent of the area under the normal curve lies between μ − $1.65\sigma_{\bar{x}}$ and μ + $1.65\sigma_{\bar{x}}$. These two facts can now be combined to form the following conclusion. If a random sample

FIGURE 7.3_____

Sampling Distribution of $\overline{X}$ with Intervals

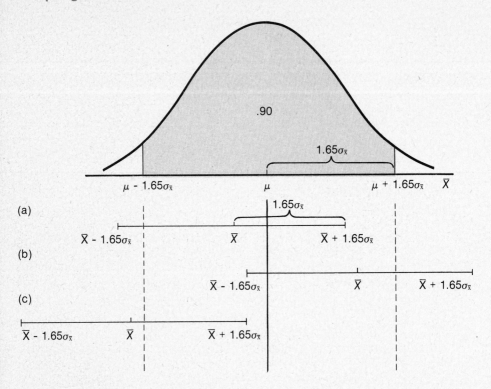

yields a sample mean of $\overline{X}$, and if an interval is constructed around $\overline{X}$ which extends from $\overline{X} - 1.65\sigma_{\overline{x}}$ to $\overline{X} + 1.65\sigma_{\overline{x}}$, then this interval will contain the true population mean 90 percent of the time. This interval from $\overline{X} - 1.65\sigma_{\overline{x}}$ to $\overline{X} + 1.65\sigma_{\overline{x}}$ is the .90 interval estimate of μ and is usually called a 90 percent *confidence interval* for μ. In other words, the analyst can say, "I am 90 percent confident that μ will fall between $\overline{X} - 1.65\sigma_{\overline{x}}$ and $\overline{X} + 1.65\sigma_{\overline{x}}$."

If the analyst prefers an 80 percent confidence interval, only one minor alteration need be made. Recall that 90 percent of the area under any normal curve falls within 1.65 standard deviations of the mean. This is why "1.65" appears in the 90 percent confidence interval. From Appendix N it is seen that 80 percent of the area falls within 1.28 standard deviations of the mean. Therefore, an 80 percent confidence interval will extend from $\overline{X} - 1.28\sigma_{\overline{x}}$ to $\overline{X} + 1.28\sigma_{\overline{x}}$. Table 7.2 gives the respective Z values that are used for a variety of confidence levels.

We may now summarize the whole process of interval estimation. After giving the summary, a further word of explanation will be added.

TABLE 7.2
Confidence Levels and Z

Confidence Level	Z
99%	2.58
98%	2.33
95%	1.96
90%	1.65
80%	1.28
50%	0.67

Confidence Interval for μ

If   1. a random sample is taken from a population of size N

2. the sample size n is at least 25

3. $\overline{X}$ is computed from the sample

Then   1. $\overline{X}$ is the point estimate of the population mean μ

2. an interval estimate of μ is given by

$$\overline{X} - Z\sigma_{\overline{X}} \quad \text{to} \quad \overline{X} + Z\sigma_{\overline{X}}$$

where $\overline{X}$ is computed from the sample, Z controls the level of confidence, and $\sigma_{\overline{X}}$ is the standard error which is computed by $\sigma/\sqrt{n}$ if n is less than 10 percent of N and by $(\sigma/\sqrt{n})\sqrt{1 - n/N}$ if n is 10 percent or more of N. If the standard deviation σ of the population is unknown, it may be estimated by s, and thus the standard error is estimated by $s_{\overline{X}}$ where $s_{\overline{X}} = s/\sqrt{n}$ or $s_{\overline{X}} = (s/\sqrt{n})\sqrt{1 - n/N}$. This implies that the confidence interval would be given by

$$\overline{X} - Zs_{\overline{X}} \quad \text{to} \quad \overline{X} + Zs_{\overline{X}}$$

when σ is unknown and must be estimated by s.

Several comments will now be made about this detailed summary of the construction of a confidence interval for the population mean.

First of all, it is assumed that the population mean μ is unknown and that the analyst wants to estimate it. A random sample of at least 25 items must be taken; this guarantees the normality of the sampling distribution which forms the theoretical foundation for this type of interval estimation. From the sample, $\overline{X}$ is computed. The actual confidence interval will then extend from $\overline{X} - Z\sigma_{\bar{X}}$ to $\overline{X} + Z\sigma_{\bar{X}}$. The Z regulates the level of confidence. The analyst chooses the level of confidence from Table 7.2 and thereby determines Z. All that remains is computing $\sigma_{\bar{X}}$. If the standard deviation σ of the population is known, then $\sigma_{\bar{X}}$ equals $\sigma/\sqrt{n}$ or $(\sigma/\sqrt{n})\sqrt{1 - n/N}$ depending on whether n is less than 10 percent of N or not. However, the population standard deviation is usually unknown. In such cases, the sample standard deviation s is used as a point estimate of σ. It therefore replaces σ in the expressions for the standard error. Hence, the estimate of the standard error becomes $s_{\bar{X}}$ and it is equal to $s/\sqrt{n}$ or $(s/\sqrt{n})\sqrt{1 - n/N}$. Thus, the interval estimate or confidence interval of μ becomes $\overline{X} - Zs_{\bar{X}}$ to $\overline{X} + Zs_{\bar{X}}$.

All of this will become clearer as we return to Poohmer, the Little Big Horn Bank auditor. Pooh had decided that he wanted an interval estimate of μ where μ is the mean amount of cottonseed oil per tank. Pooh went ahead and randomly sampled $n = 25$ tanks. The amounts of cottonseed oil in the 25 sampled tanks were (in gallons):

$$2098, 2011, 2435, 1847, 2350, \ldots.$$

From these 25 observations Pooh computed the sample mean and sample standard deviation:

$$\overline{X} = \frac{2098 + 2011 + 2435 + 1847 + 2350 + \ldots}{25}$$
$$= 2100 \text{ gallons}$$

$$s = \sqrt{\frac{(2098-2100)^2 + (2011-2100)^2 + (2435-2100)^2 + \ldots}{25 - 1}}$$
$$= 300 \text{ gallons}$$

Pooh therefore concluded that his best estimate for the mean amount of cottonseed oil per tank is 2100 gallons. However, Pooh wanted a 90 percent confidence interval. The form of such an interval estimate is

$$\overline{X} - Zs_{\bar{X}} \quad \text{to} \quad \overline{X} + Zs_{\bar{X}}$$

where $s_{\bar{X}}$ is the estimate of the standard error. From Table 7.2, it is seen that the desired value for Z is 1.65 if a 90 percent interval is to be constructed. Because $n = 25$ is less than 10 percent of $N = 500$ tanks, the estimate of the standard error is

$$s_{\bar{X}} = \frac{s}{\sqrt{n}}$$

$$= \frac{300}{\sqrt{25}}$$

$$= 60 \text{ gallons}$$

Therefore, the 90 percent confidence interval for μ is

$$\overline{X} - Zs_{\bar{X}} \quad \text{to} \quad \overline{X} + Zs_{\bar{X}}$$

$$2100 - (1.65)(60) \quad \text{to} \quad 2100 + (1.65)(60)$$

$$2100 - 99 \quad \text{to} \quad 2100 + 99$$

$$2001 \quad \text{to} \quad 2199 \text{ gallons}$$

Poohmer can now claim, "I am 90 percent confident that the average amount of cottonseed oil per tank is between 2001 and 2199 gallons." Being 90 percent confident means that the true value of μ will fall within the interval that is so constructed in 90 percent of the cases. From Pooh's confidence interval for μ, an interval for the total amount of oil on the ranch can be determined; this will be studied in the last section of the chapter.

The story of Winnie and Pooh, however, does not end here. Pooh was rather proud of himself for having constructed an interval estimate of μ and so decided to celebrate. Remember that the Western sun was beating down hard and so Pooh's sweaty body was crying for a swim. Since Pooh had never been swimming in cottonseed oil, he figured that now was the time to try. Removing his outer garments, the Pooh climbed to the top of a tank and plunged in. The oil felt good. While sploshing about in the tank Pooh's thirst intensified so that he decided he needed a gulp of oil. Before Pooh had transferred into accounting at Texas Tech, he had been a physics major. At that time he learned that cold stuff sinks while the hot rises. Putting this principle to work, Pooh decided to get a gulp of the cold cottonseed oil at the bottom of the tank. Immediately he descended to the bottom where while holding his breath he took a slurp of the cool liquid. You know what happened next. With that slurp Pooh saved himself from making a monstrous nonsampling error and in so doing saved the Little Big Horn Bank a cool $900,000.

7.5

DETERMINATION OF SAMPLE SIZE (MEANS)

In the last section, the method of constructing an interval estimate of μ was presented. Constructing a confidence interval is quite easy once the sample data is given. However, before the sampling is begun, someone must determine how large the sample should be. As a general principle, we have seen that the accuracy of an estimate increases as n increases. This general principle does not furnish us with a precise value for n. Thus, the analyst is unsure as to whether n should be 25 or 50 or 100 or 500 or 1000 and so on. In this section we will consider how the appropriate sample size can be determined.

There are some general rules floating around as to how to determine the correct sample size. One such rule occasionally heard is, "Sample about 10 percent of the items in the population." An analogous rule in the realm of dieting would be, "You should always eat about 10 percent of the food which is within 20 feet of you." Be very suspicious of simple rules which tell you how large a sample should be no matter what the circumstances.

If it is the goal of the analyst to construct an interval estimate for μ, the appropriate sample size can be determined if and only if three questions are answered. The three questions are

1. What level of confidence is desired?

2. How wide should the interval be?

3. How heterogeneous is the population?

Let us briefly think about each of these questions in their relationship to n; then they will be illustrated.

First, the analyst must determine the level of confidence. If the analyst wants to be 99 percent confident as opposed to 80 percent confident, then a larger sample must be taken. On the other hand, if a low level of confidence will suffice, then a smaller sample will be adequate. The general principle is that the higher the level of confidence, the larger must be n.

In the second place, the analyst must decide how wide the interval estimate should be. If a very narrow interval is needed, then a very large sample would typically be required. On the other hand, if a wide interval is acceptable, then only a small sample would be needed. For example, if the auditor is attempting to construct an interval estimate for the mean value of a company's accounts receivable, a relatively large sample would be needed if the interval were to be something like from \$140.00 to \$141.00 (this interval has a total width of $1.00). But if an interval from something like $20 to $400 were desired, only a few accounts receivable would need to be sampled to assure the analyst that μ falls within such wide bounds.

The third question concerns the heterogeneity of the population. If a population is heterogeneous, a larger sample would be needed; if it is homogeneous, a smaller sample would suffice. For example, this morning I filled two classrooms with various objects. In room A I put 1,000 basketballs. In room B I put a wide variety of items including a rusty muffler, a bulldozer blade, a toothbrush, an elephant tusk, and so on. You are now charged with the task of estimating the mean weight of the items in room A and in room B. Further assume that in both cases an interval estimate is desired with the same width and at the same level of confidence. From which room will you have to sample more items? Obviously, a sample of size $n = 1$ would be adequate from room A since all the objects are the same; that is, it is a perfectly homogeneous population. However, a fairly large sample would be required from room B because of the extreme heterogeneity or diversity of the population. Consider an example now where these three questions are used to determine n.

Chincoteague Island is a famous, small island off the coast of Virginia. Chincoteague is famous for its wild ponies, which are driven across the bay each year and auctioned off by the fire fighters. Though there's a lot of excitement with the pony drive each year, the fire fighters are getting tired of riding through the salt marshes and have decided to sell off the entire herd of 3,000 ponies. So the fire fighters notified potential buyers from all over about the intended sale and asked each interested buyer to submit a sealed bid for the entire herd of 3,000 ponies. One of the potential buyers is Ronald, the chief purchasing agent for a world-famous chain of restaurants. Ronald is not about to submit a bid until he has a fair idea as to the mean weight of the ponies. Therefore, Ronald wants to sample some of the ponies in order to compute $\overline{X}$, which will serve as an estimate of μ. However, Ronald does not know how many ponies ought to be sampled for this purpose.

In order to determine n, Ronald faced the three questions listed earlier in this section. Ronald decided that since he was considering the purchase of the herd which might involve quite a bit of money, he wanted a relatively high confidence level, like 90 percent. Next, Ronald felt that he should have an interval for μ, which has a total width of no more than 20 pounds. In other words, an interval like 280–300 pounds or 236–256 pounds is the size desired.

Finally, Ronald had to consider the heterogeneity of the population or herd of ponies. As explained in Chapter 5, the variability

of a population may be measured by its standard deviation. Therefore, Ronald needed to estimate the population standard deviation. There are three ways in which an analyst might estimate the
value for σ. They are

1. σ is already known from a previous study.

2. σ is estimated by s from a pilot sample.

3. σ is conservatively guessed.

In the first case, the standard deviation of the population might be
known from some previous study of the population or from a population which is very similar to the population under study. Another way to estimate σ would be to take a small preliminary
(pilot) sample and compute s from this sample. This s would then
serve as a point estimate of σ. Finally, the analyst might guess the
value of σ based on the analyst's knowledge of the population. The
guess must always be on the high side, since it is better to sample
too many than too few. It was this third alternative that Ronald
chose in order to measure the heterogeneity of the population.

Ronald began his thinking about the value of σ by realizing
that the herd of 3,000 ponies included young and old, and male and
female animals. This implies that the population would not be normal. However, Ronald always pictured standard deviations in
terms of a normal distribution where about 2/3 of the items fall
within one standard deviation of the mean. Ronald therefore decided to temporarily assume that the population was roughly normal for the sake of getting a rough idea as to the value of σ. Then
he would increase the σ to be on the safe side. Ronald first thought
about a σ of 30 pounds. Would it be reasonable to think that 2/3 of
the ponies have a weight within 30 pounds of the mean? In other
words, if the mean weight were $\mu = 250$ pounds, would 2/3 of the
ponies in the population fall between 220 and 280 pounds? The
reader should recognize that such a σ is too small. On the other
hand, a guess for σ of 300 pounds would be way too high. After
Ronald spent some time chatting with the fire fighters about the
sizes of the ponies, he decided on a conservative (high) guess of σ
$= 80$ pounds. In fixing σ at 80 pounds Ronald has now satisfac-
torily answered the third question.

In summary, Ronald's answers to the three questions are:

1. What level of confidence is desired? Answer: 90 percent.

2. How wide should the interval be? Answer: Total width of 20
   pounds.

3. How heterogeneous is the population? Answer: σ is no more
   than 80 pounds.

With these three questions answered, Ronald can proceed directly to the determination of the sample size n.

Recall that a confidence interval for μ is given by

$$\overline{X} - Z\sigma_{\overline{X}} \quad \text{to} \quad \overline{X} + Z\sigma_{\overline{X}}$$

This could alternately be expressed by

$$\overline{X} \pm Z\sigma_{\overline{X}}$$

which means that the upper value for the interval is found by adding $Z\sigma_{\overline{X}}$ to $\overline{X}$ and the lower value of the interval is found by subtracting $Z\sigma_{\overline{X}}$ from $\overline{X}$. Since $Z\sigma_{\overline{X}}$ is added and then subtracted from $\overline{X}$ which is the center of the interval, the total width of the confidence interval is $2Z\sigma_{\overline{X}}$. That is,

$$W = 2Z\sigma_{\overline{X}}$$

where W refers to the total width of the interval. This could also be shown by merely subtracting the lower value from the upper value:

$$
\begin{aligned}
W &= (\overline{X} + Z\sigma_{\overline{X}}) - (\overline{X} - Z\sigma_{\overline{X}}) \\
&= 2Z\sigma_{\overline{X}}
\end{aligned}
$$

Next it should be recalled that the standard error $\sigma_{\overline{X}}$ is found by

$$\sigma_{\overline{X}} = \frac{\sigma}{\sqrt{n}}$$

when n is less than 10 percent of N. Therefore, the total width of the confidence interval can be expressed by

$$W = 2Z\sigma_{\overline{X}}$$
$$W = 2Z\,\frac{\sigma}{\sqrt{n}}$$

This last equation permits Ronald to determine the required sample size n. It also shows that the width of a confidence interval decreases as n increases.

Ronald, according to the first question, wants a 90 percent confidence interval. Since Z controls the level of confidence, it is seen from Table 7.2 that Z must equal 1.65 if a 90 percent interval is desired. In answer to the second question, Ronald stated that he wanted an interval with a total width of 20 pounds; that is, $W = 20$.

Finally, Ronald conservatively guessed the standard deviation of the population of ponies to be $\sigma = 80$ pounds. These values of $Z = 1.65, W = 20$, and $\sigma = 80$ pounds are now substituted into

$$W = 2Z \frac{\sigma}{\sqrt{n}}$$

thereby yielding

$$20 = (2)(1.65) \frac{(80)}{\sqrt{n}}$$

This is a single equation with one unknown value, n. It should therefore be solved for n:

$$\sqrt{n} = \frac{(2)(1.65)(80)}{20}$$

$$\sqrt{n} = 13.2$$

$$n = 174$$

Therefore, Ronald has to randomly sample 174 ponies to get a 90 percent confidence interval that is no more than 20 pounds wide.

It has been shown that the key to determining n lies in W, Z, and σ according to the relationship $W = 2Z(\sigma/\sqrt{n})$. This equation can be first solved for n and then the appropriate values of W, Z, and σ substituted in order to find n. That is

$$W = 2Z \frac{\sigma}{\sqrt{n}}$$

$$\sqrt{n} = \frac{2Z\sigma}{W}$$

$$n = \frac{(2Z\sigma)^2}{W^2}$$

This last expression for n can be used to determine the sample size once W, Z, and σ are given.

One problem remains which concerns the supposition that $\sigma_{\bar{x}} = \sigma/\sqrt{n}$ instead of $(\sigma/\sqrt{n})\sqrt{1 - n/N}$ is used for the standard error in the process of seeking the value of n. If the analyst suspects that n may be more than 10 percent of N, then $(\sigma/\sqrt{n})\sqrt{1 - n/N}$ should be used. In fact, this expression for the standard error can be used anytime, even if n is less than 10 percent of N. Using this expression for the standard error results in the following equation for the determination of n:

$$W = 2Z\,\sigma_{\bar{x}}$$

$$W = 2Z\,\frac{\sigma}{\sqrt{n}}\sqrt{1 - \frac{n}{N}}$$

Both sides of this equation are squared and then it is solved for n yielding

$$n = \frac{(2Z\,\sigma)^2}{W^2 + \dfrac{(2Z\,\sigma)^2}{N}}$$

The determination of the appropriate sample size will now be summarized.

Let $\quad W =$ total width of the confidence interval

$\qquad Z\;=$ value which controls the level of confidence

$\qquad \sigma\;=$ population standard deviation

The appropriate sample size for the sake of constructing a confidence interval for μ is

$$n = \frac{(2Z\,\sigma)^2}{W^2}$$

However, if the n computed by this expression is about 10 percent or more of N, or if initially it is known that n will probably exceed 10 percent or N, then instead use the following to find n

$$n = \frac{(2Z\,\sigma)^2}{W^2 + \dfrac{(2Z\,\sigma)^2}{N}}$$

N may have to be guessed if it is not known precisely. In such a case, guess its value on the high side.

Finally, since the method of constructing interval estimates as presented in this chapter is dependent on the requirement that n must not fall below 25, the foregoing procedure for determining n is not valid if n turns out to be less than 25.

Consider one more quick example. There are 200 restaurants in the mid-Atlantic states for which Ronald is purchasing the meat. The mean annual gross income μ for these 200 restaurants is desired. In particular, a 95 percent confidence interval for μ is desired where the interval will have a total width of $20,000. From studies in previous years, the standard deviation of the annual gross incomes of the 200 restaurants is about $60,000. How many restaurants should be sampled in order to get the desired interval estimate of μ?

From the given details,

$$W = 20,000$$

$$Z = 1.96$$

$$\sigma = 60,000$$

Since the population is quite small ($N = 200$), it is reasonable to assume that n will exceed 10 percent of N. Therefore, n should be computed according to

$$n = \frac{(2Z\,\sigma)^2}{W^2 + \dfrac{(2Z\,\sigma)^2}{N}}$$

By substitution

$$n = \frac{[(2)(1.96)(60,000)]^2}{(20,000)^2 + \dfrac{[(2)(1.96)(60,000)]^2}{200}}$$

$$n = 82$$

Hence 82 restaurants should be sampled.

7.6

INTERVAL ESTIMATES OF THE POPULATION PROPORTION

The scientists at Ding-a-Ling Labs, after years of tireless research, have succeeded in impregnating paper with the scent of potato chips. With news of the breakthrough, the Ding-a-Ling System is beginning to formulate plans for the issuance of potato chip scented bills to its residential telephone customers. Before going ahead with these plans, the Ding-a-Ling System wants to determine what proportion of its residential telephone customers have potato chips in their homes. Knowledge of this proportion would give the Ding-a-Ling System some idea as to how popular the new bills might be. Thus, a random sample of 100 residential telephone customers has been taken. Of the 100 customers sampled, 40 reported that they currently have potato chips in their cupboards. What conclusions can be drawn concerning the proportion p of Ding-a-Ling customers who have potato chips in their homes?

To begin, the point estimate of the population proportion p is $\bar{p}$, which is the sample proportion. In the Ding-a-Ling System case

$$\bar{p} = \frac{X}{n}$$

$$= \frac{40}{100}$$

$$= .40$$

Thus, Ding-a-Ling's point estimate of p is .40. However, Ding-a-Ling wishes to construct a confidence interval for p. We will now consider how this can be accomplished.

In Section 7.4 the theory of constructing an interval estimate was set forth. An analogous piece of theory that involves the sampling distribution of $\bar{p}$ forms the basis of interval estimation in the case where the estimated parameter is p. Little would be gained by going through this type of theoretical development again, so it will not be repeated. The following summary sets forth the manner of constructing confidence intervals for the population proportion. This method will subsequently be used in the Ding-a-Ling System case.

Confidence Interval for p

If   **1.** A random sample is taken from a population of size N

          2. The sample size n is at least 25

          3. $\bar{p}$ is computed from the sample

Then **1.** $\bar{p}$ is the point estimate of the population proportion p

          2. An interval estimate of p is given by

$$\bar{p} - Z\sigma_{\bar{p}} \quad \text{to} \quad \bar{p} + Z\sigma_{\bar{p}}$$

where $\bar{p}$ is computed from the sample, Z controls the level of confidence, and $\sigma_{\bar{p}}$ is the standard error which is computed by $\sigma_{\bar{p}} = \sqrt{(\bar{p})(1 - \bar{p})/n}$ if n is less than 10 percent of N, and by $\sigma_{\bar{p}} = \sqrt{(\bar{p})(1 - \bar{p})/n}$ $\sqrt{1 - n/N}$ if n is 10 percent or more of N.

Returning to the Ding-a-Ling case, 40 percent or $\bar{p} = .40$ of the sample of $n = 100$ customers had potato chips. Since the population consists of the hundreds of thousands of Ding-a-Ling customers, n is much less than 10 percent of N. Now assume that a 99 percent interval is desired. From Table 7.2 the appropriate Z is 2.58. Ding-a-Ling's interval estimate is therefore,

$$\bar{p} - Z\sigma_{\bar{p}} \quad \text{to} \quad \bar{p} + Z\sigma_{\bar{p}}$$

$$\bar{p} - Z\sqrt{(\bar{p})(1 - \bar{p})/n} \quad \text{to} \quad \bar{p} + Z\sqrt{(\bar{p})(1 - \bar{p})/n}$$

$$.40 - (2.58)\sqrt{(.40)(1 - .40)/100} \quad \text{to} \quad .40 + (2.58)\sqrt{(.40)(1 - .40)/100}$$

$$.40 - (2.58)(.049) \quad \text{to} \quad .40 + (2.58)(.049)$$

$$.40 - .126 \quad \text{to} \quad .40 + .126$$

$$.27 \quad \text{to} \quad .53$$

This is the Ding-a-Ling System's 99 percent confidence interval for p, where p is the true proportion of all their residential customers who have potato chips at their residences. Ding-a-Ling can be 99 percent confident that the true proportion lies between .27 and .53.

7.7

DETERMINATION OF SAMPLE SIZE (PROPORTIONS)

The television industry has retained the Giddap Poll to estimate the proportion p of the 50,000 Navajos on the Arizona-New Mexico reservation who have seen a television program within the last month. The Giddap Poll, therefore, needs to determine how many Navajos should be sampled in order to construct an interval estimate for p.

Just as in Section 7.5, several questions must be answered before n can be determined. They are

1. What level of confidence is desired?

2. How wide should the interval be?

3. Within what range of values is p sure to fall?

Giddap decided that a 90 percent confidence interval would be suitable. Next, it was decided that the interval should have a total width of .10. An example of an interval for p which is .10 wide is .30 to .40. Finally, Giddap had very little information about the true proportion of Navajos who had seen television in the past month and thus stated that p could be anywhere from 0 to 1.

A confidence interval for p is of the form

$$\bar{p} - Z\sigma_{\bar{p}} \quad \text{to} \quad \bar{p} + Z\sigma_{\bar{p}}$$

Alternately this interval can be expressed as

$$\bar{p} \pm Z\sigma_{\bar{p}}$$

The total width W of the interval is

$$W = 2Z\sigma_{\bar{p}}$$

Furthermore, the standard error $\sigma_{\bar{p}}$ is usually equal to $\sqrt{(\bar{p})(1 - \bar{p})/n}$, therefore the width of the interval equals

$$W = 2Z \sqrt{(\bar{p})(1 - \bar{p})/n}$$

This may be solved for n yielding

$$n = \frac{4Z^2(\bar{p})(1 - \bar{p})}{W^2}$$

This equation shows how n can be determined.

The problem with the expression for n which was just developed is that it involves a sample statistic, namely, $\bar{p}$, which is only known after the sample is taken. Since we must find n *before* taking the sample, we must initially supply a value for $\bar{p}$. The third question asked is, "Within what range of values is p sure to fall?" From the answer to this question a value for $\bar{p}$ can be determined for the sole purpose of finding n. The rule is this:

> Choose a value for $\bar{p}$ within the interval given in answer to Question 3, such that the value is as close as possible to .50.

For example, if Giddap were sure that p is somewhere between .05 and .40, then a value of $\bar{p} = .40$ would be used to determine n. If Giddup were sure that p is between .65 and 1.00, then a $\bar{p} = .65$

would be used for the sake of determining n. If Giddap were sure, in answer to Question 3, that p is between .30 and .80, then a $\bar{p}$ of .50 would be used in order to find n. Since in reality the range for p that Giddap gave in response to Question 3 was from 0 to 1, the $\bar{p}$ to be used for computing the sample size is $\bar{p} = .50$.

Recall that in answer to Question 1 a 90 percent confidence interval is desired. This implies from Table 7.2 that Z must be 1.65. Second, the total width of the interval is to be .10; that is, $W = .10$. Finally, it was seen that the $\bar{p}$ to be used solely for the sake of computing n is $\bar{p} = .50$. Substituting these values into the expression for n which is given above yields

$$n = \frac{4Z^2(\bar{p})(1 - \bar{p})}{W^2}$$

$$= \frac{(4)(1.65)^2(.50)(1 - .50)}{.10^2}$$

$$= 272$$

This means that Giddap should sample 272 Navajos.

The situation where n might be more than 10 percent of N has not been considered. The following summary deals with this case along with the method just developed for determining n.

Let W = total width of the confidence interval

      Z = value which controls the level of confidence

      $\bar{p}$ = a value as close as possible to .50 within the subjectively determined range of values for p. This value of $\bar{p}$ is used solely for the sake of determining sample size; it is not used in constructing a confidence interval.

The appropriate sample size for the sake of constructing a confidence interval for p is

$$n = \frac{4Z^2(\bar{p})(1 - \bar{p})}{W^2}$$

However, if the n computed by this expression is about 10 percent or more of N, or if initially it is known that n will probably exceed 10 percent of N, then use the following to find n:

$$n = \frac{4Z^2(\bar{p})(1 - \bar{p})}{W^2 + \dfrac{4Z^2(\bar{p})(1 - \bar{p})}{N}}$$

N may have to be guessed if it is not known precisely. In such a case, guess its value on the high side.

Finally, this whole procedure is not valid if n turns out to be less than 25, since the confidence interval for p is based on a sample of at least 25 items from the population.

7.8

INTERVAL ESTIMATES OF TOTAL VALUES

Confidence intervals for the population mean μ and the population proportion p have been studied. These intervals become the basis for constructing an interval estimate of certain total values for the population. For example, suppose the 90 percent confidence interval for the mean value of a company's 1,000 accounts receivable is from \$50 to \$56. The corresponding 90 percent confidence interval for the total value of the company's accounts receivable is therefore from (\$50)(1,000) to (\$56)(1,000) or from \$50,000 to \$56,000. This is because there are $N = 1,000$ accounts receivable in the population. The general form for this confidence interval for a total value in such cases is

$$N(\overline{X} - Z\sigma_{\bar{X}}) \quad \text{to} \quad N(\overline{X} + Z\sigma_{\bar{X}})$$

Similarly, suppose that an appliance distributor has found that the 95 percent confidence interval for the proportion of apartment families that expect to buy a microwave oven in the next year is between .015 and .025. Since the total population consists of 20,000,000 apartment families, the corresponding 95 percent interval for the expected total microwave oven sales to apartment families is

$$(.015)(20,000,000) \quad \text{to} \quad (.025)(20,000,000)$$

$$300,000 \quad \text{to} \quad 500,000 \text{ ovens}$$

The general form for the confidence interval of a total value which is based on the population proportion is

$$N(\bar{p} - Z\sigma_{\bar{p}}) \quad \text{to} \quad N(\bar{p} + Z\sigma_{\bar{p}})$$

In concluding this chapter on estimation, it should be noted that confidence intervals for other population parameters such as σ do exist. However, our study of inferential statistics in this chapter and the next is limited to inferences concerning the parameters μ and p.

PROBLEMS

7.1

Describe inferential statistics.

7.2

What are the two branches of inferential statistics? Describe each.

7.3

Give and illustrate the four reasons why a sample might be preferable to a census.

7.4

Explain sampling error and nonsampling error. Give an example of how a nonsampling error could occur.

7.5

The state legislature has asked each faculty member employed by the state university to estimate how many hours a week he or she spends in job-related activities such as teaching, research, and service. Why will such a plan result in nonsampling errors?

7.6

The employees of McKenzie Incorporated who work in a large office are trying to decide if smoking should be permitted during working hours. Sandy Schaum, the office manager, has asked each employee to write out his or her reactions to the smoking question and then anonymously mail them to a group of consultants who are studying this matter. Describe how nonsampling error will result from such a plan.

7.7

Gary Christenson, a pollster, calls 100 randomly selected phone numbers and asks the person receiving the call who he or she favors in the upcoming senatorial election. Describe how nonsampling error will occur.

7.8

Cleansene Toiletries has recently introduced a new bar soap called Jungle. After several months of television advertising, Cleansene randomly selected a group of adults and asked each, "Have you seen the new Jungle soap ads?" Explain why nonsampling error might occur. Give a suggestion which, if implemented, would tend to reduce the nonsampling error.

7.9

How can sampling error be reduced?

7.10

What is the difference between a point estimate and an interval estimate?

7.11

What is an unbiased estimator? What does it mean to be a consistent estimator?

7.12

Budget Rent-A-Reck has randomly sampled three of its automobiles, finding that the annual maintenance costs for the three are $142, $67, and $98. Estimate the mean annual cost for all their automobiles as well as the population standard deviation. Use point estimates only.

7.13

A sample of 100 Rent-A-Reck cars shows that the mean distance traveled in the past year was 9,000 miles and the standard deviation was 4,000 miles. Construct a 90 percent and a 95 percent confidence interval for the mean distance traveled for all the company's rental cars.

7.14

Okla-oil has 200 stations in the state of Oklahoma. A random sample of 50 of the stations reveals that the mean price per gallon of regular at these stations is $0.68 and the standard deviation is $0.03. Compute an 80 percent and a 90 percent confidence interval for the true mean price for the population of 200 stations.

7.15

What Z value should be used to compute a 70 percent confidence interval? an 86 percent confidence interval?

7.16

The Chiller Chemical Company's flying ace, Darlene Andersen, has dropped fertilizer pellets from a plane over a large tract of forest in Washington. Twenty-five plots from the forest tract were subsequently tested with the result that the mean amount of fertilizer per plot was 205 with a standard deviation of 82 per plot. Determine a 90 percent and a 99 percent confidence interval for the mean amount of fertilizer that each of the thousands of plots in the forest received.

7.17

Henry Pont, a production supervisor for Pont's film division, has randomly sampled 49 squares of film from a run of 300 squares. The mean number of defects per square in the sample is 3.2 with a standard deviation of 1.9. Determine a 90 percent and a 99 percent confidence interval for the mean number of defects per square for the run.

7.18

The National Park Service reports that the average number of occupants in a sample of 50 cars entering the Grand Canyon National Park is 3.9 per car with a standard deviation of 1.8 per car. Compute an 80 percent and a 95 percent confidence interval for the true mean. Find a 95 percent interval assuming that n had been 400.

7.19

The J. P. Morgan Bank wishes to estimate the mean balance owed by the thousands of persons holding its credit card. If a 90 percent confidence interval which has a total width of $40 is desired, how many credit card holders should be sampled? Assume that the standard deviation of the balances is no more than $200.

7.20

A large automobile manufacturer wishes to estimate the average age of all the registered automobiles in Utah, which has a population of 200,000 automobiles. A 99 percent confidence interval is desired, which has a total width of .2 years. Assuming that the standard deviation of the ages is no more than three years, how many automobiles must be sampled? If the auto manufacturer is also interested in a 99 percent interval of the same width for California automobiles, how many California automobiles must be sampled? Assume that the standard deviation of the automobiles in California is the same as in Utah; however, there are 5,000,000 registered automobiles in California.

7.21

Dixie Jones is the chief researcher for Dominion Biological Systems. She wishes to sample bluefish from Chesapeake Bay in order to determine the mean Kepone levels in the fish. A 95 percent confidence interval is desired which has a width of four units. The standard deviation of units of Kepone is certainly no more than about 24 units. How many bluefish must be sampled?

7.22

The real estate firm headed by Juanita DeJarnette wishes to estimate the mean value of the homes in a certain district. If a 99 percent confidence interval is desired which is $2,000 wide, how many homes should be sampled and appraised? There are 200 homes in the district and the standard deviation of their values is no more than $12,000.

7.23

In order to determine the sample size n for the sake of constructing an interval estimate of μ, what three questions must be answered?

7.24

Show how changes in W, σ, and Z will affect the required sample size n when a sample is to be taken in order to construct a confidence interval for the population mean. What happens to the width of the confidence interval as n increases? Show why this is true.

7.25

Comment on the rule, "Always sample about 10 percent of the items in the population." Show why this rule is not reasonable.

7.26

A breakfast food company wants to determine the proportion of cornflake eaters who prefer the flakes soggy when eaten. A sample of 100 cornflake eaters reveals that 30 prefer soggy flakes. Construct a 90 percent and a 99 percent confidence interval for the true proportion of all cornflake eaters who like soggy flakes. Compute a 99 percent interval assuming that n had been 400 and X had been 120.

7.27

The Alabama Motor Vehicle Division sampled 50 vehicles and found that six had improperly aimed highlights. Find an 80 percent and a 90 percent confidence interval for the true proportion of all Alabama vehicles with improperly aimed headlights.

7.28

McLennan Inc. has 100 employees. A sample of 25 employees revealed that 14 of them claimed they would prefer a four-day work week where each work day would be ten hours long. Construct a 99 percent confidence interval for the true proportion of the employees who would prefer a four-day work week.

7.29

The proportion of apartments that are vacant in Shreveport is unknown. A sample of 1,000 apartments in the city revealed that 50 were vacant. If there are 5,000 apartments in the city, find a 90 percent confidence interval for the proportion of vacant apartments in the city.

7.30

The Organic Gardener magazine has 80,000 subscribers. Roxy Rodale, an editor for the magazine, wants to determine what proportion of the subscribers actually have an organic garden. If a 90 percent interval with a width of .10 is desired, how many subscribers must she sample in order to estimate the proportion who have an organic garden? Roxy has no idea as to what proportion of the subscribers might have such a garden.

7.31

A television network wishes to determine what proportion of the homes in a metropolitan area had a particular program on. If a 95 percent interval with a total width of .08 is desired, how many homes should be sampled? The network suspects that somewhere between 5 percent and 20 percent of the homes watched the program.

7.32

Fred DiMarco is a quality control engineer for a large hospital. A shipment of 100 electronic thermometers has been received. DiMarco wants to determine the proportion of the thermometers which will need adjustment. If an 80 percent confidence interval for p with a total width of .05 is desired, how many thermometers should be tested? In the past no more than 10 percent of the thermometers needed adjustment.

7.33

Refer to Problem 7.16. Each plot in the forest tract is .2 square miles. The entire forest tract is composed of 500 square miles. Find a 90 percent confidence interval for the total amount of fertilizer that was dropped on the entire tract of forest.

7.34

Refer to Problem 7.18. If 400,000 cars entered the Grand Canyon National Park last year, find a 95 percent confidence interval for the total number of visitors.

7.35

Refer to Problem 7.26. If there are 20 million people who frequently eat cornflakes, find a 90 percent confidence interval for the total number of people who like soggy cornflakes.

7.36

Refer to Problem 7.27. If there are 800,000 vehicles in Alabama, find an 80 percent confidence interval for the total number in the state which have improperly aimed headlights.

7.37

Refer to Problem 7.29. Find a 90 percent confidence interval for the total number of vacant apartments in Shreveport.

7.38

The E.P.A. tested $n = 25$ mid-size cars and found that they averaged 20 miles per gallon. The standard deviation was 5 miles per gallon for the tested cars. Compute a 90 percent confidence interval for the mean miles per gallon for all mid-size cars. Now compute the interval assuming n had been 100. Finally, compute the interval assuming n had been 400 mid-size cars. What happens to the size of the interval as n increases?

8.1

INTRODUCTION

The second branch of inferential statistics is hypothesis testing. In *hypothesis testing* a claim is made with regard to the value of a population parameter. After the claim is made sample evidence is gathered, and on the basis of the sample evidence the claim is either accepted or rejected. For example, an automobile manufacturer claims that its new model gets an average of 24 miles per gallon in highway driving. In order to test this claim, we sample several of the new cars and drive them on the highway. The miles per gallon achieved for each of the test vehicles is then measured. On the basis of the average miles per gallon of the test vehicles, as expressed by $\overline{X}$, we would then either accept or reject the auto manufacturer's claim. If the test vehicles averaged $\overline{X} = 23.98$ miles per gallon, we would be inclined to accept the claim. On the other hand, if they averaged only 15.6 miles per gallon, we would reject the claim.

In the situation just described, the automobile manufacturer's claim is the hypothesis. After formulating the hypothesis, it is accepted or rejected on the basis of sample evidence. Since the hypothesis deals with a population parameter such as μ, the analyst is in fact making an inference about the nature of the population when the hypothesis is accepted or rejected. Furthermore, the inference is based on sample evidence; therefore, hypothesis testing is rightly categorized as a type of inferential statistics.

In this chapter, hypotheses involving the population mean and population proportion will be considered. In Chapters 9, 10, and 11 there will be additional hypothesis tests. The same principles apply in all hypothesis testing situations.

8.2

HYPOTHESIS TESTING FUNDAMENTALS

Koduck puts a projector bulb in each new projector it sells. A new company from Germany has begun to produce projector bulbs according to a new design. Gesundheit Leit, the new company from Germany, has received a contract from Koduck to supply a large quantity of these new projector bulbs. In the contract, Gesundheit Leit agreed to supply bulbs which have an average life of 40 hours.

In time Koduck received the first shipment of 10,000 Gesundheit Leit bulbs; but before it was willing to accept the shipment, Koduck decided that some of the bulbs should be tested to see if they meet the specifications listed in the contract. Hence, $n = 25$ bulbs were randomly selected for testing. Koduck would decide to either accept the shipment or reject it (or perhaps do some more testing) based on the test results.

The situation being considered is an application of hypothesis testing known as *acceptance sampling*. The fundamental elements of hypothesis testing may be illustrated by such an example. We shall proceed to identify these elements and in a general way describe the essence of hypothesis testing by means of this example.

To begin, Geshundheit Leit claims that its bulbs last an average of at least 40 hours. This claim becomes a hypothesis. In particular, it is called the *null hypothesis* and is designated by H_o:

H_o: The mean life is at least 40 hours

The null hypothesis is a hypothesis about a population parameter. In this case the parameter is the population mean μ. Therefore, the null hypothesis could be stated more succinctly as

H_o: $\mu \geq 40$ hours

where μ is the mean life of the 10,000 bulbs in the shipment.

By sampling 25 bulbs from the incoming shipment, Koduck is attempting to prove that the Gesundheit Leit bulbs fall short of meeting specifications. If Koduck cannot prove that they fall short, then the shipment will be accepted. The possibility that the bulbs may not meet specifications is expressed by a competing hypothesis which is called the *alternate hypothesis*. In this case the alternate hypothesis is

H_a: $\mu < 40$ hours

Once the hypotheses have been formulated, a *decision rule* may be established. The decision rule is a rule which tells the analyst on the basis of sample evidence whether the null hypothesis should be accepted or rejected. For example, it was determined in the Gesundheit Leit case that Koduck would randomly sample 25 bulbs from the large shipment. These 25 bulbs would be burned to determine how long they last. The mean life of the sample bulbs is denoted by the statistic $\overline{X}$. The decision rule in this situation might be something like

If $\overline{X}$ is less than or equal to 39.5 hours, then reject the null hypothesis.

If $\overline{X}$ is greater than 39.5 hours, then accept the null hypothesis.

According to this decision rule, Koduck would take the sample of 25 bulbs, burn them, and determine their mean life. The mean life of these 25 bulbs might be $\overline{X} = 39.86$ hours. Thus, the null hypothesis would be accepted, which means that Koduck would accept the entire shipment. On the other hand, if the sample mean were $\overline{X} = 37.6$ hours, then Koduck would reject the null hypothesis, and in so doing would reject the shipment.

In brief, the decision rule defines two distinct ranges of possible values for the sample statistic $\overline{X}$. All the $\overline{X}$'s within one range (e.g. above 39.5) are assumed to be consistent with the null hypothesis. Hence, H_o is accepted if $\overline{X}$ falls within this range. The values of $\overline{X}$ in the second range or region (e.g. below 39.5) are considered to be inconsistent with the null hypothesis. These values of $\overline{X}$ seem to indicate that the null hypothesis is probably false. Therefore, H_o is rejected and H_a is accepted if such an $\overline{X}$ occurs. The decision rule therefore tells what kind of sample evidence leads to accepting or rejecting the null hypothesis.

It has just been indicated that the decision rule tells the analyst whether to accept or reject H_o depending on the value of a sample statistic like $\overline{X}$. Figure 8.1 pictures the decision rule that was given for the Gesundheit Leit case. Notice that the decision rule tells the analyst whether to accept or reject the null hypothesis depending on whether $\overline{X}$ falls within the *acceptance region* or the *rejection region*. The value 39.5, which divides these two regions, is called the *critical value*. Once the critical value has been established, the decision rule is determined. We shall consider how the critical value is determined in a moment. First let us review the general process of hypothesis testing as it has been described so far.

FIGURE 8.1

Koduck's Decision Rule

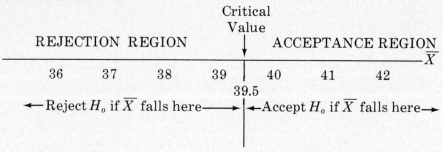

First, the null and alternative hypotheses are formulated. These hypotheses deal with a population parameter like μ. A decision rule is then established which will guide the analyst in either accepting or rejecting the null hypothesis. The analyst then compares the sample statistic to the decision rule. Specifically, the statistic like $\overline{X}$ is compared to the critical value which is given in the decision rule. If the statistic falls within the acceptance region, then the null hypothesis is accepted. If the value of the statistic falls within the rejection region, then the null hypothesis is rejected in favor of the alternative hypothesis. In other words, the rejection region describes the kinds of sample evidence which are incompatible with accepting the null hypothesis. Such is the general procedure of hypothesis testing. The only matter that has not been explained yet is how the value of the critical value is determined. This will be considered in the following sections.

8.3

THE CRITICAL VALUE

The outlines of hypothesis testing have been painted with a broad brush. In this section the determination of the critical value will be studied further. An entire section is devoted to determining the critical value of the decision rule because there are a number of weighty matters that must be considered.

In the Koduck-Gesundheit Leit case the critical value was 39.5 hours. If the sample mean were to fall below 39.5 hours, the null hypothesis would be rejected and hence the entire shipment of bulbs would be rejected. But why was the value of 39.5 chosen as this critical value or cutoff value? Some readers might think that Koduck should have used a critical value of 40, saying: "Since the entire shipment is supposed to have a mean life of at least 40 hours, then the shipment should only be accepted if a sample from this shipment has a mean of at least 40 hours." Such a rule could be used. However, upon further thought it would probably be discarded. Let us see why.

Koduck required that the mean life μ of the 10,000 bulbs be at least 40 hours. This does not mean, however, that every bulb must last exactly 40 hours or more. Some could last 35 hours, some 45, some 37, and some 43 hours, and so on, such that the mean still turns out to be 40 hours or more. In other words, half the bulbs (5,000 bulbs) could last less than 40 hours and half last more than 40 hours, and the total shipment could still have a mean life of at least 40 hours. If Koduck randomly samples a mere 25 bulbs under such conditions, it is quite possible that these 25 bulbs would have an average life $\overline{X}$ less than 40 hours if the sample happened to include relatively more of the short burning bulbs. In other words, to expect the sample mean to equal or exceed 40 hours when perhaps 5,000 of the 10,000 bulbs last less than 40 hours is being too stringent. Therefore, a critical value of 40 hours should not be used. Because of the potential for sampling error (see Section 7.2 of Chapter 7), Koduck should allow $\overline{X}$ to fall at least somewhat below 40 hours and still accept the shipment. Thus, a critical value of 39.5 might be appropriate.

Having seen that the critical value should fall below the hypothesized value of the mean in the case at hand, it next must be decided how far below it should be. For example, should Koduck use a critical value of 39.5 or 39.0 or 37.0 and so on?

The value of the critical value is determined by keeping in mind two distinct types of errors which may result in the hypothesis testing situation being faced. This is very important. Suppose that the shipment of Gesundheit Leit bulbs does have a mean life of 40 hours. We are here assuming that H_o is in fact true. It is conceivable that a sample of 25 of these bulbs could have a sample mean below a critical value like 39.5 hours. If $\overline{X}$ did fall below 39.5 in this case where $\mu = 40$, Koduck would reject the null hypothesis and hence reject the entire shipment. Such a decision would be a mistake. This error consists in rejecting the null hypothesis when the null hypothesis is true. This kind of error is called a *Type I error*. In the case at hand, a Type I error results in returning (rejecting H_o) a good shipment ($\mu = 40$) to the manufacturer.

Now suppose that the bulbs in the shipment have a mean life of less than 40 hours. Thus, the null hypothesis (H_o: $\mu \geq 40$) is false and the alternate hypothesis (H_a: $\mu < 40$) is true. Koduck proceeds to test 25 bulbs whose mean life turns out to be 39.7 hours. According to the decision rule where the critical value equals 39.5, Koduck would accept H_o and therefore accept this shipment of bulbs which does not meet specifications. This is a *Type II error*. A Type II error consists in accepting the null hypothesis when it is false.

To repeat, a Type I error is sending back a good shipment and a Type II error is accepting a bad shipment. Koduck does not want to make either type of error. Figure 8.2 presents the decisions (accept or reject H_o) in relationship to the nature of the population. In so doing, the two types of errors are shown. Notice that accepting H_o when it is true is a correct decision as is rejecting H_o when in fact it is false.

FIGURE 8.2_____

Decisions and Errors in Hypothesis Testing

Population

	H_o IS TRUE *Shipment is good,* $\mu \geq 40$	*H_o IS FALSE* *(H_a is true)* *Shipment is bad,* $\mu < 40$
ACCEPT H_o	CORRECT DECISION	TYPE II ERROR
REJECT H_o	TYPE I ERROR	CORRECT DECISION

Decision

The critical value is determined by the analyst based on how the analyst views the relative evils of the two types of errors. Consider the decision rule given earlier where the critical value is 39.5; also consider another decision rule which has a critical value of 36.5 hours. With this second decision rule, Koduck would reject the null hypothesis if $\overline{X}$ is less than or equal to 36.5 hours and would accept H_o and the shipment if $\overline{X}$ exceeded 36.5 hours. One of these decision rules is especially vulnerable to a Type I error and the other has a tendency to yield a Type II error. Let us discover which is which.

We begin by assuming that the null hypothesis is true. In other words, we are assuming that the shipment is a good shipment (has a mean of at least 40 hours). If Koduck samples 25 bulbs from this good shipment, it is quite possible that $\overline{X}$ will fall below 40 hours. The mean life of all the bulbs taken together can be $\mu = 40$ hours and yet individual bulbs may have lives greater or less than 40 hours. If quite a few of the bulbs with lives of less than 40 hours happen, by pure chance, to end up in the sample, then $\overline{X}$ will fall below the mean of 40 hours. According to the first decision rule, this good shipment will be rejected if $\overline{X}$ is less than or equal to 39.5 hours. According to the second decision rule, $\overline{X}$ must be less than or equal to 36.5 in order for the shipment to be rejected. Therefore, it is more probable that the null hypothesis will be rejected when the critical value is 39.5 than when it is 36.5. This is because it is more likely, by pure chance, that $\overline{X}$ will be less than or equal to 39.5 than less than or equal to 36.5 when the population mean is $\mu = 40$ hours. Since rejecting H_o when the shipment is good (H_o is true) is a Type I error, we may conclude that the first decision rule which has a critical value of 39.5 is more vulnerable to yielding a Type I error.

Now let us assume that the shipment is bad. To be specific, let's assume that the mean life of the bulbs is $\mu = 37$ hours. A Type II error would consist of accepting a bad shipment. This is equivalent to accepting the null hypothesis when in fact it is false. The first decision rule states that Koduck should accept H_o only if $\overline{X}$ exceeds 39.5 hours. However, according to the second decision rule, the shipment will be accepted if $\overline{X}$ exceeds 36.5 hours. If the true mean life is $\mu = 37$ hours, it is apparent that there is a pretty good chance that $\overline{X}$ will exceed 36.5 hours if a sample of 25 is taken. Therefore, if the second decision rule were being used, Koduck might easily end up accepting this shipment, thus making a Type II error. Since an $\overline{X}$ of more than 39.5 is not as likely, the first decision rule would not be as prone to yield a Type II error.

In view of this discussion, the two decision rules may be summarized in terms of their tendencies to make errors as follows:

Decision rule with a critical value of 39.5 —

  A high probability of making a Type I error

  A low probability of making a Type II error

Decision rule with a critical value of 36.5 —

  A low probability of making a Type I error

  A high probability of making a Type II error

So which decision rule should Koduck use? The answer depends on how seriously Koduck regards each type of error.

In order to be more precise in our language, the probability of making a Type I error is denoted by the Greek letter alpha, that is, α. The probability of making a Type II error is denoted by beta, that is, β.

$$\alpha = P(\text{Type I error})$$

$$\alpha = P(\text{Rejecting } H_o | H_o \text{ is true})$$

$$\beta = P(\text{Type II error})$$

$$\beta = P(\text{Accepting } H_o | H_o \text{ is false})$$

These definitions should be committed to memory.

As was demonstrated by the study of the two Koduck decision rules, the probability of a Type I error varies inversely with the probability of a Type II error. This is always the case in hypothesis testing. If the critical value is changed in order to reduce α, then β will increase. If the critical value is changed the other way in order to decrease β, then α will automatically increase. The only way to simultaneously decrease both α and β is to increase the sample size.

It is usual procedure for the analyst to begin hypothesis testing by specifying a value for α; in so doing, β is not specified. The value of α is said to represent the *level of significance* of the test. Typically α is fixed somewhere between .10 and .01. In other words, the analyst initially determines what chance he/she is willing to take in making a Type I error. Of course if an α of .01 is chosen, then there is a better chance that a Type II error could occur because α and β vary inversely. Once α is established, the critical value may be determined relatively easily by referring to the sampling distribution. In the next section, some attention will be devoted to selecting a significance level and to formulating hypotheses. Then in the section after that we will study the mechanics of actually finding a critical value and conducting a hypothesis test.

In summary, the following constitute the basic steps of hypothesis testing. Numerical examples based on the Gesundheit Leit case are given in parentheses.

Five Steps of Hypothesis Testing

1. Formulate H_o and H_a. ($H_o: \mu \geq 40, H_a: \mu < 40$)
2. Specify the value of α and n. (Let $\alpha = .10$ and $n = 25$)
3. Take a random sample and compute the relevant statistics. (Compute $\overline{X}$ and s)
4. Determine the critical value and decision rule. (Critical value = 39.5)
5. Either accept or reject the null hypothesis.

Steps 1 and 2 will be considered in detail in the following section.

8.4

FORMULATION OF HYPOTHESES AND DETERMINATION OF α

Generally speaking, there are two types of hypothesis tests — *one-tailed tests* and *two-tailed tests*. When testing the mean, a one-tailed test involves a null hypothesis which is written as

$$H_o: \mu \geq K$$

or, $H_o: \mu = K$

and the alternate hypothesis is

$$H_a: \mu < K$$

Of course everything could be switched so that the hypotheses are

$$H_o: \mu \leq K \quad \text{or} \quad \mu = K$$
$$H_a: \mu > K$$

In all these cases K is some constant. The Gesundheit case is a one-tailed test since

$$H_o: \mu \geq 40 \text{ hours}$$
$$H_a: \mu < 40$$

A two-tailed test has a null hypothesis given by

$$H_o: \mu = K$$

and the alternate hypothesis given by

$$H_a: \mu \neq K$$

An example of such a test would be a case in which the mean breaking strength of a cable produced in the past by a certain machine has been $\mu = 3{,}000$ pounds. There is now reason to suspect that the machine is producing cable which is too thick ($\mu > 3{,}000$) or too thin ($\mu < 3{,}000$). In this case, the null and alternate hypotheses are

$$H_o: \mu = 3{,}000 \text{ pounds}$$
$$H_a: \mu \neq 3{,}000$$

In such a situation, the null hypothesis would be rejected if a sample of the cable proved to be much too strong (an $\overline{X}$ quite a bit greater than 3,000 pounds) or much too weak (an $\overline{X}$ quite a bit less than 3,000 pounds). Hence, two critical values exist in two-tailed tests.

Sometimes it is not clear as to what the null hypothesis should be and what the alternate hypothesis should be. For example, in the Gesundheit Leit case, why was the null hypothesis chosen as $\mu \geq 40$ and the alternate as $\mu < 40$? Why not the other way around? It is hard to give a rule which works in every possible hypothesis-testing situation. However, some rules of thumb which are usually valid will be given.

As a general rule, the null hypothesis expresses how things have been in the past. Something new comes along and we wonder if that something new has changed how things were in the past. The anticipated change that the "something new" will cause is typically stated in the alternate hypothesis. A couple of examples of this general rule follow.

In the past, the mean strength of the cable has been 3,000 pounds. The machine may be getting out of adjustment (the "something new"). Therefore, the hypotheses are

H_o: $\mu = 3,000$ (how machine operated in past)

H_a: $\mu \neq 3,000$ (the effect of a suspected change)

As another example, last year the mean number of accidents per 100,000 vehicle miles was 3.4. This year the speed limit has been reduced. Has the new speed limit reduced the accident rate? In this test,

H_o: $\mu = 3.4$

H_a: $\mu < 3.4$

Another rule of thumb, similar to the first, is that the null hypothesis states that a particular product, treatment, or whatever, is ineffective. The alternate hypothesis states that it is effective. For example, the mean time for a flu victim to return to normal with no medication is 5.3 days. A new flu medication may speed recovery. We wish to test it, so we administer it to a sample of people who have just contracted the flu. In such a case

H_o: $\mu = 5.3$ days

H_a: $\mu < 5.3$

The null hypothesis says that the mean recovery period for those receiving the new medication is 5.3 days, which is the same as that for people who have received no medication. Accepting H_o implies that the new medication is ineffective. The alternate hypothesis states that the new medication is effective in reducing the mean recovery time. In a similar fashion, if you wish to test a new method of producing components, a new job training program, a new advertising campaign, a new regulation, and so on, the alternate hypothesis states that it is effective and the null hypothesis states that it makes no difference.

If an outright claim is made about some product or method, and there is no attempt to prove whether or not it is effective or that a change has taken place, then the claim is often expressed by the null hypothesis. This third rule of thumb is exemplified by the case where Gesundheit Leit claims that their bulbs have a mean life of 40 hours. This claim becomes the null hypothesis. Koduck takes an adversary position and tries to disprove the claim, thereby accepting the alternate hypothesis which states that μ is less than 40 hours. Similarly, an auto manufacturer claims that one of its luxury cars gets an average of 20 miles per gallon on the highway. This becomes the null hypothesis. The alternate hypothesis is that μ is less than 20 miles per gallon. As another example, an economist claims that the mean family income for residents of Minnesota is \$16,400. If you wish to test this claim, the null hypothesis would be

$$H_o: \mu = \$16,400$$

and the alternate hypothesis would be

$$H_a: \mu \neq \$16,400$$

With continued exposure to hypothesis-testing situations, the reader will gain experience in deciding what the null hypothesis should be. Deciding if the alternate hypothesis is one- or two-tailed is usually an easier matter.

The five steps of hypothesis testing were listed at the end of the last section. We have now spent some time dealing with the first step. A few comments should next be made with regard to the second step which involves specifying n and α.

In Chapter 7, considerable attention was devoted to finding the appropriate sample size when the analyst intends to construct an interval estimate for either μ or p. Determining the right sample size in hypothesis testing situations is a bit complex and will not be discussed in this text. Therefore, in each problem the n will be given. As a general principle, it should be stated that if the sample size n increases, then both α and β will decrease. This is analogous to the situation in interval estimation where the width of the confidence interval decreases as n increases. This phenomenon in both hypothesis testing and estimation is due to the decrease in the standard error as n increases. More will be said about this in Section 8.8. In concluding this brief comment on sample size, it should be emphasized that the hypothesis-testing procedures of this chapter are all based on the assumption that n is at least 25. The necessity of this assumption, as will be seen, resides in the fact that only when n is at least 25 are we assured of the normality of the sampling distribution.

In the last section, it was stated that the analyst usually fixes the level of significance α somewhere between .10 and .01. For a given sample size, a relatively large α will result in less chance of making a Type II error, and a smaller α like .01 will result in a greater chance of making a Type II error. The analyst must decide what is better, a large α or a small α. The following example will demonstrate how an analyst might decide upon the value of α.

A large corporation, Rolamotor, has just received two orders for relays. One order came from NASA, the other from Dorf Automobile Company. NASA plans to use the relays in a manned space flight to Mars; Dorf will use them in the ignition system of a new Dorf model that is slated for production in the near future. Rolamotor spends a month manufacturing the relays and then sends a shipment to NASA and a shipment to Dorf.

Both NASA and Dorf want to sample some of the relays before accepting them. Let us suppose that the specifications called for the relays to respond to an electrical stimulus in a mean time of .03 seconds. Hence,

$$H_o: \mu = .03 \text{ seconds}$$

$$H_a: \mu \neq .03$$

Both NASA and Dorf have the same hypotheses. However, their decision rules will differ. One decision rule is

Decision Rule A:

Accept H_o if $\overline{X}$ falls between .025 and .035 seconds,

Reject H_o if $\overline{X} \leq .025$ or $\overline{X} \geq .035$,

and the other is

Decision Rule B:

Accept H_o if $\overline{X}$ falls between .01 and .05 seconds,

Reject H_o if $\overline{X} \le .01$ or $\overline{X} \ge .05$.

Which of these two decision rules would NASA use? would Dorf use?

In order to answer these questions, we must determine what type of error NASA abhors and what type Dorf abhors. Recall the following definitions:

Type I Error — Rejecting H_o when H_o is true.
(i.e., rejecting the shipment of relays when the shipment is in fact good)

Type II Error — Accepting H_o when H_o is false.
(i.e., accepting the shipment when the shipment is bad)

It should be obvious that since NASA is very safety conscious in manned space flights, NASA would especially hate to make a Type II error. In order to keep the probability of a Type II error down, NASA must be willing to live with an increased probability of a Type I error. Hence, NASA would prefer a decision rule which offers a low β and high α. Dorf, on the other hand, would be in a rush to get production of the new model on the way. Dorf would hate to have to return (reject) a good shipment. Hence, there would be more of a willingness to make a Type II error in order to keep α low. Dorf would prefer a decision rule with a low α like .01 and thus a higher β. The circumstances of the hypothesis test therefore guide the analyst in establishing α at a low value like .01 or a high value like .10 or even .20.

Finally, we need to determine which decision rule given above, A or B, offers the high α and low β and which offers the low α and high β. Certainly Decision Rule A makes it harder to accept the shipment of relays since the acceptance region is so narrow. With such a stringent standard it would be easy to reject a good shipment of relays. Thus, Decision Rule A yields a high α. However, its tough standards (narrow acceptance region) keeps the probability of making a Type II error small. NASA would therefore prefer Decision Rule A. The sample results would have to be pretty bad in the case of Decision Rule B in order to reject H_o. It is not very likely that through using Decision Rule B a good shipment will be rejected. Hence, Decision Rule B offers a low α and is the decision rule that Dorf would prefer to use.

Having considered the general outline of hypothesis testing as represented by the five step process indicated earlier, and with further study concerning the first two steps, we are ready to conduct a hypothesis test.

8.5

TESTING ONE-TAILED HYPOTHESES ABOUT THE POPULATION MEAN

As stated earlier, the five steps of hypothesis testing are

1. Formulate the hypotheses.

2. Specify n (at least 25) and α.

3. Take the sample and compute the statistics.

4. Construct the decision rule.

5. Accept or reject the null hypothesis.

This process will now be illustrated.

Last year Captain Kidd, a manufacturer of waterbeds, found that the mean age of the people buying a waterbed was $\mu = 34$ years. Captain Kidd, as a result of this study, felt that older people were not sufficiently interested in waterbeds. In order to increase interest in waterbeds among older folk, Captain Kidd retained the Mermaid Advertising Agency of Copenhagen to redirect the Captain's advertising toward older people. Captain Kidd is now wondering if this change in advertising has proved successful.

To begin, the relevant hypotheses are

H_o: $\mu = 34$ years

H_a: $\mu > 34$

where μ is the mean age of the population of people who have purchased a waterbed since the Mermaid Agency began the new advertising campaign. Captain Kidd next decided that the level of significance should be $\alpha = .10$ and that a random sample of $n = 100$ recent waterbed buyers would be taken. This sample was taken and yielded the following statistics:

$\overline{X} = 37$ years

$s\ \ = 15$ years

In other words, the mean age of the 100 sampled buyers was 37 years. Furthermore, there was a lot of variability in their ages, as indicated by the large sample standard deviation of 15 years.

Captain Kidd now wishes to determine if the new advertising campaign was effective. In order to do this, a decision rule must be constructed. It has already been stipulated that the decision rule should yield an α of .10. Captain Kidd needs to find the appropriate critical value. For the time being, let us assume that the critical value is C; hence, the decision rule would be

> Accept H_o if $\overline{X} < C$
>
> Reject H_o if $\overline{X} \geq C$

where C is some value in excess of 34.

The critical value C is determined on the basis of the level of significance α. Recall that α equals the probability of making a Type I error:

$$\alpha = P(\text{Type I Error})$$

This means that α equals the probability of rejecting H_o when H_o is true; that is,

$$\alpha = P(\text{Rejecting } H_o | H_o \text{ is true})$$

With the decision rule as given above, H_o will be rejected if $\overline{X}$ is greater than or equal to C. Therefore,

$$\alpha = P(\overline{X} \geq C | H_o \text{ is true})$$

Furthermore, to say that H_o is true implies that μ equals 34. This yields

$$\alpha = P(\overline{X} \geq C | \mu = 34)$$

In Chapter 6 it was shown that probabilities concerning $\overline{X}$ are easily determined from the sampling distribution of $\overline{X}$. Remember that the sampling distribution of $\overline{X}$ lists all the possible values that $\overline{X}$ might take on depending on what items actually end up in the random sample. Under the assumption that H_o is true, the sampling distribution of $\overline{X}$ will have a mean of 34. In the last paragraph, α was shown to equal

$$\alpha = P(\overline{X} \geq C)$$

when the sampling distribution has a mean of 34 as hypothesized in the null hypothesis. This probability can be determined once the distribution of $\overline{X}$ is known. Since the sample size is $n = 100$, the central limit theorem states that the $\overline{X}$ distribution is normal. Figure 8.3 pictures the normal distribution of $\overline{X}$ along with the critical value C and α. Figure 8.3 will now be used to find the specific value of C.

FIGURE 8.3

Critical Value and Sampling Distribution of $\overline{X}$ when H_o is True

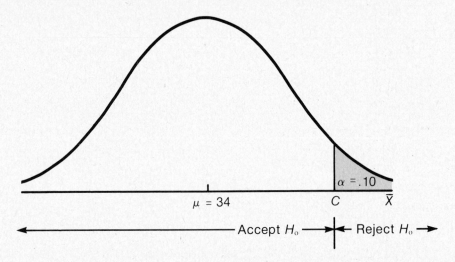

Notice in Figure 8.3 that the mean of the sampling distribution of $\overline{X}$ is $\mu = 34$. This is because we are presently assuming that the null hypothesis is true. Under these circumstances, the sample statistic $\overline{X}$ can vary depending on who happens to get chosen in the random sample of 100 buyers. If $\overline{X}$ gets above C, we will reject H_o, thereby making a Type I error. The chance of making such an error has been specified to be $\alpha = .10$, which in this case is the probability that $\overline{X}$ will equal or exceed C. Since α has been fixed at .10, we can determine C.

Following the procedure of Section 4.6 of Chapter 4, we can determine the value C which has an area of .10 beyond it and thus an area of .40 between it and the mean. According to Appendix N, C must be 1.28 standard deviations above the mean. This Z value of 1.28 was found, as in Section 4.6, by looking in the heart of Appendix N for an area as close to .40 as possible. The Z value which corresponds to this area is 1.28. Therefore, it follows that the critical value is

$$C = \text{mean} + (1.28)(\text{standard deviation})$$

For the sampling distribution of $\overline{X}$, it was shown in Chapter 6 that the mean is $\mu_{\overline{X}} = \mu = 34$ years and the standard deviation or standard error is $\sigma_{\overline{X}}$, which equals $\sigma/\sqrt{n}$ if n is less than 10 percent of N. Since the population standard deviation σ is unknown, it is estimated by s. The resulting estimate of the standard error is denoted by $s_{\overline{X}}$, which equals $s/\sqrt{n}$. Captain Kidd has already computed the sample standard deviation which is $s = 15$. Therefore, the estimate of the standard error is

$$s_{\overline{X}} = \frac{s}{\sqrt{n}}$$

$$= \frac{15}{\sqrt{100}}$$

$$= 1.5$$

This implies that the critical value is

$$C = \mu + (1.28)(s_{\overline{X}})$$
$$= 34 + (1.28)(1.5)$$
$$= 35.9$$

The decision rule is

Accept H_o if $\overline{X} < 35.9$

Reject H_o if $\overline{X} \geq 35.9$

Since Captain Kidd found $\overline{X}$ to equal 37 years, H_o is rejected. The sample evidence as expressed by $\overline{X} = 37$ is inconsistent with the null hypothesis that μ equals 34 years. Captain Kidd should conclude that the mean age of the waterbed buyers has increased.

Figure 8.4 portrays the situation as it has been presented. In addition, some other information is given in the lower part of Figure 8.4. Each of the values is given in terms of its equivalent standard deviation units. Recall that the following relationship is used to calculate the standard deviation units Z:

$$Z = \frac{\text{value} - \text{mean}}{\text{standard deviation}}$$

In the case at hand this becomes

FIGURE 8.4_____

Sampling Distribution of $\overline{X}$ with Decision Rule for Captain Kidd
where $C = 34 + (1.28)(1.5)$

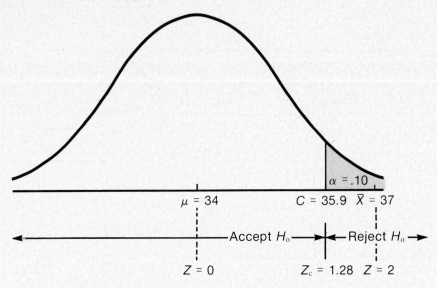

From this it follows that 34 is equivalent to a Z of 0. The critical
value which is $C = 35.9$ is equivalent to a Z of 1.28 since

$$Z = \frac{35.9 - 34}{1.5}$$

$$= 1.28$$

This value, in terms of standard deviation units, which corresponds to C is denoted by Z_c. Z_c is the critical value expressed in
standard deviation units. Finally, the value of the sample statistic
which is $\overline{X} = 37$ is converted to standard deviation units according
to

$$Z = \frac{37 - 34}{1.5}$$

$$= 2$$

It should be emphasized that this particular Z value is a statistic, since it is based on the $\overline{X}$ statistic. This particular Z value is actually computed from sample data because it is based on $\overline{X}$ which is computed directly from the sample. In the case at hand, the statement "The sample mean is $\overline{X} = 37$" is equivalent to the statement "The sample mean is $Z = 2$." This Z value, which is equivalent to the statistic $\overline{X}$, is sometimes called the *test statistic*.

As shown in Figure 8.4, the decision rule for Captain Kidd is

$$\text{Accept } H_o \text{ if } \overline{X} < 35.9$$
$$\text{Reject } H_o \text{ if } \overline{X} \geq 35.9$$

since C equals 35.9. The same rule may be equivalently expressed in terms of standard deviation units:

$$\text{Accept } H_o \text{ if } Z < Z_c$$
$$\text{Reject } H_o \text{ if } Z \geq Z_c$$

Since Z_c equals 1.28, this becomes

$$\text{Accept } H_o \text{ if } Z < 1.28$$
$$\text{Reject } H_o \text{ if } Z \geq 1.28$$

where Z is the statistic computed by $Z = (\overline{X} - \mu)/s_{\bar{x}}$. This Z value has already been found to equal 2; therefore, the null hypothesis is rejected. Regardless of the form of the decision rule used, the conclusion is the same.

That form of the decision rule which is expressed in standard deviation units is the more commonly used form. It is more useful because the critical value Z_c can be more easily adjusted for differing levels of significance. For example, if Captain Kidd changed to an α of .01, the critical value Z_c could be determined directly by using Appendix N. Figure 8.5 shows the relationship between Z_c and $\alpha = .01$. A probability (area) of .49 is sought in the heart of Appendix N; the value of Z which corresponds to this probability is 2.33. This 2.33 is Z_c when the level of significance is .01. Therefore, Captain Kidd would accept H_o with the significance level at .01 because the test statistic is $Z = 2$ as computed earlier.

Figure 8.6 presents the critical value Z_c for differing significance levels. These are all determined from Appendix N and are appropriate for one-tailed tests only. Although the test illustrated here has been an upper-tailed test, the same principles apply for one-tailed tests that are lower-tailed tests. Lower-tailed tests are based on an alternate hypothesis such as $\mu < 20$. In such tests, the

critical value is below the mean; therefore, the critical value will
be $-Z_c$. A brief example will be given shortly.

FIGURE 8.5
Finding Z_c for $\alpha = .01$

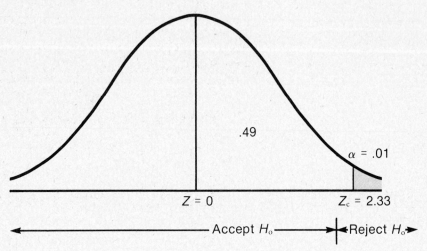

.49

$\alpha = .01$

$Z = 0$ $Z_c = 2.33$

◄───────── Accept H_o ────────►◄Reject H_o►

FIGURE 8.6
Critical Values for One-Tailed Tests

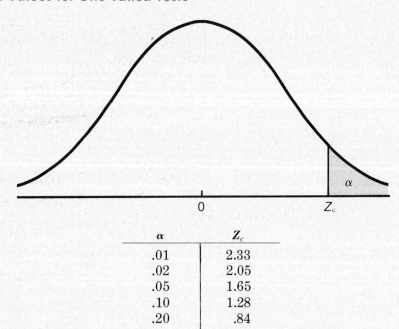

α	Z_c
.01	2.33
.02	2.05
.05	1.65
.10	1.28
.20	.84

The subject of one-tailed hypothesis testing for null hypotheses concerned with the population mean may now be summarized.

1. Formulate the hypotheses. For an upper-tailed test the hypotheses are $H_o: \mu = k$ and $H_a: \mu > k$. For a lower-tailed test the alternate hypothesis is $H_a: \mu < k$.

2. Specify n and α. The sample size n must be at least 25 and the level of significance is typically between .10 and .01.

3. Take the sample and compute $\overline{X}$ and s. Then compute the test statistic Z according to $Z = (\overline{X} - \mu)/s_{\overline{X}}$ where μ is the hypothesized mean and $s_{\overline{X}}$ is the estimated standard error of the sampling distribution.

4. Formulate the decision rule in terms of Z_c. For upper-tailed tests, reject H_o if the test statistic Z is greater than or equal to Z_c. For lower-tailed tests, reject H_o if Z is less than or equal to $-Z_c$.

5. Compare the actual value of the test statistic as computed in Step 3 to the decision rule. On the basis of this comparison, make a decision to either accept or reject H_o.

A lower-tailed test will now be briefly presented.

An automobile manufacturer claims that one of its models, the Firecat, gets 22 miles per gallon in highway driving. The E.P.A. wishes to test this claim. The hypotheses are

$$H_o: \mu = 22 \text{ m.p.g.}$$

$$H_a: \mu < 22$$

where μ is the mean miles per gallon. The E.P.A. decides to test n = 25 Firecats at the $\alpha = .05$ significance level. The 25 Firecats are tested and yield a sample mean of $\overline{X} = 21.2$ m.p.g. with a standard deviation of $s = 5$ m.p.g. The estimate of the standard error is therefore $s_{\overline{X}} = s/\sqrt{n} = 5/\sqrt{25} = 1$. The $\overline{X}$ of 21.2 is next translated into standard deviation units to yield the value of the test statistic:

$$Z = \frac{\overline{X} - \mu}{s_{\overline{X}}}$$

$$= \frac{21.2 - 22}{1}$$

$$= -.8$$

The decision rule is

> Accept H_o if $Z > -1.65$
>
> Reject H_o if $Z \leq -1.65$

The critical value of -1.65 is determined from Figure 8.6, since $\alpha =$ .05. A negative sign is affixed, since in a lower-tailed test the critical value falls below the mean. Finally, since the test statistic value of $Z = -.8$ is greater than the critical value of -1.65, H_o should be accepted. The E.P.A. is not able to disprove the manufacturer's claim and hence concludes that μ is 22 miles per gallon. Figure 8.7 pictures this test.

FIGURE 8.7
Lower-Tailed Test for Firecats

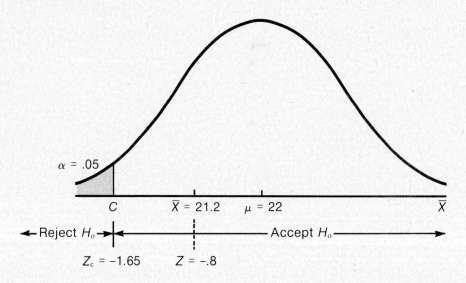

8.6

TESTING TWO-TAILED HYPOTHESES ABOUT THE POPULATION MEAN

A large copper mining company operating in Arizona presently has 1,000 ore cars filled with copper ore. The company wishes to sell this ore at an equitable price. It does not want to sell the ore for too much, as this would be treating the buyer unfairly. Neither does the company wish to sell it too cheaply, as this would be unfair to its owners. In order to estimate the amount of copper in these ore cars, the mining company checked its records and found that a previous 1,000 ore cars proved to have a mean of 200 pounds of copper per car. Since the company has continued to mine in the same area of the open pit, it seems reasonable to assume that this new set of 1,000 cars will have the same copper content. Therefore, the hypotheses become

$$H_o: \mu = 200 \text{ pounds of copper per car}$$

$$H_a: \mu \neq 200$$

This is a two-tailed test because the company is concerned about the possibility of μ being either below or above 200 pounds per car.

It was next decided that $n = 25$ of the population of 1,000 cars would be sampled and assayed. Furthermore, a level of significance of $\alpha = .10$ seemed appropriate.

Upon sampling 25 ore cars, the following statistics were computed:

$$\overline{X} = 194 \text{ pounds per car}$$

$$s = 50 \text{ pounds}$$

Assuming that H_o is true, the sampling distribution of $\overline{X}$ has a mean of

$$\mu_{\overline{X}} = \mu = 200$$

and an estimate of its standard error is

$$s_{\overline{X}} = \frac{s}{\sqrt{n}}$$

$$= \frac{50}{\sqrt{25}}$$

$$= 10$$

Because of the central limit theorem and the fact that n equals 25, the $\overline{X}$ distribution is normal.

The sample result of $\overline{X} = 194$ may now be expressed in standard deviation units. The resulting value of the test statistic is

$$Z = \frac{\overline{X} - \mu}{s_{\overline{X}}}$$

$$= \frac{194 - 200}{10}$$

$$= -.6$$

The mining company now wonders if a sample result of $Z = -.6$ standard errors below the mean is a sample result which is inconsistent with the null hypothesis. It is the decision rule which specifies the sample results which are inconsistent with H_o. If a sample result is inconsistent with H_o, then the null hypothesis is rejected.

For a two-tailed test, the null hypothesis can be rejected if X is quite a bit greater than μ or if it is quite a bit lower than μ. In the case at hand, if $\overline{X}$ were something like 385 pounds, certainly the mining company would reject H_o. Likewise, if $\overline{X}$ proved to be only 114 pounds, then H_o would also be rejected. Figure 8.8 gives a picture of the decision rule for a two-tailed test. The distribution of Figure 8.8 is the sampling distribution of $\overline{X}$, which is normal since n is at least 25. As shown in Figure 8.8, the general form of the decision rule is

Accept H_o if $C_L < \overline{X} < C_U$

Reject H_o if $\overline{X} \le C_L$ or $\overline{X} \ge C_U$

FIGURE 8.8_____

Sampling Distribution of $\overline{X}$ with Decision Rule

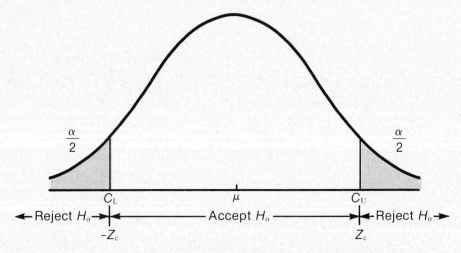

Notice that there are two critical values in a two-tailed test. The lower critical value is denoted by C_L and the upper is C_U. Stated in standard deviation units, the decision rule is

Accept H_o if $-Z_c < Z < Z_c$

Reject H_o if $Z \le -Z_c$ or $Z \ge Z_c$

where Z is the test statistic which is computed by $Z = (\overline{X} - \mu)/s_{\overline{X}}$. Hence, the two critical values are $-Z_c$ and Z_c.

In two-tailed tests, α is still the probability of making a Type I error. By definition,

$$\alpha = P(\text{Type I error})$$

$$\alpha = P(\text{Reject } H_o | H_o \text{ is true})$$

$$\alpha = \text{Area associated with the rejection region}$$

$$\alpha = P(\overline{X} \leq C_L) + P(\overline{X} \geq C_U)$$

$$\alpha = P(Z \leq -Z_c) + P(Z \geq Z_c)$$

Since the rejection region is split into two parts in a two-tailed test, α is also split. Thus, $\alpha/2$ is the area in each tail. The mining company chose the level of significance to be $\alpha = .10$; this implies that .05 must be the area or probability in each tail. According to Appendix N, .05 of the area under any normal curve lies beyond 1.65 standard deviations above the mean. Therefore, a total area or probability of .10 lies beyond ± 1.65 standard deviations from the mean. Figure 8.9 shows these specific values for Z_c. There is no need to actually determine C_L and C_U if the critical values of $-Z_c$ and Z_c are used.

FIGURE 8.9

Sampling Distribution of $\overline{X}$ with Decision Rule for a Copper Mining Company

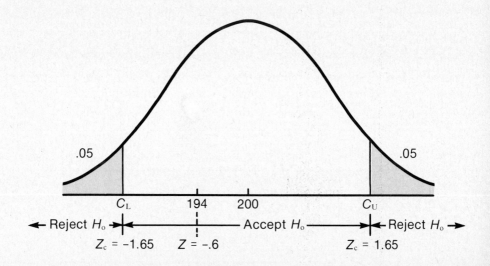

It has already been shown that the sample mean of $\overline{X} = 194$ is equivalent to a Z of $-.6$. Since this sample value of Z is well within the acceptance region as shown in Figure 8.9, it follows that H_o is accepted. In other words, an $\overline{X}$ of 194 is quite consistent with the hypothesis that the mean of the population of 1,000 ore cars is 200 pounds of copper. Thus, the company may act as if the cars contain a mean of 200 pounds of copper.

For two-tailed tests where the decision rule is expressed in terms of standard deviation units, the critical values of $-Z_c$ and Z_c for a variety of significance levels are given in Figure 8.10. For example, the critical values for $\alpha = .04$ would be $-Z_c = -2.05$ and $Z_c = 2.05$. If the test statistic Z falls between these critical values, then H_o is accepted. Otherwise, it is rejected.

FIGURE 8.10

Critical Values for Two-Tailed Tests

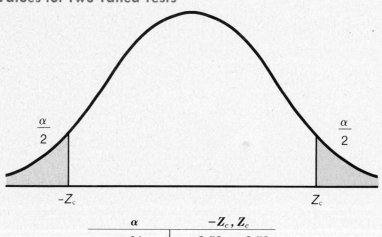

α	$-Z_c, Z_c$
.01	$-2.58, +2.58$
.02	$-2.33, +2.33$
.04	$-2.05, +2.05$
.05	$-1.96, +1.96$
.10	$-1.65, +1.65$
.20	$-1.28, +1.28$

8.7

TESTING HYPOTHESES ABOUT THE POPULATION PROPORTION

Testing a hypothesis involving p, the population proportion, is analogous to testing a hypothesis about μ. The only difference lies in the fact that $\bar{p}$, rather than $\overline{X}$, is computed from the sample. The test statistic Z based on this $\bar{p}$ is then determined according to

$$Z = \frac{\bar{p} - p}{\sigma_{\bar{p}}}$$

where p is the hypothesized population proportion, and the standard error is computed by

$$\sigma_{\bar{p}} = \sqrt{\frac{(p)(1 - p)}{n}}$$

The test statistic Z is compared to the critical value Z_c in order to accept or reject the null hypothesis. As before, the procedure is based on the assumption that n is at least 25. Two examples will now be given.

Chief Yellowhorse has a trading post located along I40 near the Arizona-New Mexico border. Piled behind the trading post is a veritable mountain of burlap sacks filled with sand from the painted desert. The Chief advertises that at least 30 percent of the sacks contain a piece of petrified wood in addition to the sand. However, the sacks with the petrified wood are unmarked. While the Chief was holding his sale, a well-known consumer advocate, Raphel, drove up in her Corvair. Spotting the sacks in back of the trading post, Raphel immediately suspected that the Chief was not putting petrified wood in 30 percent of the sacks. She therefore decided to run a hypothesis test.

The hypotheses in this situation are

$$H_o: p = .30$$
$$H_a: p < .30$$

where p represents the true proportion of the sacks in the pile which contain petrified wood. Having something of an ornery disposition, Raphel chose a level of significance of .10. Such an α would make it easier to reject H_o than would an α like .01. Next, Raphel purchased 50 sacks from the Chief. Taking these to her motel, Raphel found that only 11 had petrified wood. Is Raphel justified in rejecting H_o and therefore making trouble for the Chief? Before conducting the test, it should be noted that if Raphel intended to bring the Chief to court, she would prefer to use a level of significance like .01 in order to protect herself from bringing a false charge.

If $X = 11$ out of $n = 50$ sacks have petrified wood, then the sample proportion is

$$\bar{p} = \frac{X}{n}$$

$$= \frac{11}{50}$$

$$= .22$$

Assuming that H_o is true, the statistic $\bar{p}$ has a sampling distribution which is normal with a standard error of

$$\sigma_{\bar{p}} = \sqrt{\frac{(p)(1-p)}{n}}$$

$$= \sqrt{\frac{(.30)(1-.30)}{50}}$$

$$= .065$$

Notice that p is the value which is hypothesized in H_o. The Z statistic corresponding to a $\bar{p}$ of .22 is

$$Z = \frac{\bar{p} - p}{\sigma_{\bar{p}}}$$

$$Z = \frac{.22 - .30}{.065}$$

$$= -1.23$$

From Figure 8.6 which gives critical values for one-tailed tests, the critical value $-Z_c$ is -1.28 if α is .10. Therefore, Raphel should accept H_o, since the test statistic has a value of $Z = -1.23$ which is within the acceptance region. In accepting H_o, Raphel concludes that the sample evidence does not warrant bringing a charge against the Chief. The decision rule and test statistic for this one-tailed test are pictured in Figure 8.11.

Consider another example which involves a two-tailed test of p. The Purple Stamp Company is attempting to talk Xmart into giving purple stamps. The Purple Stamp Company says that purple stamps will serve to increase the proportion of customer purchases exceeding $10. A marketing consultant, on the other hand, says that the effect of the purple stamps will be the exact opposite. The consultant says that issuing stamps will mar Xmart's reputation of offering the lowest price possible; today's sophisticated shoppers will not believe that they are getting something for nothing. Thus, customers will in fact buy less once the stamps are given.

FIGURE 8.11 _____

Sampling Distribution of $\bar{p}$ and Decision Rule

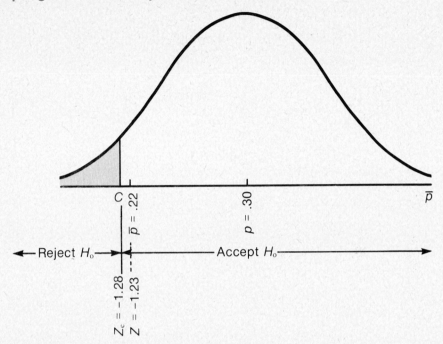

Faced with all of these arguments, Xmart decided to try purple stamps for awhile. Xmart knew that prior to the stamps, 20 percent of the purchases made by customers exceeded $10. Xmart wants to be sensitive to a change in this proportion in either direction. Letting p denote the proportion of purchases which exceed $10 *after* the purple stamp program has been instituted, the hypotheses are

$$H_o: p = .20$$

$$H_a: p \neq .20$$

In essence, the null hypothesis says that the purple stamps are ineffective in changing p. Xmart wishes to test the null hypothesis at the .02 significance level.

After the purple stamps had been introduced, Xmart proceeded to randomly sample 500 customer purchases. A total of 130 of these purchases exceeded $10. In view of this sample evidence, should H_o be rejected?

The test is begun by computing the statistic $\bar{p}$ and then the test statistic Z. In this case,

$$\bar{p} = \frac{X}{n}$$

$$= \frac{130}{500}$$

$$= .26$$

The standard error, assuming H_o is true, is

$$\sigma_{\bar{p}} = \sqrt{\frac{(p)(1 - p)}{n}}$$

$$= \sqrt{\frac{(.20)(1 - .20)}{500}}$$

$$= .018$$

Therefore, the statistic expressed in standard deviation units is

$$Z = \frac{\bar{p} - p}{\sigma_{\bar{p}}}$$

$$= \frac{.26 - .20}{.018}$$

$$= 3.33$$

Xmart next wonders if a Z of 3.33 is to be considered as inconsistent with H_o. In order to make a decision, the decision rule in terms of $-Z_c$ and Z_c must be determined. From Figure 8.10, if the level of significance is .02 for a two-tailed test, then the decision rule will be

Accept H_o if $\quad -2.33 < Z < 2.33$

Reject H_o if $\quad Z \le -2.33 \quad$ or $\quad Z \ge 2.33$

Since the value of the test statistic Z is 3.33, which is in the rejection region, Xmart should reject H_o, thereby concluding that the purple stamps do have an effect on the proportion of customer purchases which exceed \$10.

8.8

LOOKING BACK AT HYPOTHESIS TESTING

It is the purpose in this section to briefly summarize the process of hypothesis testing and to emphasize several details which were not previously emphasized. In hypothesis testing the analyst sets forth a hypothesis, the null hypothesis, about the value of a population parameter like μ or p. The analyst then seeks sample information which will either confirm or disprove the hypothesis. Since sample information by nature is not necessarily representative of the population, the analyst always runs the risk of drawing an erroneous conclusion. The two types of errors that can be made are called Type I and Type II errors. Even though the possibility of making an error exists, the analyst proceeds to either accept or reject the null hypothesis on the basis of the sample evidence.

In order to test the null hypothesis, a statistic like $\overline{X}$ or $\bar{p}$ is computed from the sample data. If the value of this statistic (which is usually expressed in standard deviation units) is quite a bit different from the hypothesized value of the parameter, then the analyst discards or rejects the null hypothesis. On the other hand, if the value of the statistic is relatively close to the hypothesized value of the parameter, then the analyst accepts the hypothesis. In this procedure, it is the decision rule which defines what values of the statistic should be considered as "quite a bit different" from the hypothesized value of the parameter and what values of the statistic are "relatively close."

The challenging part of hypothesis testing is determining the decision rule. Usually the decision rule is determined as a result of the analyst first stipulating an acceptable probability of making a Type I error. Once α or the level of significance is specified, then the decision rule is determined. Most often the decision rule is expressed in terms of standard deviation units. The test statistic Z, which is based on $\overline{X}$ or $\bar{p}$, is then directly compared to the critical value Z_c in order to make a decision.

In the hypothesis testing procedure that was developed, it was stated that the sample size n must always be at least 25. This, by reason of the central limit theorem, guarantees the normality of the sampling distributions of the statistics $\overline{X}$ and $\bar{p}$. Using an n which is much larger than 25 has an important advantage. Very large sample sizes reduce the probability β of making a Type II error. In this chapter the probability of a Type I error has been fixed usually between .10 and .01. Recalling that α and β vary inversely, this means that if a small α in the .01 to .10 region is used, then β will be relatively large. However, if n is increased and α is held constant, then β will decline. Therefore, it is a good idea to use a fairly large n in order to reduce the probability of making a Type II error. There is a real danger of making a Type II error when α is fixed at a low level and n is relatively small. Because of the great chance of making a Type II error in these circumstances, many analysts, if accepting the null hypothesis, say "The evidence does not disprove H_o" rather than "The evidence proves

H_o is true." This cautious wording is something of a hedge in situations where Type II errors are very likely.

The theoretical entity which links together the probabilities of Type I and II errors, the decision rule, and the sample size is the standard error of the sampling distribution. Figure 8.12, for example, shows how an increase in sample size will reduce α if the critical value of the decision rule remains unchanged. When n is small, the standard error is relatively large, yielding a sampling distribution which is spread out. Notice that with this sampling distribution there is a considerable probability α that $\overline{X}$ will fall below C, thus yielding a Type I error. However, when n is increased then $s_{\bar{x}}$ is reduced, since a large value in the denominator of $s_{\bar{x}} = s/\sqrt{n}$ causes $s_{\bar{x}}$ to decline. The $\overline{X}$'s of the resulting sampling distribution then become more tightly packed about μ. This means that it is unlikely that an $\overline{X}$ will fall below C and thus yield a Type I error. In a similar fashion, the effects on α and β of changes in the decision rule as well as in changes in n may be determined.

In concluding this section, it should be noted that in this chapter the standard error has been estimated by $s_{\bar{x}}$ where $s_{\bar{x}} = s/\sqrt{n}$. If the hypothesis test is conducted in a situation where n is

FIGURE 8.12_____

The Effect on α of a Change in n

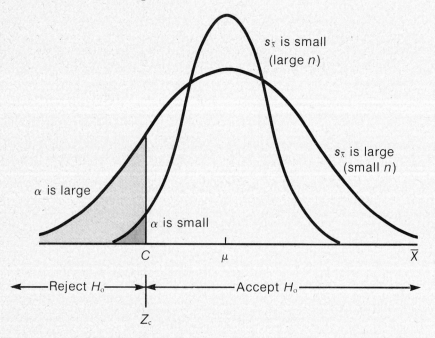

10 percent or more of N, then the estimate of the standard error is computed by

$$s_{\bar{x}} = \frac{s}{\sqrt{n}}\sqrt{1 - \frac{n}{N}}$$

None of the problems in this chapter, however, will require the use of the finite population correction factor.

8.9

TESTING THE EQUALITY OF TWO MEANS AND TWO PROPORTIONS

In this section two more tests will be presented. These two tests are based on the same kind of theory involving sampling distributions as the tests that have already been considered. In each of these two tests, a test statistic Z is computed from sample evidence. This Z is then compared to the critical value(s) Z_c for the sake of accepting or rejecting the null hypothesis. Such a procedure is exactly the same as has been previously presented in this chapter.

At times it is desirable to determine if the means of two populations are the same or if the proportions of two populations are the same. For example, we might wish to determine if the mean miles per gallon using Gasoline S in an automobile is the same as the mean miles per gallon achieved using Gasoline M. Here the null hypothesis would be

H_o: $\mu_s = \mu_m$

With regard to population proportions, we might be interested in determining if the proportion of people in Atlanta who eat out regularly is the same as the proportion of people in Boston who eat out regularly. Hence, the null hypothesis would be

H_o: $p_a = p_b$

In either case the test could be two-tailed or one-tailed. For example, with Gasolines S and M the alternate hypothesis might be

H_a: $\mu_s \neq \mu_m$

In the Atlanta and Boston example the alternate hypothesis might be

$$H_a: \ p_a < p_b$$

thus indicating a one-tailed test.

When a test regarding the equality of two means is to be conducted, as in the gasoline case, the analyst begins by stipulating the level of significance and the number of items which are to be randomly sampled from each population. After the samples of at least 25 items are taken from each of the populations, the test statistic Z is computed according to

$$Z = \frac{\overline{X}_1 - \overline{X}_2}{\sqrt{\dfrac{s_1^2}{n_1} + \dfrac{s_2^2}{n_2}}}$$

where $\overline{X}_1$ is the sample mean from the first population, s_1^2 is the sample variance from the first population, and n_1 is the number of items sampled from the first population. $\overline{X}_2$, s_2^2, and n_2 are the respective values corresponding to the second population. This test statistic is then compared to the appropriate critical value(s) as taken from either Figure 8.6 or 8.10. Then a decision is made either to accept or reject H_o. Notice that the test statistic Z will have a value close to 0 whenever $\overline{X}_1$ and $\overline{X}_2$ are approximately the same size. In these cases H_o would be accepted. However, if $\overline{X}_1$ and $\overline{X}_2$ substantially differ, this will cause Z to be a very large negative number or a very large positive number. The null hypothesis is then rejected when Z is far from 0.

If the test concerns the equality of two proportions, as in the Atlanta and Boston case, then the test statistic is computed from a sample of at least 25 items from each of the populations according to

$$Z = \frac{\bar{p}_1 - \bar{p}_2}{\sqrt{\left(\dfrac{X_1 + X_2}{n_1 + n_2}\right)\left(1 - \dfrac{X_1 + X_2}{n_1 + n_2}\right)\left(\dfrac{1}{n_1} + \dfrac{1}{n_2}\right)}}$$

where n_1 is the number of items sampled from the first population, X_1 is the number of successes obtained from the first population, and $\bar{p}_1$ is the sample proportion from the first population which equals X_1/n_1. The values $\bar{p}_2$, X_2, and n_2 are similarly defined for the second population. The test statistic is then compared to the critical values, as found in Figure 8.6 or Figure 8.10, in order to make a decision. Two examples of these two kinds of tests will now be given.

An analyst for a medical insurance company wishes to determine if the mean length of stay per patient in the Phoenix General Hospital is the same as that for St. Paul's Hospital of Phoenix. The analyst subsequently samples $n_1 = 100$ patient records from General Hospital and finds the sample mean to be $\overline{X}_1 = 7.6$ days, with a sample standard deviation of $s_1 = 5$ days. Then $n_2 = 50$ patient records are sampled from St. Paul's yielding $\overline{X}_2 = 8.2$ days and $s_2 = 6$ days. With a significance level of .10, what should the insurance analyst conclude?

To begin, the hypotheses are

$$H_o: \mu_1 = \mu_2$$

$$H_a: \mu_1 \neq \mu_2$$

where μ_1 represents the mean time per patient in General Hospital and μ_2 represents the mean for St. Paul's. This is a two-tailed test, since the analyst is not particularly concerned about which mean might be greater.

The test statistic Z is next computed. It is

$$
\begin{aligned}
Z &= \frac{\overline{X}_1 - \overline{X}_2}{\sqrt{\dfrac{s_1^2}{n_1} + \dfrac{s_2^2}{n_2}}} \\[2ex]
&= \frac{7.6 - 8.2}{\sqrt{\dfrac{5^2}{100} + \dfrac{6^2}{50}}} \\[2ex]
&= \frac{-.6}{.98} \\[2ex]
&= -.61
\end{aligned}
$$

According to Figure 8.10, the critical values for a two-tailed test where $\alpha = .10$ are $-Z_c = 1.65$ and $Z_c = 1.65$. Since $Z = -.61$ falls within the acceptance region, the analyst should accept H_o. In other words, the sample evidence does not indicate that the two population means differ.

An example of a test for the equality of two population proportions will now be given. The Small Business Administration wonders if the proportion of loans which go to minority businesses is the same in different regions of the country. To begin a study into this matter, the SBA singles out Texas and Massachusetts. Let p_t equal the proportion of loans in Texas that have gone to minority businesses and let p_m equal the proportion of loans in Massachusetts that have gone to minority businesses. The relevant hypotheses are

$$H_o:\ p_t = p_m$$
$$H_a:\ p_t \neq p_m$$

These hypotheses are to be tested at the .05 significance level.

A sample of 50 Texas loans reveals that 10 went to minority businesses. Symbolically, this may be expressed as

$$n_t = 50$$
$$X_t = 10$$
$$\bar{p}_t = 10/50 = .20$$

A sample of 80 Massachusetts loans revealed that 4 of these loans went to minority businesses. Symbolically, this sample information may be expressed as

$$n_m = 80$$
$$X_m = 4$$
$$\bar{p}_m = 4/80 = .05$$

In order to test H_o, the test statistic Z must be computed:

$$Z = \frac{\bar{p}_t - \bar{p}_m}{\sqrt{\left(\dfrac{X_t + X_m}{n_t + n_m}\right)\left(1 - \dfrac{X_t + X_m}{n_t + n_m}\right)\left(\dfrac{1}{n_t} + \dfrac{1}{n_m}\right)}}$$

$$= \frac{.20 - .05}{\sqrt{\left(\dfrac{10 + 4}{50 + 80}\right)\left(1 - \dfrac{10 + 4}{50 + 80}\right)\left(\dfrac{1}{50} + \dfrac{1}{80}\right)}}$$

$$= \frac{.15}{.056}$$

$$= 2.68$$

From Figure 8.10, the critical values for a two-tailed test where α equals .05 are $-Z_c = -1.96$ and $Z_c = 1.96$. Since the test statistic Z has a value of 2.68, H_o is rejected. The SBA should conclude that the proportions in Texas and Massachusetts are not the same.

8.10

THE t DISTRIBUTION IN HYPOTHESIS TESTING AND ESTIMATION

In this final section of the chapter a special case of hypothesis testing and estimation will be studied. The principles to be discussed here are identical to those outlined earlier; only a few details will vary.

Throughout this chapter it has been assumed that the sample size is large; that is, $n \geq 25$. A special situation may arise where the population is normal and where a small sample, $n < 25$, is drawn from this population in order to compute $\overline{X}$ and s for the sake of testing a hypothesis about μ. In this case, the test statistic is given by

$$t = \frac{\overline{X} - \mu}{s_{\overline{X}}}$$

where μ is the hypothesized value of the population mean and $s_{\overline{X}} = s/\sqrt{n}$. In this chapter the test statistic has always been designated as Z; however, under the special conditions just mentioned (small sample size from a normal population where μ and σ are unknown) it has been shown by statisticians that Z is not appropriate. Rather, the t statistic should be used.

The statistic t has a symmetrical distribution which is quite similar to the normal or Z distribution and is called the Student's t distribution. The test statistic t, as shown above, is compared to the critical values of the t distribution, t_c, in order to determine if the null hypothesis should be rejected. This procedure is directly analogous to that involving the Z test statistic, which is compared to critical values in order to reject or accept H_o. Appendix T gives the critical values of t corresponding to different levels of significance for both one-tailed and two-tailed tests. It should be noted that the critical values, t_c, vary depending on the sample size n. An example will now be considered which will illustrate the essentials of hypothesis testing with the t distribution.

A manufacturer of 40-foot extension ladders claims that its ladder will hold, on the average, at least 900 pounds before buckling. A testing agency wishes to test this claim, and therefore obtains 5 ladders. To begin, the relevant hypotheses are

H_o: $\mu \geq 900$

H_a: $\mu < 900$

where μ is the mean strength of all the ladders produced by the manufacturer. The sample of $n = 5$ ladders are next tested yielding a mean breaking strength of $\overline{X} = 888$ pounds and $s = 46$ pounds. Based on this test data, should the manufacturer's claim be rejected if a .10 level of significance is used?

We notice first that n is small, σ is unknown and thus estimated by s, and it is reasonable to assume that the population of ladders is normally distributed with regard to strength. Hence, the t statistic is the appropriate test statistic:

$$t = \frac{\overline{X} - \mu}{s_{\overline{X}}} = \frac{\overline{X} - \mu}{s/\sqrt{n}}$$

$$= \frac{888 - 900}{46/\sqrt{5}}$$

$$= -.58$$

Turning now to Appendix T, the critical value for this lower-tail test when $\alpha = .10$ and $n - 1 = 5 - 1$ or 4 is $t_c = -1.533$. Analogous to hypothesis testing with Z, the decision rule is

Accept H_o if $t > -1.533$

Reject H_o if $t \leq -1.533$

Therefore, it follows that H_o should be accepted since $-.58$ is greater than $t_c = -1.533$ in this left-tail test.

Following the general procedure of hypothesis testing using the Z statistic (as developed earlier in this chapter), two-tailed tests involving the t distribution may also be performed with ease. In these cases, the t statistic is computed and then H_o is rejected if t falls outside the two critical values. Again, the critical values corresponding to different sample sizes are given in Appendix T.

In Chapter 7 interval estimation was presented. It was seen there that a confidence interval for μ when σ is unknown has the form

$$\overline{X} - Zs_{\overline{X}} \quad \text{to} \quad \overline{X} + Zs_{\overline{X}}$$

where $\overline{X}$ and $s_{\overline{X}} = s/\sqrt{n}$ are based on samples of size 25 or more. If the population is normal, σ is unknown, and n is less than 25, then the confidence interval will have the form

$$\overline{X} - ts_{\overline{X}} \quad \text{to} \quad \overline{X} + ts_{\overline{X}}$$

where t is taken from the Student's t distribution. Let us consider a brief example which will demonstrate how this confidence interval is constructed.

A purchaser of marine flares wishes to estimate the mean burning time of Twinkle flares. Nine flares are tested, yielding a mean burning time of $\overline{X} = 40$ minutes and a standard deviation of $s = 10$ minutes. From this information a 95 percent confidence interval for μ is desired. Turning to Appendix T, it is seen that the values of t in

$$\overline{X} - ts_{\overline{X}} \quad \text{to} \quad \overline{X} + ts_{\overline{X}}$$

are -2.306 and 2.306 for a 95 percent confidence level if $n - 1$ equals $9 - 1$ or 8. Therefore, the 95 percent confidence interval for μ, the mean burning time of all the flares in the population, is

$$40 - (2.306)\left(\frac{10}{\sqrt{9}}\right) \quad \text{to} \quad 40 + (2.306)\left(\frac{10}{\sqrt{9}}\right).$$

$$40 - 7.69 \quad \text{to} \quad 40 + 7.69$$

$$32.31 \quad \text{to} \quad 47.69 \text{ minutes}$$

To summarize this section of the use of the t distribution in hypothesis testing and estimation, the t distribution should be used when a sample of less than 25 is drawn from a normal population for the sake of computing $\overline{X}$ and s. The ensuing hypothesis testing or estimation procedures then follow those involving the normal distribution.

PROBLEMS

8.1

How is the decision rule used in hypothesis testing? What is the critical value?

8.2

How is the decision rule determined?

8.3

Describe the two types of errors that are faced in hypothesis testing.

8.4

Suppose the null hypothesis states that a denarius is a fair coin. A denarius is flipped 100 times yielding 31 heads. If you conclude that the denarius is an unfair coin when in fact it is fair, what type of error have you made?

8.5

If a decision maker accepts the null hypothesis, is there a chance that a Type I error has been made?

8.6

If a decision maker rejects the null hypothesis, is there a chance that a Type II error has been made?

8.7

A person has been arrested and charged with robbery. In our system of justice the arrested person is assumed to be innocent until proven otherwise. Letting the null hypothesis state that the arrested person is innocent, describe the two types of errors the jury might make.

8.8

A yellow car sits on a used car lot. Let the hypotheses be

> H_o: This is a good used car.
>
> H_a: This is a lemon.

Two potential purchasers come to the car lot seeking a yellow used car. Dick operates with a decision rule with a high α and a low β. Phoebe operates with a low α and a high β. If the car is good, who is more likely to buy it? If it is a lemon, who is more likely to reject it?

8.9

Two sporting goods companies (S and W) have ordered a shipment of baseball bats which are supposed to have a mean diameter of 3 inches. Both companies will sample 25 bats from the incoming shipment before deciding to accept or reject the shipment. In the case of Company S, the shipment will be accepted only if the sample mean falls between 2.95 and 3.05 inches. In the case of Company W the shipment will be accepted only if the sample mean falls between 2.98 and 3.02 inches. What type of error is relatively more likely with Company S? with Company W? If in the past the supplier of the bats has always shipped exactly what was ordered, would this cause the decision maker to use a higher or lower α?

8.10

What is the danger in specifying α to be a very low value like .005?

8.11

How does an increase in the sample size affect α and β?

8.12

Give and illustrate the three rules of thumb which guide in deciding what the null hypothesis should be and what the alternate hypothesis should be.

8.13

In a one-tailed test, what is Z_c if the level of significance is .005? is .08?

8.14

In a two-tailed test, what are $-Z_c$ and Z_c if the level of significance is .18? is .06?

8.15

If a statistician is undertaking a one-tailed test where $Z_c = +1.80$, what is alpha?

8.16

Heimer Production Systems Inc. is being audited by the accounting firm of Wingman & Scot. Heimer claims that the mean value of its accounts receivable is \$180. Wingman & Scot proceeds to sample 100 accounts receivable and finds $\overline{X} = \$176$ and $s = \$80$.

(a) Why should this be a one-tailed test?
(b) State the hypotheses.
(c) In the past Heimer has proven to be an honest company which has a good accounting system. In view of this, should a small

or large α be used by Wingman & Scot?

(d) Using a .05 significance level, what is the critical value in terms of standard deviation units?

(e) Compute the test statistic and determine if H_o should be accepted or rejected.

8.17

At Disco Ltd. the mean number of sick days taken per employee for last year was 3.8 days. A new management policy has been instituted this year which is aimed at reducing this figure. A sample of 36 employees this year reveals that they took an average of 3.4 sick days. The sample standard deviation is 1.2 days. At the .10 significance level, should Disco conclude that μ has been reduced?

8.18

The mean size of the stock purchases by customers of Peril Pynch last month was $2,800. This month Peril Pynch has reduced its sales commissions hoping to induce larger purchases. A sample of 100 purchases this month had a mean size of $2,900 with a sample standard deviation of $1,500. At the .01 significance level, can it be concluded that the reduced commissions have been effective?

8.19

The Universal Metal Workers claims that the average size of the monthly mortgage payments for its members is at least $300. In order to test this claim, a sample of 100 metal workers is taken. The mean mortgage payment for these sampled metal workers is $240 with a sample standard deviation of $80. Using a one-tailed test with $\alpha = .02$, determine if the UMW's claim can be accepted.

8.20

The Life Insurance Institute, based on a projection from last year's figures, claims that the mean face value of the life insurance policies sold this year is $35,000. A random sample of 49 of this year's policies has an average face value of $38,000 with a sample standard deviation of $20,000. Using a two-tailed test, should the Institute's claim be rejected? Use a .05 level of significance.

8.21

Burger Chemical of Newark claims that the mean daily amount of pollutants spewing forth from one of its stacks is 880 kilograms.

Newark monitors the stack on 25 randomly selected days in order to see if the mean is greater or less than 880 kilograms per day. For the 25 sampled days, the mean was 910 kilograms with a sample standard deviation of 200 kilograms. At the .01 significance level, can Newark conclude that there has been a change in the mean amount of pollutants spewing from the stack?

8.22

Greypooch claims that at least 90 percent of the packages they deliver arrive on time. One hundred packages are sent at differing times from differing locations via Greypooch. Eighty arrive on time. Can Greypooch's claim be accepted at the .10 significance level?

8.23

A Florida citrus grower states that no more than 20 percent of the oranges they ship are sour. A sample of 50 oranges reveals that 14 are sour. If $\alpha = .05$, can the grower's claim be rejected?

8.24

A television station claims that at least 30 percent of the homes in a city watch Star Trek. An advertiser randomly samples 60 homes and finds that 15 are watching Star Trek. Should the television station's claim be rejected? Use $\alpha = .02$.

8.25

In the past 40 percent of a grocery store's shoppers have purchased the store's brand of spinach. The grocery store wonders if this percentage has declined because of intensive advertising by the name brand canneries. A sample of 80 shoppers shows that 25 percent of them have purchased the store brand of spinach instead of another brand. At the .05 significance level, should the store conclude that fewer shoppers now buy the store brand?

8.26

Last month the proportion of vacant apartments in Chicago was .10. It is desired to know if the vacancy rate has changed in either direction. A sample of 50 apartments this month shows that 7 are vacant. At the .10 significance level, should it be concluded that there has been a change in the vacancy rate?

8.27

An economist has stated that 60 percent of the U.S. manufacturing firms plan to increase their capital budget expenditures. We are interested in determining the accuracy of this statement. Intending to use a .02 significance level, 25 firms are polled. If 10 of these firms indicate that their capital budget expenditures will increase, should the economist's claim be rejected?

8.28

A political candidate claims that 54 percent of the electorate favors her. In seeking to test if the true proportion is different from 54 percent, a sample of 1,000 voters is taken. Fifty-one percent of the 1,000 favor the candidate. Should the candidate's claim be disputed? Use a two-tailed test with $\alpha = .01$.

8.29

An automobile manufacturer wishes to determine if the age of a sales representative is related to the number of cars the representative sells. One hundred old sales reps were sampled. The mean annual number of cars sold by these reps was 48 with a sample standard deviation of 20 cars. A sample of 50 young reps had a mean annual sales of 37 cars with a sample standard deviation of 24. At the .05 significance level, can the auto manufacturer conclude that the young and old sales reps differ in sales?

8.30

Northern Arizona University would like to know if the mean income of its MBA graduates five years after receiving the degree differs from the mean of the MBA's from the University of Arizona. A sample of 25 MBA's from NAU has a mean salary of $28,000 with a sample standard deviation of $8,000. A sample of 30 MBA's from the University of Arizona has a mean salary of $26,000 with a standard deviation of $10,000. Can NAU conclude that a difference exists? Use $\alpha = .10$.

8.31

The makers of Coldent toothpaste wish to determine if the proportion of students at the University of Michigan who use Coldent is the same as the proportion of students at the University of Florida who use Coldent. Of the 100 Michigan students that were sampled, 40 use Coldent. Of the 200 Florida students sampled, 70 use Coldent. Should the company conclude that the population proportions are the same? Use a .04 level of significance.

8.32

The Internal Revenue Service believes that the propensity to make "computational" errors on tax forms is related to the gross income of the taxpayer. A sample of 100 tax forms from high income taxpayers revealed that 8 had computational errors. A sample of 50 tax forms from middle income taxpayers was taken and 3 had computational errors. At the $\alpha = .05$ level of significance, can the IRS conclude that a difference exists?

8.33

A researcher who is testing a new drug has taken a sample of 25 cases. Using a .01 significance level, the researcher has accepted the null hypothesis which states that the drug is ineffective. However, in reporting the conclusion the researcher stated: "Limited sample evidence has not proven the drug to be effective" rather than "The drug is ineffective." Why is the researcher being cautious in the wording of the conclusion?

8.34

Under what conditions is the t distribution used in hypothesis testing and estimation?

8.35

The mean score of the men who took a psychological test was 80. A sample of four women were then given the same test. The four women had a mean score of 75 with a standard deviation of 20. At the .05 significance level, can it be concluded that the mean score for all women differs from that of the men? Use a two-tailed test.

8.36

The mean pollution index in Denver was 176 last winter. A random sample of 12 days this winter yielded a mean of 158 with a standard deviation of 40. At the .01 significance level, can it be concluded that the pollution index has declined?

8.37

A retailer wishes to estimate the mean time it takes for a wholesaler to fill an order. From a sample of 10 orders, the retailer finds the mean time is 15 days with a standard deviation of 4 days. Determine a 90 percent confidence interval for the mean time it takes to get an order filled by the wholesaler.

8.38

Determine a 99 percent confidence interval for the mean pollution index for this winter in Denver. Use the sample data given in Problem 8-36.

CHAPTER 9

ANALYSIS OF VARIANCE

9.1

INTRODUCTION

The branch of inferential statistics known as hypothesis testing was introduced in Chapter 8. One type of hypothesis test studied in that chapter were tests involving the mean of a population. For example, an auditor might hypothesize that for a given company the mean or average size of the accounts receivables is $280. With this null hypothesis, denoted by

$$H_o: \mu = 280$$

the auditor would then proceed to take a random sample from the total population of receivables. Depending on the outcome of the random sample, the auditor would then either accept the null hypothesis or reject it in favor of some alternative hypothesis.

In this chapter, another hypothesis testing procedure will be presented where the null hypothesis involves several means. Consider an example of a situation where several means are involved in a hypothesis. Suppose National Advertising is a firm which markets new products through television advertising. National Advertising not only produces television commercials but also purchases television time across the nation for the sake of airing its ads. When National Advertising decides to advertise a product, several alternative commercials for that product are produced, each with a somewhat different appeal and format. A market researcher from National Advertising would then test these different commercials on television stations in different cities in order to determine their effectiveness. Suppose that in each case the effectiveness of the commercial could be judged easily since orders would be received by toll-free phone calls only.

In order to determine if the commercials were or were not of equal persuasiveness, the researcher might have tested the following null hypothesis

$$H_o: \mu_1 = \mu_2 = \mu_3 = \mu_4$$

where μ_1 equals the average or mean sales per run of the first commercial, μ_2 equals the mean sales per run of the second commercial, and so on. Then with the test results, the researcher would either accept or reject this null hypothesis. Accepting the hypothesis would imply that the empirical evidence indicates that there is no reason to suppose one commercial is any better than the others. *Analysis of variance* is the name of the statistical testing procedure by which such cases can be resolved.

In summary, analysis of variance is a hypothesis testing procedure which tests whether the means of several populations are the same.

9.2

THE THEORY OF ANOVA

In order to understand how the analysis of variance works, an example will be introduced which will be carried throughout the chapter. In 1896 Skookum Jim and Tagish Charlie struck gold on Bonanza Creek, one of the tributaries of the Klondike River which in turn flows into the Yukon. At about the same time, the Torres Mining Company set up operations in Dawson and hired Skookum and Tagish to oversee the placer mining business. In his spare time, Skookum was reading Frederick W. Taylor, the father of scientific management. Through Skook's interest in these matters, Torres Mining became obsessed with finding the most productive way to extract gold from the sand, mud, and gravel fields of the Yukon. Three pieces of placer mining equipment were used in those days; they were the (1) pan, (2) rocker, and (3) sluice box. Torres Mining wanted to determine if the three methods of placer mining were equally effective. To this purpose, Torres Mining established the null hypothesis

$$H_o: \mu_1 = \mu_2 = \mu_3$$

where μ_1 equals the average or mean amount of gold a miner recovers in a day using a pan, μ_2 equals the mean amount of gold a miner recovers in a day using a rocker, and μ_3 equals the mean amount of gold recovered in a day when a miner uses a sluice box. Accepting or rejecting this null hypothesis would obviously have implications for how Torres Mining would go about mining and hence would have cost and revenue consequences.

In order to test the null hypothesis, Torres Mining gathered 12 miners and randomly assigned 4 miners to each type of equipment. In other words, each of 4 miners got a pan, each of 4 miners got a rocker, and each of 4 miners got a sluice box. It is important to note that miners were randomly assigned to the type of equipment. Next, 12 plots along Bonanza Creek were marked off and the miners with their equipment were randomly assigned to the plots. This way each miner would have an equal chance of being stationed on a plot which was especially rich in gold.

Having made all the random assignments, Torres Mining put the 12 miners to work. Table 9.1 gives the results of this experiment. Notice that the first miner who used a pan ended the day with 25 ounces of gold, the second got 31 ounces, the third got 25, and the fourth miner using a pan got 27 ounces of gold. The average or mean for these four miners was 27 ounces. The four miners who used a rocker got 29, 32, 30, and 25 ounces, respectively, for an average of 29 ounces per miner. Finally, the four miners using sluice boxes averaged 34 ounces.

TABLE 9.1_____

Comparison of Placer Mining Methods

	Pan	*Rocker*	*Sluice Box*
Miner 1	25 ounces	29 ounces	33 ounces
2	31	32	32
3	25	30	33
4	27	25	38
MEAN	27	29	34

Do these experimental results run contrary to the claim of the null hypothesis? (Remember that the null hypothesis says in essence that each of the three methods of placer mining is equally effective.) On the basis of a quick reaction, one might conclude that the sluice box is the best method, and hence all the methods are not equal. But we should not be too hasty in coming to such a conclusion. What if, by pure chance, the sluice boxes happened to get assigned to miners who were more energetic and furthermore that these miners ended up on better plots. This could happen and would give the illusion that the sluice box is the best, when in fact it might not be any better than the others. You might respond by saying that it is not very likely that the energetic miners would happen to get randomly assigned to the sluice boxes and then in turn get randomly assigned to the better plots. This is a good point; nevertheless, chance could still in some measure affect the results so that one method looks better than another when they are really equal in effectiveness. It is necessary to precisely determine what pure chance can do in making one method of mining look better than another. Then it will be possible to say something substantive about whether there is a real difference between the methods of mining.

Let us now carefully rethink why a person might conclude that the three methods of placer mining are not equal in view of the experimental data of Table 9.1. It is because the three means, 27, 29, and 34, seem to differ quite a bit. Someone who contends that the methods are equal might maintain that the variability or differences between these means is really not that great if the variability within each particular method is considered. In other words, if those miners using the rocker only can differ from 25 to 32 ounces, what is so unusual about the variability from 27 to 34 in the case of the means from method to method? This is a good rebuttal; however, its force is diminished somewhat by the fact that means do not vary as much as individual values and so variation from 27 to 34 among the means may be relatively great in comparison to the variation from 25 to 32 within one of the methods. It is the essence of the analysis of variance to compare these two kinds of variabilities in order to accept or reject the null hypothesis. Briefly, if there is a lot of variability or difference among the means (from method to method) relative to the variability within the methods, then the null hypothesis should be rejected. Two special examples will demonstrate this.

Suppose that Torres Mining was interested in comparing the effectiveness of pans whose undersides were painted different colors. To run a test, four miners used blue pans, four miners used purple pans, and four miners used green pans. It should be obvious that in reality there is no difference between the effectiveness of these three types of pans. But still, due to chance, the purple pans might prove to be better in a test. Table 9.2 shows what happened in this experiment or test. Notice that there were some differences in the means from pan to pan; the mean of the blue pans was 28.25 ounces, the mean of the purple pans was 28.75 ounces, and the mean of the green pans was 28.50. These means don't vary much. However, there was considerable variation within each differently colored pan, that is, the blue pans for example varied from 29 to 26 to 30 to 28 ounces. Suppose we summarize this as follows. There was relatively little variation *between* different

TABLE 9.2

Comparison of Different Colored Pans

	Blue Pan	*Purple Pan*	*Green Pan*
Miner 1	29 ounces	30 ounces	25 ounces
2	26	27	30
3	30	28	28
4	28	30	31
MEAN	28.25	28.75	28.50

colors of pans (witness 28.25, 28.75, and 28.50), and there was considerable variation *within* each of the three columns or colors (witness 29, 26, 30, and 28 within the blue column). Now form the ratio F as follows:

$$F = \frac{\text{Variation } Between \text{ Columns or Colors}}{\text{Variation } Within \text{ Columns or Colors}}$$

In the case of Table 9.2 where the null hypothesis ($\mu_b = \mu_p = \mu_g$) is obviously true, the F ratio will be

$$F = \frac{\text{Little Variation } Between \text{ Columns or Colors}}{\text{Considerable Variation } Within \text{ Columns or Colors}}$$

When a little number is divided by a considerable number, the result is a value for F which is small (less than 1). We might then conclude that when the null hypothesis is true there will be a tendency to get a small F value.

Now consider the other extreme. Some Eskimos paddled up to the Torres Mining camp and claimed that they could pan more gold than any miner by using their cupped hands as a pan. Also at the same time a hoard of cowpeople came wandering by and dogmatically claimed that by bowing their legs and thereby cupping their feet, they could out-pan both cupped hands and the ordinary pan. Torres was of a mind to put the whole matter to a test. The null hypothesis as always was that these three methods (cupped foot, cupped hand, pan) were of equal effectiveness, that is,

$$H_o: \mu_{cf} = \mu_{ch} = \mu_p$$

Torres then assigned four miners to each method. The results of this experiment are recorded in Table 9.3.

Even before looking at Table 9.3, it should be apparent to everyone who operates with a thawed brain that the null hypothesis

TABLE 9.3 _____

Comparison of Drastically Different Placer Mining Methods

	Cupped Feet	_Cupped Hands_	_Pan_
Miner 1	2 ounces	0 ounces	30 ounces
2	0	2	28
3	0	4	24
4	1	2	28
MEAN	.75	2.00	27.50

is false. There is no way that these three methods of mining can be equally effective (except in the special case where there is no gold). This shows up in Table 9.3 where the cupped feet average .75 ounces per miner, the cupped hands average 2.00 ounces, and the mean of the ordinary pan is 27.5 ounces. In this situation there is very great variation between columns or methods, and there is only considerable variation within each of the columns or methods (witness 0, 2, 4, and 2 within the cupped hands column). The F ratio in this case will be

$$F = \frac{\text{Variation } Between \text{ Columns}}{\text{Variation } Within \text{ Columns}}$$

$$= \frac{\text{Very Great Variation } Between \text{ Columns}}{\text{Considerable Variation } Within \text{ Columns}}$$

When a very great number is divided by a considerable number, the result is an F value that is large (much larger than 1).

It may be concluded now that whenever the null hypothesis is false, then the between variation will tend to numerically overshadow the within variation and therefore yield a large F ratio. Large F ratios therefore imply that the null hypothesis is false.

Knowing that small F ratios imply that the null hypothesis is true and large F ratios imply that it is false, it is now necessary to determine how an F value can be precisely computed. It is obviously impractical to use terms like "very great" or "considerable" when speaking of the variability of data. This is especially true when the experimental data is not derived from some extreme case. Thus, the between and within variabilities must be mathematically determined in order to ultimately find the F value.

The technique of computing the F ratio will be carried out in the next section using the experimental data of Table 9.1 where the pan, rocker, and sluice box are compared. In this case it is not yet apparent whether a large or small F ratio will occur. Once the

F ratio is mathematically determined, more will be said concerning how large it must be in order to warrant the rejection of the null hypothesis. This will pave the way for Torres Mining to make a decision with regard to the three mining methods.

9.3

THE MECHANICS OF ANOVA

In this section the technique for computing the *Between* and *Within* variations and the F ratio will be presented. Also, making a decision in regard to the null hypothesis will be considered.

Table 9.4 gives the experimental data for Torres Mining. This is the same data as originally given in Table 9.1; however, some symbols have been introduced which will make possible the writing of certain general formulas that will be needed for computing the two types of variability and hence F.

TABLE 9.4

Experimental Data for Torres Mining

	Pan $j = 1$	Rocker $j = 2$	Sluice Box $j = 3$
Miner $i = 1$	$X_{11} = 25$	$X_{12} = 29$	$X_{13} = 33$
$i = 2$	$X_{21} = 31$	$X_{22} = 32$	$X_{23} = 32$
$i = 3$	$X_{31} = 25$	$X_{32} = 30$	$X_{33} = 33$
$i = 4$	$X_{41} = 27$	$X_{42} = 25$	$X_{43} = 38$
MEAN $\overline{X}_j$:	$\overline{X}_1 = 27$	$\overline{X}_2 = 29$	$\overline{X}_3 = 34$

r = number of rows = 4, c = number of columns = 3, $\overline{\overline{X}}$ = 30

In Table 9.4, X_{ij} refers to the amount of gold that the ith miner using the jth method recovers in a day of work. That is, the subscript i refers to the miner, and the subscript j refers to the method. For example, $X_{13} = 33$ implies that the first miner using the sluice box recovered 33 ounces of gold, and $X_{32} = 30$ implies that the third miner ($i = 3$) who used the rocker ($j = 2$) recovered 30 ounces. $\overline{X}_1$ is the mean amount of gold recovered by the users of the $j = 1$ method which is the pan; in this case $\overline{X}_1 = 27$ ounces. In general, $\overline{X}_j$ is the mean for the jth method or column. $\overline{\overline{X}}$ is called the *grand mean*. The grand mean is the mean of all 12 entries in the table

$$\overline{\overline{X}} = \frac{\Sigma X_{ij}}{n}$$

where n equals the total number of entries. The grand mean may alternately be computed by averaging the three column means; that is,

$$\overline{\overline{X}} = \frac{\Sigma \overline{X}_j}{c} = \frac{27 + 29 + 34}{3} = 30$$

where c is the number of columns. (It is assumed here and in this entire chapter that the number of observations in each column is the same.)

The F value, which is crucial to the decision whether to accept or reject the null hypothesis, is computed by

$$F = \frac{Between \text{ Column Variation}}{Within \text{ Column Variation}}$$

The technical terminology for the *Between* column variation is the *Mean Square variation Between columns*, and that for the *Within* variation is the *Mean Square variation Within columns*. Therefore, F may be written as

$$F = \frac{MSB}{MSW}$$

Next, the mean square in the numerator and the denominator are broken down as

$$F = \frac{SSB/d_1}{SSW/d_2}$$

Here *SSB* refers to the *Sum of Squares Between columns* and *SSW* refers to the *Sum of Squares Within columns*. Also, d_1 and d_2 are the degrees of freedom associated with each of the types of variation. Finally this last expression for F may be written in the computational format

$$F = \frac{r\Sigma(\overline{X}_j - \overline{\overline{X}})^2/(c - 1)}{\Sigma(X_{ij} - \overline{X}_j)^2/(cr - c)}$$

where c is the number of columns and r is the number of rows in a table like Table 9.4.

Before using this last expression for the computation of F, it might be pointed out that MSB and MSW are nothing more than specially adjusted variances which measure the variability between and within columns. The degrees of freedom, d_1 and d_2, in

$$MSB = SSB/d_1$$
$$MSW = SSW/d_2$$

are analogous to the $n - 1$ in the typical formula for the variance which was introduced in Chapter 5:

$$s^2 = \frac{\Sigma(X - \overline{X})^2}{n - 1}$$

Furthermore, the SSB and SSW are logically analogous to the sum of squares, $\Sigma(X - \overline{X})^2$, in the numerator of s^2. Finally, the SSB, d_1, SSW, and d_2 are defined implicitly in the last expression presented for F in the previous paragraph. It is seen, for example, that the degrees of freedom d_1 for the numerator is $c - 1$ and the degrees of freedom for the denominator is $d_2 = cr - c$.

We are now ready to compute F for the Torres Mining case. First, the sum of squares between rows is computed:

$$\begin{aligned}
SSB &= r \Sigma (\overline{X}_j - \overline{\overline{X}})^2 \\
&= 4[(27\text{--}30)^2 + (29\text{--}30)^2 + (34\text{--}30)^2] \\
&= (4)(26) \\
&= 104
\end{aligned}$$

Notice that each column mean is compared to the grand mean with their respective differences being squared and then added or summed. Next, the sum of squares within columns is computed. In this case, each X_{ij} within a column is compared to the mean of the respective column. The differences are squared and summed, and then this continues by moving to the next column:

$$\begin{aligned}
SSW &= \Sigma(X_{ij} - \overline{X}_j)^2 = \Sigma(X_{i1} - \overline{X}_1)^2 + \Sigma(X_{i2} - \overline{X}_2)^2 + \Sigma(X_{i3} - \overline{X}_3)^2 \\
&= (25\text{--}27)^2 + (31\text{--}27)^2 + (25\text{--}27)^2 + (27\text{--}27)^2 \\
&\quad + (29\text{--}29)^2 + (32\text{--}29)^2 + (30\text{--}29)^2 + (25\text{--}29)^2 \\
&\quad\quad + (33\text{--}34)^2 + (32\text{--}34)^2 + (33\text{--}34)^2 + (38\text{--}34)^2 \\
&= 24 + 26 + 22 \\
&= 72
\end{aligned}$$

The primary computational effort has now been accomplished. As is shown in Table 9.5, the degrees of freedom for the numerator are $d_1 = 2$ and for the denominator are $d_2 = 9$. Hence MSB, which

TABLE 9.5

Analysis of Variance Table

Variation	Sum of Squares	Degrees of Freedom	Mean Square
Between	$SSB = 104$	$d_1 = c - 1 = 3 - 1 = 2$	$MSB = SSB/d_1 = 104/2 = 52$
Within	$SSW = 72$	$d_2 = cr - c = (3 \times 4) - 3 = 9$	$MSW = SSW/d_2 = 72/9 = 8$

$$F = \frac{MSB}{MSW} = \frac{52}{8} = 6.5$$

measures the variability between columns or mining methods, is 52, and MSW, which measures the within variation, is 8. Therefore,

$$F = \frac{SSB/d_1}{SSW/d_2} = \frac{104/2}{72/9}$$

$$= \frac{MSB}{MSW} = \frac{52}{8}$$

$$= 6.5$$

Having computed F, it merely remains to determine if this is a large F, in which case H_o should be rejected, or a small F, in which case H_o should be accepted. We then ask, "Is $F = 6.5$ large?" This is something like the question, "Is a 45 pound bandersnatch a big one or a small one?" It is impossible to tell about the size of such a bandersnatch unless we know what the distribution of the weights of bandersnatches looks like. If 95 percent of all bandersnatches weigh less than 35 pounds, then we would say that a 45 pounder is a big one. Likewise, if a judgment about an F or 6.5 is to be made, we first need to know what the distribution of F values is like.

A distribution of F values was computed for the special case where there were $c = 3$ columns (like three mining methods), and where there were $r = 4$ rows (like four miners being assigned to each method). This special distribution is distinguished from other distributions of F, which might be based on a different number of columns and rows, by saying that this distribution has d_1 and d_2 degrees of freedom. The F distribution for $d_1 = 2$ and $d_2 = 9$ degrees of freedom looks something like that of Figure 9.1. It is apparent from this graph that 95 percent of the F values fall below 4.26. Since the F value in the Torres Mining case is 6.5, it is fair to say that it is a large F and hence that the null hypothesis should be rejected. There is a difference between mining methods.

FIGURE 9.1

The Distribution of F when $d_1 = 2$ and $d_2 = 9$

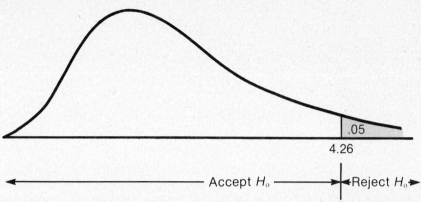

Let us now express the thoughts of the last paragraph in a manner more compatible with the discussion of hypothesis testing as set forth in Chapter 8. After the null hypothesis has been stated, it is customary to establish the level of alpha which is the probability of a Type I error. Remember that alpha is the probability of rejecting the null hypothesis when in fact the null hypothesis is true. After alpha, which is the level of significance that has been established, the rejection region is constructed. If the sample statistic (for example, $\overline{X}$ was one of the statistics used in the last chapter) falls within the rejection region, then the null hypothesis is rejected. Otherwise, it is accepted. In the context of the analysis of variance, F is a sample statistic since it is a ratio of variances derived completely from sample evidence. When the null hypothesis is true (all the means are the same), F will vary because of pure chance. Sometimes F is low and sometimes it is high, even when the null hypothesis is true; that is, when all the three mining methods are of equal efficiency. The F distribution of Figure 9.1 gives all the values for F with their respective probabilities for the case when the null hypothesis is true. It is seen here that F will take on a value in excess of 4.26 about 5 percent of the time when the null hypothesis is true. If the rejection region consists of all F values above 4.26, this implies that there is a .05 probability of making a Type I error. Hence, alpha equals .05 in such a case.

As the experiment is being set up in the case of the analysis of variance, an alpha or level of significance is to be chosen. This serves to establish the rejection region for the ensuing test. If Torres had selected a .05 significance level beforehand, the rejection region of Figure 9.1 would have been established before the F was computed from the experimental evidence. Then, when the F of 6.5 was computed, Torres would immediately know that the null hypothesis should be rejected since 6.5 exceeds the critical value of F which is

$$F_{\text{crit}} = 4.26$$

Critical values of F (the value which separates the rejection region from the acceptance region) for experiments where there are different numbers of rows and columns may be found from Appendix F in the back of the text. First d_1 and d_2 are determined. Then the level of significance is chosen; only two levels of significance may be used with Appendix F, namely, $\alpha = .05$ or $\alpha = .01$. Then the critical value of F is read from the table. The light faced type gives the critical value for a .05 test and the dark faced type gives the critical F for a .01 test. To illustrate, suppose Elephant Brand Fertilizer Corporation is testing four types of fertilizers. Each fertilizer is tested on three different plots of soil. The null hypothesis is that the average yield for the crop for each of the fertilizers is the same; that is,

$$H_o: \mu_1 = \mu_2 = \mu_3 = \mu_4$$

Furthermore, Elephant Brand wants to test this hypothesis at the .01 significance level. In this circumstance, what is the critical value of F?

In the fertilizer test, there will be $c = 4$ columns (one for each type of fertilizer) and $r = 3$ rows (3 plots tested per type of fertilizer). This implies that F will have $d_1 = c - 1 = 3$ and $d_2 = cr - c = 8$ degrees of freedom. With an alpha of .01 the critical value for F is $F_{\text{crit}} = 7.59$. Therefore, if the F computed from the experimental data exceeds 7.59, Elephant Brand should reject the null hypothesis, thereby concluding that there is a difference between the fertilizers.

9.4

THE ASSUMPTIONS OF ANOVA

In presenting the theory and mechanics of the analysis of variance, not much was said concerning the assumptions of such a procedure. There are three conditions which should be met before ANOVA is applied.

Random Assignments

In the course of the discussion of Torres Mining it was noted that the 12 miners were randomly assigned to the various methods of placer mining, and then the miners with their respective pieces of equipment were randomly assigned to plots along the creek. In all applications of the analysis of variance, there must be a similar random assignment procedure; this keeps the influence of the designer of the experiment out of the experiment, thereby allowing chance alone to operate.

Homoscedasticity

According to the *homoscedasticity* condition, the variability of the data within any column must be roughly the same as the variability of the data within any other column. Look back at Table 9.1 for a moment and notice that the values in the first column (25, 31, 25, 27) are about as variable as the values in any other column. An example where the homoscedasticity requirement would not be met would be where one column contained the values 56, 57, 56, and 55, and another column contained the values 56, 79, 44, and 48.

Normality

The last condition is that the values in each column must be approximately normally distributed. It is typically difficult to verify this requirement in a particular case because there are usually just a few values in each column. If a column contained 8, 9, 11, and 9, for example, there would be no reason to hesitate. However, if a column contained 18, 19, 12, 21, 10, and 10, then it would appear that this requirement might not be satisfied. Further investigation into the matter would be necessary.

The importance of these assumptions and methods for statistically determining whether they are satisfied are treated in more advanced texts.

9.5

EXTENSIONS

This chapter has dealt with *one-way analysis of variance*. Only one type of factor has been considered in the tests. In the Torres Mining illustration the factor was the type of mining equipment; in the Elephant Brand case the factor was type of fertilizer. In the Torres case it should be apparent that other factors might play an important role in determining the relative merits of the pan, rocker, and sluice box. The consistency of the mud and sand might affect the efficiency of the methods. In the experiment as presented, no attempt was made to measure the efficiency of the different methods relative to the consistency of the mud in the creek bottom. Other factors that also might be important in judging the methods are the size of the miners, the weather conditions, the age of the miners, and the like.

Analysis of variance can be extended so that it will take into account more than one factor. The Pocahontas Apple Company of Virginia is seeking to find the optimal way to store red delicious apples. Chief Executive Powhatan, the father of Pocahontas, has designed an experimental storage warehouse which contains 12 compartments or rooms. The temperature and humidity of each room can be regulated as desired. Table 9.6 presents a bird's-eye view of the storage warehouse. Pocahontas has loaded each room with apples and sets the temperature and humidity as indicated. For example, the room in the northwest corner of the warehouse will have a temperature of 2° Celsius and a relative humidity of 10 percent. After six months, each room is checked to see how many rotten apples occur. With this data, Pocahontas can determine if temperature makes a difference and if humidity makes a difference in the storage of apples.

By suitably designing a two-way experiment, information concerning the interaction of the two variables can also be gained. In the Pocahontas case, it might be that a certain combination of temperature and humidity is extremely good for the sake of preserving apples. Interactions between factors often do occur; when they do, it is helpful to know of it. For example, Drug A may stop your coughing and Drug B may reduce nausea, but if you take A and B simultaneously what will happen? Maybe you will stop

TABLE 9.6

Floor Plan for Storage Warehouse

	temperature			
	2°	4°	8°	16°
humidity 10%				
20%				
40%				

$$H_o: \mu_2 = \mu_4 = \mu_8 = \mu_{16}$$
$$H_o: \mu_{10\%} = \mu_{20\%} = \mu_{40\%}$$

coughing and be less nauseated; however, there is also the possibility that you will stop coughing, be less nauseated, and also experience a drop in blood pressure, loss of breath, sweaty feet, internal bleeding, and a few other such reactions. In such a case these two drugs have interacted within your body to produce a sum of effects greater than their separate effects combined. So it might be that a certain combination of humidity and temperature may interact to produce unusual effects. In many other sorts of applications the manager may be interested in possible interactions that produce unusual results. For example, in selecting advertising media for different products it might be discovered that a certain medium like television is especially effective in advertising a particular type of product like toys. The advertising manager can optimize the results obtained by allocating the advertising budget accordingly.

PROBLEMS

9.1

When the null hypothesis in the analysis of variance is in fact true, the ratio of the between variation to the within variation will approach what value?

9.2

Name and discuss the various assumptions which underlie the analysis of variance.

9.3

In an analysis of variance problem the following have been computed:

$$SSB = 220$$
$$SSW = 40$$
$$d_1 = 4$$
$$d_2 = 10$$

At the $\alpha = .05$ significance level, should the null hypothesis be accepted or rejected? What does this imply about the means of the populations being tested?

9.4

In an ANOVA test the following have been determined:

$r = 6$

$c = 4$

$\Sigma(\overline{X}_j - \overline{\overline{X}})^2 = 52$

$\Sigma(X_{ij} - \overline{X}_j)^2 = 80$

At the $\alpha = .01$ significance level, should the null hypothesis be accepted or rejected? What does this imply about the means of the four populations that are being tested?

9.5

In an ANOVA test with $d_1 = 5$ and $d_2 = 9$ degrees of freedom and where $MSW = 100$, what must MSB equal in order to reject the null hypothesis if the test is to be carried out at the .05 significance level?

9.6

The lives of three different top-of-the-line radial tires are being tested to see if they differ. Five tires of each brand have been tested with the following results (all figures are in thousands of miles):

Aircloud	Maliroll	Duostreak
46	42	47
41	49	51
40	43	44
44	45	48
44	41	40

State the null hypothesis and then test it at the $\alpha = .01$ significance level. Are the tires different?

9.7

At the Virginia Commonwealth University-Medical College of Virginia three types of post-operative therapy for heart surgery patients are being tested. Three patients have been randomly assigned to each of the three methods and the amount of time until certain physiological functions returned to normalcy was recorded. The results are given in the table on the top of page 277 where the times are recorded in hours.

Type of Therapy

Draper	*Fantl*	*Dunn*
48	100	56
61	60	92
71	80	62

State the null hypothesis and then test it at the $\alpha = .05$ significance level. Are the types of therapy different in regard to their effectiveness?

9.8

The Australian Health Spas of America must decide which diet plan to institute in their weight losing program. The first is the "coffee and peanuts" diet; the second is the "locusts and beans" diet. Ten women, all of which are about the same size, have been selected to participate in the test. The five who were assigned to the coffee and peanuts diet lost 18, 12, 21, 14, and 15 pounds, respectively. The five subjected to the locusts and beans lost 31, 28, 19, 23, and 19 pounds. At the .05 significance level, can it be concluded that the diets differ in their effectiveness?

9.9

The Coconino Corporation is testing four types of automatic machinery to see if they differ in the number of defective extrusions they produce. Each machine is tested for three days. The number of defective extrusions produced each day by each machine is recorded in the table below.

Machine

A	*B*	*C*	*D*
6	11	8	7
5	9	8	8
7	10	8	9

At the .05 significance level, can it be concluded that the machines differ with respect to the average number of defective extrusions produced?

9.10

Rolamotor makes three types of special guidance systems for planes which are fertilizing forests for the sake of increased lumber production. With the guidance system, the plane is able to fly over a large parcel of forest without skipping certain areas or applying fertilizer twice on other spots as the plane flies back and forth over the forest. Rolamotor wants to determine if the three different systems are equally effective and therefore wishes to field test them. The Quaritone System is tested six times by different pilots flying in the Cascade mountains of the Northwest. The Peeker System is tested by six pilots flying over the forests of southern Alabama. The Donovaloff System is tested by six pilots who fly in the mountains of Arizona. The test data resulting from these three sets of six flights are given below where a low number indicates good results.

Quaritone System	Peeker System	Donovaloff System
426	390	248
918	456	641
741	389	720
561	296	304
549	340	902
888	381	285

Consider the data and description of the problem in light of the assumptions which must be satisfied if the analysis of variance is to be applied. Can ANOVA be used in this problem? Be thorough in stating why or why not.

CHAPTER 10

REGRESSION AND CORRELATION ANALYSIS

10.1

INTRODUCTION

When we think of learning, we often picture a person learning some fact. For example, we might think of the child who has just learned that in 1492 Columbus sailed the ocean blue. Learning at a higher level, however, involves more than memorizing bare facts. Learning at a higher level involves understanding relationships between various phenomena. The same child has learned that the closer the hand comes to a pot of boiling water, the hotter the hand feels. This child has learned that there is a certain relationship between the variable d, which is the distance from the pot to the hand, and the variable h, which is how hot the hand feels. Though the child would not express the relationship as such, this relationship is an inverse relationship. That is, the smaller the value of d, the greater the corresponding value of h.

All of us operate on the basis of relationships between variables. We know that taking a certain medicine is related to our recovery from a certain disease. The way we treat certain people is related to how they treat us. The amount of job training a person gets is related to that person's performance on the job. The frequency with which we take baths is related to the aroma which pervades the atmosphere about us. The amount of time we study is related to the kinds of grades we get. Our age seems to be related to how fast we can run. The speed at which we drive is related to the time it takes to get to our destination. The profitability of a company is related to its stock market performance. Such a list could go on and on.

Having established that relationships do exist between pairs of variables, it might be useful in certain cases to be able to explicitly define the nature of the relationship. In regression and correlation analysis, relationships between variables are mathematically expressed and measured. A large corporation does not need to be told that advertising is related to sales — this relationship is obvious. However, the company might wish to know the explicit nature of the relationship. If $1 million more is spent on advertising for a particular product, how much will sales increase? Through regression and correlation analysis, questions like this one can be answered.

The main thrust of this chapter will be to examine the relationship between two variables. Two different facets of this examination may be identified. Through *regression analysis*, the actual mathematical relationship between two variables is determined. By means of *correlation analysis*, the strength of the relationship between the two variables is measured. Though this chapter will deal primarily with regression and correlation analysis as it pertains to two variables, models involving more than two variables will be briefly considered at the end of the chapter.

10.2
SCATTER DIAGRAMS

It was not too long ago that the Bitoff Soors Brewing Company of Colorado entered the regional resort business. It all started when Soors refused to give local breweries in eastern United States permission to brew and sell beer under the Soors label. The eastern breweries contended that the water in the East was as good as the Rocky Mountain spring water for which Soors was noted. (As an aside, it takes only a brief visit to the Cuyahoga River in Cleveland or the Passaic in Northern Jersey to be convinced that the two eastern breweries located on these rivers were justified in their claim.) Indignant beer drinkers in the East began to write Soors in great numbers demanding that Soors sell in the East. Since Soors could not get enough Rocky Mountain spring water for the sake of brewing enough beer for the vast eastern market, the company began looking for other water sources in an effort to make its beer available nationwide.

It was at this time that Soors bought the Okefenokee Swamp in southern Georgia. The intention was to drill for beer in this great primitive swamp. Unfortunately, the drills never struck beer and Soors was left with nothing but a vast swamp. Unbeknown to Soors, however, this purchase set the stage for a chain of events which led to the development of a great regional resort in southern Georgia.

Soors at this time learned that Great Britain, being continually plagued with economic problems, was ready to sell off just about anything it owned in order to ease its balance of payment problems. To make a long story short, Soors ended up buying a famous lake (loch) in Britain. Soors bought the entire Loch Ness. All the water of the loch was drained and shipped by tanker to their new brewery located in the midst of the Okefenokee Swamp. Bitoff Soors claimed that this water alone could be substituted for Rocky Mountain spring water in the brewing of beer. Of course, in purchasing Loch Ness, the monster came along in the water. Thus, Soors relocated the monster in the Okefenokee Swamp. Obviously people wanted to see the Loch Ness monster, and so Soors developed a swamp resort which turned out to be something like a mixture of Walt Disney World, the Everglades, and the wineries of California.

What proved to be a real problem was that the monster, who was free to haunt the entire swamp, was subject to periods of severe depression. Because of concern for the monster's well-being, Soors wanted to keep the number of visitors to a minimum when the monster was depressed. Soors achieved the control of the number of daily visitors by means of regression analysis. Let us see how this was done.

The people who visit the Soors resort are usually travelers on their way to or from Florida. These people usually travel on I95. As they settle down in their motel rooms at night, they flip on the local television shows. During these programs Soors advertises the swamp resort. As the number of television ads run in a night is increased, more people see the ads, and hence more people spend the next day at the swamp instead of immediately continuing their trips. To repeat, if Soors aired no ads, no one would be reminded that the monster was close by and very few people would show up the next day. On the other hand, a large number of television ads the night before would precipitate a large number of visitors the next day.

Soors began experimenting with the relationship between the number of television ads the night before and the number of visitors the next day. For example, one night Soors ran no ads and found that there were 55 visitors the next day. One night they ran 10 television ads and found that there were 86 visitors the next day. On another occasion they ran 30 ads with the result that 158 visitors showed up the next day. Soors ran 20 tests in this manner such that in five cases no ads were run the night before, in five cases 10 ads were run, in five cases 20 ads were run, and in five cases 30 television ads were run the night before. Table 10.1 presents these 20 cases where the number of television ads are paired with the number of Okefenokee admissions the following day.

TABLE 10.1_____

Experimental Data Linking Admissions Y to Advertising X for Soors' Swamp Resort

Television Ads X	Visitors Y
0	55
0	82
0	68
0	70
0	66
10	86
10	108
10	116
10	100
10	110
20	127
20	132
20	149
20	140
20	135
30	158
30	152
30	177
30	170
30	165

A quick look at the data of Table 10.1 indicates that there seems to be a positive relationship between advertising and admissions. As the number of advertisements increases, the number of visitors to the swamp also increases. However, knowing the number of advertisements does not enable the analyst to perfectly predict the number of admissions. For example, in the five cases when 10 ads were run, the admissions the following day were 86, 108, 116, 100, and 110. Though imperfect, a relationship, nevertheless, does exist between advertising and admissions.

It is often desirable to graphically portray the relationship between a couple of variables. Such a portrayal permits visual insights into the nature of the relationship. To begin, let X represent the number of television ads that are run and let Y represent the number of admissions or visitors the day following. Since advertising influences admissions, the advertising variable is denoted by X which is called the *independent variable*. Since admissions is dependent on advertising, the admissions variable is denoted by Y

and is called the *dependent variable*. (The general relationship between an independent and a dependent variable will be more fully considered in Section 10.7.) In graphing the data, a pair of axes are constructed with the independent variable represented on the horizontal axis and the dependent variable represented on the vertical axis. Figure 10.1 gives these axes.

Having constructed the coordinate system, it is next necessary to plot each of the 20 points which constitute the observations in the study of the relationship between advertising and admissions. For example, on one occasion there were $X = 0$ ads and then $Y = 55$ admissions or visitors followed. A point is plotted in Figure 10.1 corresponding to this observation or pair of X and Y values. Each observation is similarly plotted yielding the set of 20 points or dots

FIGURE 10.1

Experimental Data Linking Admissions Y to Advertising X for Soors' Swamp Resort

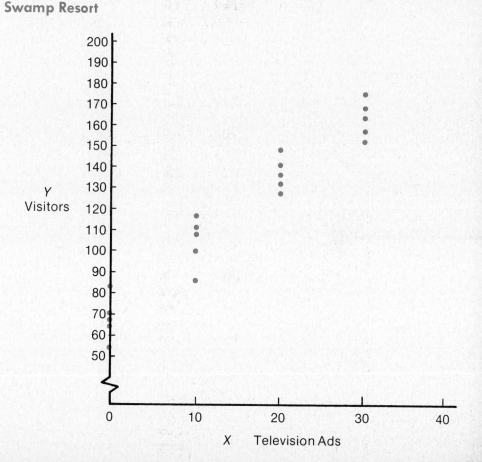

as shown in Figure 10.1. This set of points which graphically portrays the observations is called a *scatter diagram*. A glance at the
scatter diagram of Figure 10.1 confirms the earlier conclusion that
admissions increase as advertising increases.

The Soors case will be continued after we take a look at some
other scatter diagrams. Sue DeChimony, the manager in charge of
Meo Farms, is seeking to find the relationship between fertilizer
and yield. In growing corn, DeChimony has marked off 30 different
test plots of land and has applied differing amounts of fertilizer to
these plots. At harvest time, the yield for each of the 30 plots was
carefully measured. Letting X equal the amount of fertilizer applied per plot and Y equal the yield in bushels per plot, DeChimony
constructed the scatter diagram of Figure 10.2.

A worthwhile contrast to note between the scatter diagrams of
Figures 10.1 and 10.2 deals with the shape of the collection of data
points as X increases. In Figure 10.1 an analyst could draw a
straight line through the heart of the data as is done later in Figure 10.6. However, the data in the Meo Farms case follows a curvilinear line; such a line has been supplied to the scatter diagram.
The analyst must always be aware of the possibility that the data
is *curvilinear*. The data is curvilinear in Figure 10.2 because after
quite a bit of fertilizer has been administered to a plot, the application of even more fertilizer is really not needed by the corn, and

FIGURE 10.2_____

Scatter Diagram for Meo Farms (Curvilinear Relationship)

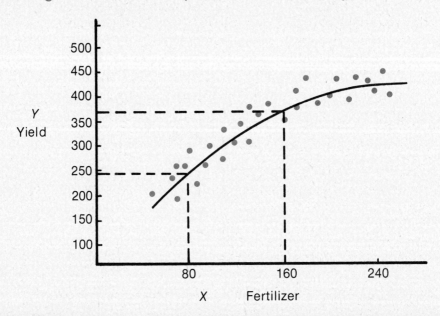

thus the yield is not materially increased. In fact, if too much fertilizer is applied, like knee-deep, it will kill the corn and result in a yield of 0 bushels per plot.

Kib Manufacturing has had a bit of trouble with high turnover in its manufacturing plants. Carol Mohr, who is the plant shrink, has devised a test which she thinks will help predict employee turnover. A number of employees have taken the test and their contentment with their jobs has been measured. Letting X equal the test score and Y equal job contentment, Dr. Mohr has constructed a scatter diagram. Figure 10.3 presents this scatter diagram. Notice that the relationship follows a straight line; this indicates that the relationship is *linear*. However, the higher the test score, the lower the job contentment. The relationship between X and Y is therefore *inverse* rather than *direct*, as is the case in Figure 10.1.

FIGURE 10.3
Scatter Diagram for Kib Manufacturing (Inverse Linear Relationship)

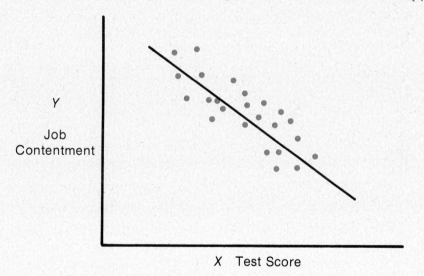

A hospital has done a study relating the age of the admitted patient to the size of the hospital bill incurred. With age as the independent variable and hospital expenditure as the dependent variable, the scatter diagram of Figure 10.4 has been constructed. Notice that the relationship between X and Y is both linear and direct. It should also be noted that since most patients are old or very young at this hospital, most of the data points correspond to low and high values of X.

FIGURE 10.4_____

Scatter Diagram for a Hospital (Direct Linear Relationship)

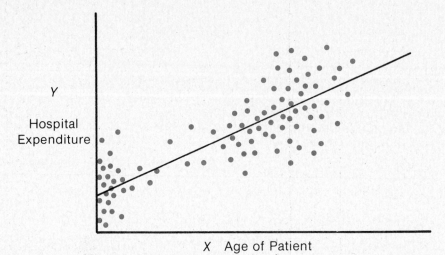

Several scatter diagrams have been discussed for the sake of showing how they visually depict the relationship between two variables. Several general comments have been made in describing a scatter diagram. For example, sometimes the relationship between the variables tends to be *linear* as in the Soors case of Figure 10.1, and sometimes *curvilinear* as in the Meo Farms case of Figure 10.2. Sometimes the relationship is *direct* as in Figures 10.1, 10.2, and 10.4, in which cases the greater values for the dependent variable are associated with the larger values of the independent variable, and sometimes the relationship is *inverse* as in Figure 10.3. Finally, sometimes the independent variable is *controlled* or fixed and sometimes it is not. For example, in the Soors case of Figure 10.1, the experiment was deliberately controlled such that on five evenings 0 ads were run, on five evenings 10 ads were run, on five evenings 20 ads were run, and on five evenings 30 ads were run. Soors determined the X values ahead of time in these cases. On the other hand, in the hospital case, as shown in Figure 10.4, a number of patients were randomly selected with no attempt to select only people, for example, of age $X = 10$ years, $X = 20$ years, $X = 30$ years, and so forth. In other words, the levels of the independent variable in this case were not preselected, and thus it is said that the independent variable was *uncontrolled*.

Having generally described the scatter diagram, it is now time to study the actual mathematical relationship which may exist between a pair of variables.

10.3

REGRESSION LINE

In the last section a visual portrayal of the relationship between a pair of variables was accomplished by means of the scatter diagram. The scatter diagram in the Soors case (see Figure 10.1) indicates that as the number of ads is increased, the number of visitors will increase. Furthermore, this relationship appears to be linear, which means that the data points seem to cluster about an imagined straight line. An imagined line of one sort or another was drawn in Figures 10.2, 10.3, and 10.4 in order to give the viewer some kind of a feel for the pattern of the data points; such a line was not drawn in Figure 10.1. In this section we wish to consider what this imagined line represents and we will also seek to mathematically determine it.

The lines supplied in Figures 10.2, 10.3, and 10.4 are called *regression lines*. The regression line passes through the set of data points in the scatter diagram in a manner which sets forth the nature of the relationship between the two corresponding variables. For example, in the Meo Farms example of Figure 10.2, it is seen that if about 80 pounds of fertilizer is applied to a plot, the yield will be about 245 bushels. Of course there is still variation among plots with about 80 pounds of fertilizer, for it is also seen from the scatter diagram that some of these plots yielded as high as 290 and some as low as 200 bushels. Nevertheless, the average yield for plots with about 80 pounds of fertilizer is close to 245 bushels of corn. When 160 pounds of fertilizer is applied, the average yield appears to be somewhere in the neighborhood of 375 bushels per plot. Notice that the regression line passes through the 245 bushel level when $X = 80$ pounds and through the 375 bushel level when $X = 160$ pounds. From this you may correctly conclude that the regression line passes through the average yield which corresponds to each value of the independent variable X. Such is the case with all regression lines. The regression line indicates the average value for Y corresponding to each of the values of X along the horizontal axis. Therefore, it is said that the regression line shows the underlying relationship between the dependent and independent variables.

In this text we will mathematically deal only with linear relationships between two variables; curvilinear situations, as illustrated by Figure 10.2, are left to more advanced texts. In the Soors case of Figure 10.1, it is visually obvious that the relationship between X and Y is linear. We now want to determine exactly where the regression line lies in this scatter diagram.

In elementary algebra it is shown that the general form for the equation of a straight line is

$$Y = a + bX$$

where a is the intercept on the vertical or Y axis and b is the slope. For example, the equation $Y = 1 + .5X$ is that of a straight line which crosses the Y axis at a height of 1 and has an upward slope such that for every unit to the right the line rises by .5 units. (See Figure 10.5.) Every straight line that can be drawn on a scatter diagram has a unique equation, and vice versa. Therefore, the regression line, wherever it may be in Figure 10.1, must have an equation.

FIGURE 10.5
Graph of $Y = 1 + .5X$ (Intercept is 1 and Slope is .5)

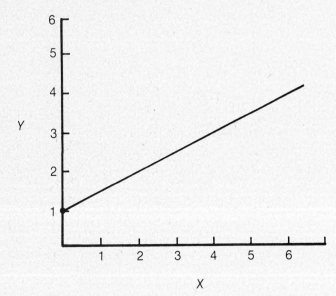

A mathematical method called the *method of least squares* has been devised to determine the equation of the regression line. Once the equation of the regression line is determined, it may then be plotted on the coordinate system of the scatter diagram. The general equation of the regression line is

$$Y_c = a + bX$$

where Y_c refers merely to the computed regression line value of Y and a and b are constants which are determined by

$$b = \frac{\Sigma XY - n\overline{X}\,\overline{Y}}{\Sigma X^2 - n\overline{X}^2}$$

$$a = \overline{Y} - b\overline{X}$$

The determination of the regression line will now be illustrated.

Initially, the regression equation for the Soors case of Figure 10.1 and Table 10.1 will be determined; afterwards, its meaning and uses will be explained. In order to compute the values for b and a in the regression equation, the values of ΣXY, $\overline{X}$, $\overline{Y}$, ΣX^2, and n must first be found. Table 10.2 gives the original 20 data points or observations; these are the same as in Table 10.1. As is typically the case, n represents the number of observations in a sample, and therefore n equals 20 in the Soors case. The first of these 20 observations is $X = 0$, $Y = 55$ and the last is (30, 165). By

TABLE 10.2

Preliminary Calculations for Regression and Correlation Analysis

X	Y	XY	X^2	Y^2
0	55	0	0	3,025
0	82	0	0	6,724
0	68	0	0	4,624
0	70	0	0	4,900
0	66	0	0	4,356
10	86	860	100	7,396
10	108	1080	100	11,664
10	116	1160	100	13,456
10	100	1000	100	10,000
10	110	1100	100	12,100
20	127	2540	400	16,129
20	132	2640	400	17,424
20	149	2980	400	22,201
20	140	2800	400	19,600
20	135	2700	400	18,225
30	158	4740	900	24,964
30	152	4560	900	23,104
30	177	5310	900	31,329
30	170	5100	900	28,900
30	165	4950	900	27,225
300	2366	43520	7000	307,346
ΣX	ΣY	ΣXY	ΣX^2	ΣY^2

$$\overline{X} = 15 \quad \overline{Y} = 118.3$$

summing up all the X values of these observations as recorded in the first column of Table 10.2, the quantity ΣX is found, which is 300. Dividing ΣX by the number of observations, which is $n = 20$, yields the mean value of X, namely, $\overline{X} = 300/20 = 15$ ads. Similarly, $\overline{Y}$ is found to be 2366/20 or 118.3 visitors. The third column in Table 10.2 is labelled XY and is composed of all the products of X and Y for each observation. Summing all the values in this column yields ΣXY or 43,520. In like manner, the X^2 column and Y^2 column are constructed based on the corresponding values of X and Y from the first two columns of the table. With the completion of Table 10.2, it is easy to compute the values of b and a in the regression equation:

$$b = \frac{\Sigma XY - n\overline{X}\,\overline{Y}}{\Sigma X^2 - n\overline{X}^2}$$

$$= \frac{43{,}520 - (20)(15)(118.3)}{7{,}000 - (20)(15^2)}$$

$$= 3.212$$

$$a = \overline{Y} - b\overline{X}$$

$$= 118.3 - (3.212)(15)$$

$$= 70.12$$

This means that the regression equation for Soors is

$$Y_c = 70.12 + 3.212X$$

The regression equation is now graphed in Figure 10.6 along with the original data points. Notice that the Y intercept is $a = 70.12$, which means that the regression line crosses the vertical axis at this point. Also, the intercept of 70.12 means that Soors will have an average of 70.12 visitors per day if there is no advertising. The slope of $b = 3.212$ means that for every additional advertisement that is run, the number of admissions increases by 3.212 people. Finally, we recall the meaning of the regression line. The value Y_c gives the average number of visitors that can be expected corresponding to any value of X. For example, if Soors runs $X = 10$ ads, then an average of

$$Y_c = 70.12 + (3.212)(10)$$

$$= 102.24$$

people will seek admission to the swamp the next day. This 102.24 serves as a *point estimate* of the number of admissions for the day

FIGURE 10.6

Regression Line for Soors' Swamp Resort

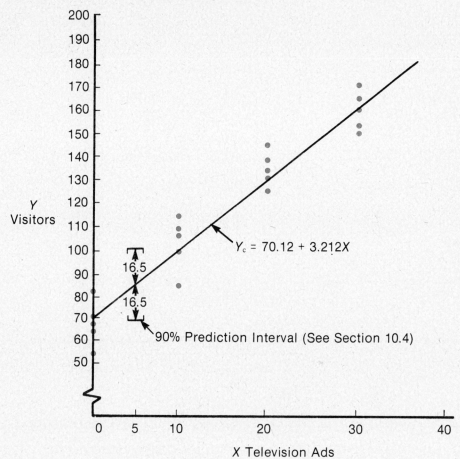

$Y_c = 70.12 + 3.212X$

16.5

16.5

90% Prediction Interval (See Section 10.4)

which follows the airing of 10 ads. If 12 ads are run, an average of 108.7 visitors will show up according to the regression equation.

Soors originally began this experiment which links advertising to admissions in order to be able to control the number of visitors by the careful use of advertising. The regression line enables Soors to accomplish this purpose with ease. For example, if Soors is shooting for admissions of about 150 visitors tomorrow, then the number of television ads for tonight may be found by solving the regression equation as follows:

$$150 = 70.12 + 3.212X$$

$$X = 24.9$$

This means that if $X = 24.9$ (or 25) ads are run, then the expected number of visitors the next day is 150. Remember, however, that the data points usually do not fall on the regression line itself. Therefore, the actual number of visitors will undoubtedly be different from 150. In the section to follow, the variability in the number of visitors when the number of ads is fixed will be studied.

One of the dangers in the kind of analysis that has been presented is in placing undue confidence in a regression equation which is based on a fairly limited number of observations. In the Soors case, there were a total of $n = 20$ observations which linked admissions to advertising. The regression line based on these 20 observations has the equation $Y_c = 70.12 + 3.212X$ which has been graphed in Figure 10.6. But what if another 20 trials had been run where on five nights 0 ads were run, on five nights 10 ads were run, et cetera? Would the resulting Y values be identical to the ones shown in Table 10.1? We would be very surprised if they were the same. Therefore, the scatter diagram would look somewhat different, and this in turn would yield a regression line that would be somewhat different. For example, maybe the regression line would be $Y_c = 72.4 + 2.98X$. This naturally leads us to wonder which, if either, of these two regression equations is the true regression line. It is quite probable that neither $Y_c = 70.12 + 3.212X$ nor $Y_c = 72.4 + 2.98X$ is the true regression line, which with perfect accuracy shows the relationship between Y and X. The regression equation $Y_c = 70.12 + 3.212X$, which is based on a sample of 20 observations, is only an *estimate* of the true regression equation. If the true regression equation is expressed as

$$Y_c = \alpha + \beta X$$

then the a of 70.12 is only an estimate of α and the b of 3.212 is only an estimate of β. Since the true values of α and β are not known, and since a and b are based on a sample of only 20 observations, the analyst should not put undue confidence in $Y_c = 70.12 + 3.212X$ or the point estimates which flow from it. This matter will be further explored in Section 10.6.

10.4

PREDICTION INTERVALS

It has been seen that the data points in a scatter diagram do not usually fall directly on the regression line but are rather dispersed about it. Throughout this text, the standard deviation or variance has been used to mathematically measure the amount of dispersion exhibited by a set of data. In order to be able to predict what Y value will occur corresponding to some X value, the dispersion of the Y values or points about the regression line must be measured. This dispersion may be measured by means of the *standard error of estimate* which is similar in concept to the standard deviation. The standard error of estimate is defined by

$$s_{Y \cdot X} = \sqrt{\frac{\Sigma (Y - Y_c)^2}{n - 2}}$$

In computing the standard error of estimate, the Y value for each point is compared to the corresponding Y_c value on the regression line. The difference between these two values is squared and then summed along with the squared differences for every other point on the scatter diagram. Figure 10.7 illustrates how $s_{Y \cdot X}$ is computed once the differences between each point and the corresponding value on the regression line have been determined. Quite obviously, $s_{Y \cdot X}$ will be greater if the points tend to be a great distance from the regression line. When the points are close to the regression line, then $s_{Y \cdot X}$ will be small; and if every point in the scatter diagram lies directly on the line, then $s_{Y \cdot X}$ would equal 0.

Instead of computing the standard error of estimate by means of the definition given above, a computational formula has been developed which uses quantities which have already been found in the process of determining the equation of the regression line.

FIGURE 10.7_____

Computing the Standard Error of Estimate, $s_{Y \cdot X}$

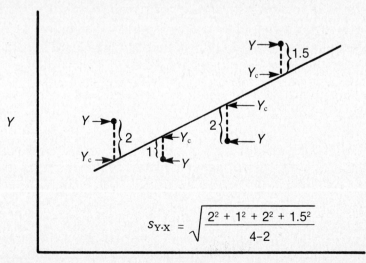

This computational formula is

$$s_{Y \cdot X} = \sqrt{\frac{\Sigma Y^2 - a\Sigma Y - b\Sigma XY}{n - 2}}$$

Using this computational formula in the Soors case of Table 10.2, the standard error of estimate is

$$s_{Y \cdot X} = \sqrt{\frac{307{,}346 - (70.12)(2366) - (3.212)(43{,}520)}{20 - 2}}$$

$$= \sqrt{91.99}$$

$$= 9.59 \text{ visitors}$$

Having measured the dispersion of the points about the regression line by the standard error of estimate, an interval estimate for individual values of the dependent variable Y can be constructed. An interval estimate can be constructed, however, only when the following conditions are satisfied:

1. *Linearity*. The scatter diagram data must exhibit a linear relationship.

2. *Normality*. The Y values corresponding to any particular value of X must be normally distributed around the regression line.

3. *Homoscedasticity*. The variance of the points about the regression line must be equal all along the line.

4. *Independence*. The Y value of any given observation (point) must not be influenced by any other observation (point).

5. *Large Sample Size*. There should be at least $n = 20$ observations.

These five conditions will be briefly amplified; then the construction of an interval estimate for Y will be considered.

The linearity requirement has been previously discussed in Section 10.2. It was stated there that curvilinear situations, as illustrated by the scatter diagram of Figure 10.2, will be left for more advanced texts and that only linear cases would be considered here. According to the normality requirement, the Y values corresponding to any X value must be normally distributed. In Figure 10.8a there is a graphical display of a case where all the values of Y corresponding to an X value are approximately normally distributed about the regression line. Notice that the data points are most dense near the regression line and are symmetrically spread about the line. A picture of a normal distribution has been drawn for the Y values corresponding to X_1; this may help in picturing the normality of the Y values about the regression line. The data of Figure 10.8b would not satisfy the condition of normality. In this case the Y values have some sort of bimodal distribution about the regression line.

FIGURE 10.8

Scatter Diagrams Illustrating Normal and Nonnormal Distributions about the Regression Line

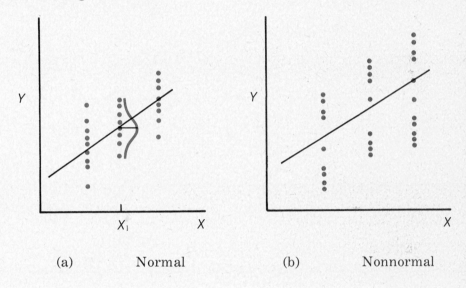

(a)   Normal   (b)   Nonnormal

With the homoscedasticity requirement, the data points must be equally spread about the regression line. More precisely, the variance of the Y values about the regression line must be the same regardless of the corresponding X value. Both scatter diagrams in Figure 10.8 satisfy the homoscedasticity requirement. However, the data in Figure 10.9 do not, since the variance of the points about the line for high values of X is much less than the variance of the Y values for low values of X. Regarding the independence criterion, this means that the location of any given point in a scatter diagram is not influenced by the location of any other point. In other words, one observation does not affect another observation. The lack of independence is typically encountered in time series, which is a topic discussed in Chapter 13. Finally, the interval estimation procedure of this section is designed for situations where there are at least 20 data points. Preferably, there

FIGURE 10.9
Lack of Homoscedasticity

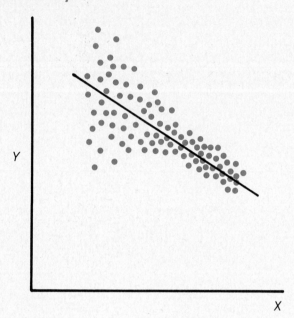

should be 30 or more observations. There is a method to construct
interval estimates when smaller samples are used; this method
will not be discussed here but is quite similar to the procedure to
be presented.

The problem at hand is predicting the value of Y when a particular X value is given. We have already seen that a point estimate of Y may be found by using the regression equation. For
example, if Soors runs five ads, then the expected number of visitors the next day is

$$Y_c = 70.12 + 3.212X$$
$$= 70.12 + (3.212)(5)$$
$$= 86.18 \text{ people}$$

Since the Y values rarely fall on the regression line, we would like
to have an interval estimate of Y. Following the general procedure
of Chapter 7 which dealt with confidence intervals, statisticians
have derived a formula for the interval estimate of Y corresponding to a given value of X. This *prediction interval* is

$$Y_c \pm Z \, s_{Y \cdot X} \sqrt{1 + \frac{1}{n} + \frac{(X - \overline{X})^2}{[\Sigma X^2 - (\Sigma X)^2/n]}}$$

where Y_c is the point estimate of Y as derived from the regression equation and Z controls the level of confidence. Just as in Chapter 7, a Z of 1.65 yields a 90 percent confidence level and a Z of 2.58 yields a 99 percent interval.

Using the interval estimation procedure just introduced, it can be claimed with 90 percent confidence in the Soors case that if $X = 5$ ads are run tonight there will be between 69.7 and 102.7 visitors tomorrow. This prediction interval is computed as follows:

$$86.18 \pm (1.65)(9.59) \sqrt{1 + \frac{1}{20} + \frac{(5-15)^2}{[7000 - 300^2/20]}}$$

$$86.18 \pm (1.65)(9.59) \sqrt{1 + .05 + .04}$$

$$86.18 \pm (1.65)(9.59)(1.04)$$

$$86.18 \pm 16.52$$

or,   69.7 to 102.7

This interval has been indicated in Figure 10.6

In like manner, a prediction interval for the number of visitors can be determined resulting from any other value of X as long as X is in the range from 0 to 30 ads. The values of X for prediction purposes must be limited to the 0 to 30 range, since the observations have been confined to this range. The effect of running more than 30 ads has never been observed, and therefore no predictions can scientifically be made.

10.5

CORRELATION

In regression analysis the mathematical relationship between a pair of variables was determined. This relationship, as expressed by the regression equation, may be used to generate either point or interval estimates of the dependent variable. Thus, regression analysis has utility as a predictive technique. Correlation analysis, on the other hand, is concerned with measuring the strength of the relationship between the pair of variables. If it is said that X and Y are highly correlated, it is meant that knowing the value of either variable gives considerable information in predicting the value of the other. For example, if it were stated that the number of teeth in a horse's mouth is highly correlated to the horse's age, then a person would be able to estimate quite accurately the age of a horse by counting its teeth, and vice versa. However, if it is said that a pair of variables are not correlated, this means that knowing the value of either is of no help in predicting the value of

the other. For example, the number of letters in a person's sur-
name and the weight of the person are not correlated. Knowing
either is of no help in predicting the other.

Figure 10.10 gives a set of four scatter diagrams with their respective regression lines. Let us generally describe the correlation
present in each of these cases. In Figure 10.10a it is apparent that
X and Y are correlated since information as to the value of X
would help in predicting Y. However, the correlation is not very
great. In Figure 10.10b there is high correlation, since once the X
value is determined there is a pretty narrow range wherein Y will
fall. In Figure 10.10c the correlation is perfect. Knowing either X
or Y gives perfect information as to the value of the other. In Figure 10.10d we have a case of no correlation. Even though the
points hug the regression line quite closely, knowing the value of
X is of no help in predicting Y because the regression line is flat
(has a slope of $b = 0$). In this case the average of all the Y values is
$\overline{Y} = 60$, and this is the best guess for Y regardless of the corresponding X value.

FIGURE 10.10

Scatter Diagrams Illustrating Correlation

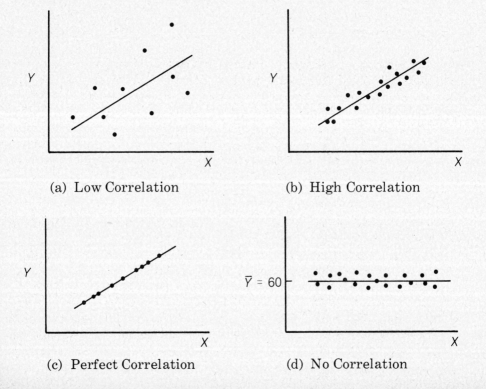

(a) Low Correlation

(b) High Correlation

(c) Perfect Correlation

(d) No Correlation

With a general feel for the meaning of correlation, it is now necessary to mathematically compute it. A mathematical quantity known as the *coefficient of determination* is the primary value used in measuring the strength of a relationship between a pair of variables. In the case where there is a sample of n observations, the *sample coefficient of determination* is defined as

$$r^2 = 1 - \frac{\Sigma(Y - Y_c)^2}{\Sigma(Y - \overline{Y})^2}$$

where Y gives the dependent variable value of an observation and Y_c gives the corresponding value on the regression line. This definition will be explained shortly. The coefficient of determination may take on any value from 0 through 1. A value of $r^2 = 0$ indicates that there is no correlation between the variables and an $r^2 = 1$ indicates perfect correlation.

Before illustrating the computation of the coefficient of determination, a word concerning its mathematical definition is appropriate. When two variables are correlated, it means that the value of either of them is useful in predicting the value of the other. When no correlation exists, as in Figure 10.10d, knowledge of X is useless for the sake of predicting Y. When no correlation exists, the regression line is a flat line (with a slope of 0) whose equation is $Y_c = \overline{Y} + 0X$ or simply $Y_c = \overline{Y}$.

A scatter diagram is given in Figure 10.11a where correlation between X and Y exists. Both the regression line (with a positive slope) and the $\overline{Y}$ line are drawn in the scatter diagram. The fact that the regression line is not identical to the $\overline{Y}$ line indicates that a relationship between X and Y exists. In order to measure the strength of this relationship, each point is compared to the $\overline{Y}$ line (the "no regression line") and each point is compared to the Y_c line (the "regression line"). Relatively speaking, the closer the points are to the Y_c line as opposed to the $\overline{Y}$ line, the higher the correlation. In order to determine how close the points are to the regression line, the vertical distance from each point to the Y_c line is found and then these distances are squared (to eliminate the minus signs) and summed. The result is that the closeness of the data points to the regression line is measured by $\Sigma(Y - Y_c)^2$. Figure 10.11b illustrates this computation. In like manner the closeness of the same points to the $\overline{Y}$ line is measured by $\Sigma(Y - \overline{Y})^2$, as illustrated in Figure 10.11c.

As was indicated, the usefulness of the regression line in predicting values of Y lies in the fact that the data points lie closer to the regression line than to the $\overline{Y}$ line. Since the closeness of the points to the Y_c line is measured by $\Sigma(Y - Y_c)^2$ and the closeness of the points to the $\overline{Y}$ line is measured by $\Sigma(Y - \overline{Y})^2$, the ratio

FIGURE 10.11

Measuring the Fits of the Y_c and $\overline{Y}$ Lines

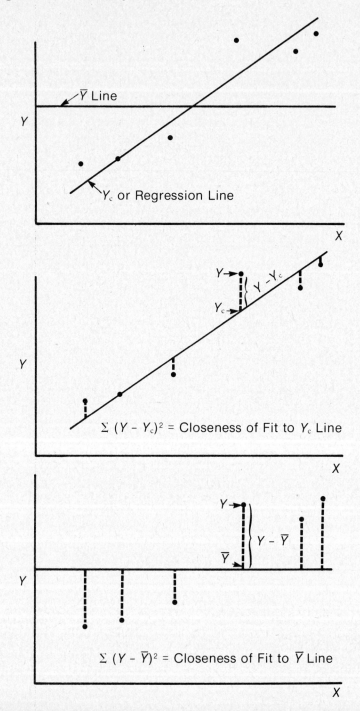

$$\frac{\Sigma(Y - Y_c)^2}{\Sigma(Y - \overline{Y})^2}$$

will approach 0 if the points tend to be much closer to the Y_c line than to the $\overline{Y}$ line. This in turn implies that the coefficient of determination, which is defined by

$$r^2 = 1 - \frac{\text{Closeness of points to } Y_c \text{ line}}{\text{Closeness of points to } \overline{Y} \text{ line}}$$

$$= 1 - \frac{\Sigma(Y - Y_c)^2}{\Sigma(Y - \overline{Y})^2}$$

would approach a value of $1 - 0$ or 1. See Figure 10.10b where r^2 would be close to 1 and Figure 10.10c where r^2 would equal 1. Therefore, when a strong relationship exists the coefficient of determination tends toward 1. On the other hand, if the Y_c line turns out to be identical to the $\overline{Y}$ line as in Figure 10.10d, then the ratio $\Sigma(Y - Y_c)^2/\Sigma(Y - \overline{Y})^2$ equals 1 and r^2 will take on a value of $r^2 = 1 - 1$ or 0. This indicates that no correlation exists since the regression line (being the same as the $\overline{Y}$ line) offers no advantage in predicting Y.

Thus, it has been shown that r^2 may vary from 0 to 1. An $r^2 = 0$ implies that no correlation exists and $r^2 = 1$ implies that perfect correlation exists. Intermediate values of r^2 imply that correlation, though not perfect, does exist between the variables. In this way r^2 measures the strength of the relationship. To say it a different way, r^2 measures the extent to which the Y_c or regression line does a better job in fitting the data than the $\overline{Y}$ line. When the Y_c line fits the data better than the $\overline{Y}$ line, as shown by r^2 being positive, it is advantageous to use the regression equation in predicting Y. If $r^2 = 0$, then X is useless in predicting Y; no relationship exists.

Having probed into the meaning of the coefficient of determination, let us now compute r^2 for the Soors case. The theoretical definition of r^2 as shown earlier is

$$r^2 = 1 - \frac{\Sigma(Y - Y_c)^2}{\Sigma(Y - \overline{Y})^2}$$

This definition can be used to compute r^2. However, a special computational formula has been derived which can be computed faster; it is

$$r^2 = \frac{a\Sigma Y + b\Sigma XY - n\overline{Y}^2}{\Sigma Y^2 - n\overline{Y}^2}$$

where a and b are the values from the regression equation and the remaining values are taken from a table such as Table 10.2.

Using the computational formula with the values as computed in Table 10.2 and remembering that the regression equation for Soors is $Y_c = 70.12 + 3.212X$, the coefficient of determination is found to be

$$r^2 = \frac{(70.12)(2366) + (3.212)(43,520) - (20)(118.3)^2}{307,346 - (20)(118.3)^2}$$
$$= .94$$

The coefficient of determination of .94 indicates that there is a very strong relationship between advertising and the number of people who visit the swamp.

Throughout this section, the coefficient of determination has been used to measure the strength of the relationship between two variables. Another measure which is commonly used but which is less meaningful is the *correlation coefficient*. The correlation coefficient is merely the square root of the coefficient of determination. Therefore, the sample correlation coefficient is denoted by r. The correlation coefficient may take on any value from -1 to $+1$. A negative sign is attached if the relationship is inverse; a positive sign indicates that the relationship is direct. Thus, the correlation of Figure 10.11c would be $r = +1$ since it is a perfect direct relationship. A correlation of $r = 0$ indicates that no relationship exists. The correlation coefficient in the Soors case is $r = \sqrt{.94} = +.97$.

In the previous paragraph it was stated that r is less meaningful than r^2. The reason r^2 is more meaningful than r is that the coefficient of determination represents the proportion of the total variation in Y that is explained by using the regression equation. For instance, in the Soors case where $r^2 = .94$ it could be stated that 94 percent of the variability in admissions is explained by changes in the number of television ads that are run. The correlation coefficient of $r = .97$ does not have any particular meaning such as this.

10.6

TEST OF CORRELATION

It was stated in Section 10.3 that danger lies in putting too much confidence in a regression line which is based on a relatively small number of observations. The same can be said about a correlation coefficient. A nonzero correlation coefficient may easily give a wrong impression regarding the strength of the relationship between the two variables; this is especially true when the sample size is small. It is quite possible to get a *sample* correlation coefficient which is not near zero when the true coefficient is 0. In other words, it is easy to conclude that a relationship exists between a pair of variables when in fact no relationship exists. This will now be illustrated.

After his many travels, Chuck Darwin returned home and made a number of bold assertions. One of these assertions was that the date within the month of a person's birth is directly related to the month of the person's birth. In other words, Chuck says that people who were born in early months like January through March tend to be born early in the month like between the first and eighth days of the month, and that people who are born late in the year like in October or December tend to be born late in the month. Therefore, Chuck claims that we would expect birthdates to be roughly like January 3, March 8, June 14, September 23, and December 30. We tell Chuck that what he claims is not true; however, Chuck won't back down. In order to resolve the situation we agree to take a random sample of three people to see if empirical evidence will support Chuck's claim. The three randomly sampled persons turned out to have birthdates of March 8, July 19, and December 24. Letting X equal the month and Y the day, the three observations are ($X = 3$, $Y = 8$), (7, 19), and (12, 24). These data points are plotted in Figure 10.12a. Using these points, the regression equation turns out to be

$$Y_c = 4.25 + 1.74X$$

and the correlation coefficient is $r = .96$. With a smug little smile Chuck says, "How about that!"

It is true that the sample correlation proved to be very high, which on the face of it would indicate that Chuck's original assertion concerning the relationship of day to month is correct. However, we are not ready to agree with Chuck. We tell Chuck that the points happened to line up by pure chance. Furthermore, when taking such a small sample like $n = 3$ it is quite easy for the points in the scatter diagram to line up in some fashion thereby giving the illusion of correlation. The proof of the pudding is in studying a much larger sample, or better yet in checking out the entire population. If everyone who is currently alive were plotted in a scatter diagram like that of Figure 10.12a, we would get a scatter diagram like that of Figure 10.12b where each point represents the birthdate of thousands of people. When everyone is considered there is no tendency for low X's to go with low Y's and so on. In reality, knowing X is of no help in predicting Y, and hence the

FIGURE 10.12

Relationship Between Birth Month and Birth Day

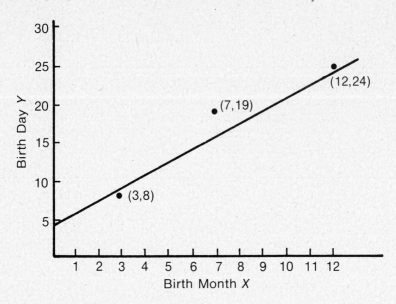

(a) Chance Correlation (Sample)

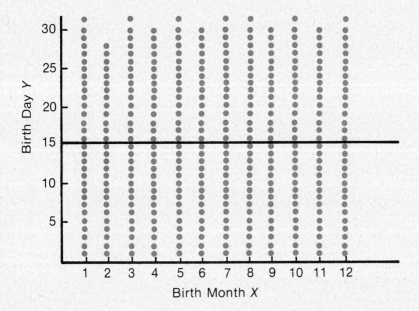

(b) No Correlation (Population)

regression line would be flat (slope of 0) and the true correlation for the entire population is 0. In conclusion, though the true correlation for an entire population is 0, it is possible especially in the case of a small sample to get a substantial sample correlation. Such a correlation is merely a chance occurrence and must not be regarded as significant.

Having established the possibility of getting a nonzero sample correlation in the case when the true population correlation is zero, it is now important to be able to determine when we can treat a sample correlation as being significant. To this end we will develop a hypothesis testing procedure.

The true correlation coefficient of a population is designated by the Greek symbol rho, that is, ρ. Whenever an r is found, it is desirable to test the following null hypothesis

$$H_o:\ \rho = 0$$

against some alternative hypothesis like

or
$$H_a:\ \rho \neq 0$$
$$H_a:\ \rho > 0$$

In order to perform the test, several conditions must be met. In the first place the linearity, normality, homoscedasticity, independence, and large sample size assumptions as listed in Section 10.4 must be satisfied. One other condition must also be satisfied. In regression analysis, as was pointed out in Section 10.2, the independent variable could either be controlled as in the Soors case or uncontrolled (left to chance) as in the cases of Figures 10.3 and 10.4. In order to run a test on the significance of the correlation coefficient, the X variable must be uncontrolled; furthermore, X must have a normal distribution. This means that the X values when compared to $\overline{X}$ must be most dense near $\overline{X}$ with relatively few in the extremes in either direction from $\overline{X}$. Looking at the X values in the Soors case, as shown in Table 10.1, and realizing that $\overline{X}$ equals 15, it is apparent that these X values, when considered by themselves, do not come close to exhibiting the shape of a normal distribution. Therefore, the testing procedure to be developed here is not appropriate for the Soors situation. In Section 11.5 of Chapter 11 an alternative procedure called the Spearman rank correlation test is presented which can be used in the Soors case. An example of the proper use of the correlation test will now be given.

Sudi Sumida is a financial analyst who is concerned with the profitability of New York Stock Exchange companies in relationship to their corporate social responsibility involvement. Sumida developed a quantitative measure of corporate social involvement, which he designated by X, and also developed a quantitative measure of corporate profitability, which is denoted by the variable Y. He then took a random sample of $n = 30$ stocks from the total population of stocks traded on the New York Stock Exchange. The resulting scatter diagram is presented in Figure 10.13. From this scatter diagram it appears that all of the conditions or assumptions mentioned earlier, which make a correlation test of significance possible, are satisfied. Notice that most of the X values are fairly close to $\overline{X}$; only a few points are found in about equal numbers in both tails. This indicates that X, which was not controlled, is approximately normal.

Since all of the conditions are satisfied, Sumida went on to compute the correlation coefficient which proved to be $r = +.20$. In order to test the hypothesis that there is in reality no correlation when the entire population of NYSE companies are considered, the following test statistic must be computed:

$$Z = \frac{r}{\sqrt{\dfrac{1 - r^2}{n - 2}}}$$

FIGURE 10.13_____

Scattergram of 30 Stocks

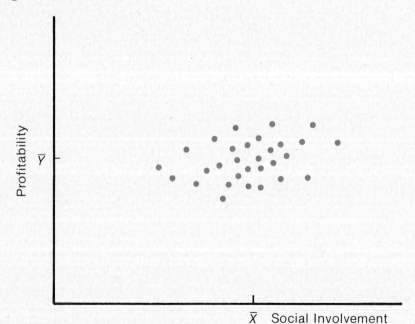

$\overline{X}$ Social Involvement

When the null hypothesis (H_o: $\rho = 0$) is true, Z will have a normal distribution with a mean of 0 and a standard deviation of 1. Following the same type of hypothesis testing procedure that was developed in Chapter 8, the null hypothesis may be tested against an alternative hypothesis like H_a: $\rho \neq 0$. In such a two-tailed test the null hypothesis would be rejected if a very negative or a large positive Z value occurs. With a significance level of .01, the critical values for Z are -2.58 and $+2.58$; this was explained in Section 8.6. Similarly, the critical values for the .05 level of significance are -1.96 and $+1.96$, and for $\alpha = .10$ are -1.65 and $+1.65$ when two-tailed tests are being conducted. In each case the null hypothesis which states that there is no correlation in the population would be accepted if the test statistic Z falls between the critical values.

Returning to the situation where Sumida found the correlation to be $+.20$ between profitability and corporate social involvement, the resulting test statistic based on the sample of $n = 30$ stocks is

$$Z = \frac{.20}{\sqrt{\dfrac{1 - .20^2}{28}}}$$

$$= 1.08$$

Therefore, the null hypothesis would be accepted at the .10 significance level. The empirical data as collected does not support the alternative hypothesis that says that correlation exists.

10.7

CAUTIONS

Along the way in the discussion of regression and correlation analysis, various assumptions have been made and warnings given. In this section some additional comments will be made concerning regression and correlation. In addition, some of the earlier comments will be briefly repeated.

Assumptions

Regression and correlation analysis is based on various assumptions. If only a regression line is to be determined or only a correlation coefficient is to be computed, relatively few conditions must be met. There must be at least $n = 3$ observations and the data should be linear. However, if prediction intervals are to be constructed based on the regression analysis as was presented, then the assumptions of normality, homoscedasticity, independence, and large sample size must be met. If the significance of the correlation coefficient is to be tested, then the additional requirement of the normality of X must be satisfied. If data does not satisfy all of the assumptions, many times the situation can still be handled. For example, if only $n = 15$ observations are available, prediction intervals and hypothesis tests of ρ can be undertaken through methods not described in this text. Also, some of the other assumptions like that of the normality of X for the sake of hypothesis testing of ρ is not too critical as long as X has a distribution which is not too unlike the normal. Therefore, the situation is often not hopeless when one of the assumptions is not met. The analyst should attempt to rectify the situation and not blindly apply the analysis as if the assumption were met.

Significance

The reader has already been warned not to put too much confidence in a regression line or correlation coefficient which is based on a relatively small sample of observations. The test of the correlation coefficient as given in the last section permits the analyst to determine if the data does in fact indicate that a significant relationship exists between the two variables under study. Even if this test indicates that a relationship does exist between X and Y, the relationship is still not necessarily the exact mathematical relationship which was determined through the regression analysis. As was pointed out in Section 10.3, the sample regression line of $Y_c = a + bX$ is only an estimate of the true regression line, just as r is a sample estimate of the true population correlation. Nevertheless, if the given sample of n observations is all that is available, and if the relationship is significant, then the sample regression line is the best estimate of the true relationship between X and Y.

Extrapolation

Once a regression line has been determined it must be used only for predictive purposes where X is within the range of the X values in the actual sample data. For example, in the Soors case X values of 0, 10, 20, and 30 television ads per night were used. The resulting regression equation is therefore to be used only when making predictions of Y corresponding to X values between 0 and 30 television ads. It would be wrong to use the regression equation to estimate Y for the case where $X = 60$ ads are run. In essence this would amount to extending or *extrapolating* the regression line beyond the data which has been observed. Such a procedure is not legitimate because, for example, values of X near 60 have never been observed in their effect on admissions.

Causality

When the discussion of regression analysis was begun, a distinction was made between the independent and dependent variables. The idea conveyed was that you might think of the dependent variable as the one which depends on the independent variable, or the independent variable as the one which has some sort of effect on the dependent variable. Therefore, advertising and fertilizer, for example, were the independent variables, and admissions and corn yield the dependent variables in the examples given early in the chapter. In another example, an employee's score on a test was selected as the independent variable and the employee's job satisfaction was the dependent variable. In reality, however, we don't think that a test score *causes* someone to be content or not. Nevertheless, the score is taken as the independent variable because for predictive purposes we would want to use the score to predict job contentment, and not the other way around. Therefore, the independent variable may be thought of as the variable to be used in predicting the dependent variable, which is what we are ultimately interested in. In other examples it is a toss up in deciding what is the independent and what is the dependent variable. In a correlation study between the length of a person's leg and the length of the person's arm, it is quite obvious that it makes no difference as to which is the dependent variable unless one of these happens to be given and the researcher is seeking the other. Either way, correlation will measure the strength of the relationship and the correlation will be the same.

In interpreting the results of regression and correlation analysis it is important to understand that causality cannot be proved. In the Soors case, a relationship between advertising X and admissions Y to the swamp was found; the statistical technique, however, did not say that advertising causes or has an effect upon admissions. Regression and correlation analysis works with numbers alone and can therefore only tell if certain numbers are related; it knows nothing of the meanings of the variables and hence says nothing about causation. It has been found, for example, that there is a significant relationship between smoking and the incidence of lung cancer. This does not mean that smoking causes lung cancer. Regression and correlation analysis merely states that these two variables are statistically related. It is the researcher who, from outside the data, makes the claim that smoking causes cancer, or that latent cancer causes people to smoke, or that some other factor causes both cancer and smoking. All three of these statements can explain the statistical relationship between smoking and lung cancer. Thus, statements concerning causation are not within the domain of statistics; only statistical relationships can be determined by statistical procedures. It is the manager or researcher that interprets the statistical relationship as resulting from some cause and effect process.

10.8

MULTIPLE REGRESSION AND CORRELATION ANALYSIS

In this chapter *simple regression and correlation analysis* has been the topic under consideration. In simple regression and correlation analysis there is one dependent variable and one independent variable. In *multiple regression and correlation analysis* there is one dependent variable and several independent variables. Multiple linear regression and correlation is nothing more than a generalization or extension of the simple regression and correlation analysis which has been presented. The same kinds of assumptions must hold and the same types of point estimates, interval estimates, and measures of the strength of various relationships can be determined.

Multiple regression and correlation is a powerful tool for the prediction of the dependent variable because it takes into consideration the simultaneous influences of several independent variables. An example of a multiple linear model will now be given.

A chain of convenience food markets known as the Mess Express markets is continually looking for new spots to build more markets. Based on the experience of dozens of their markets which are already in operation, Mess Express has isolated certain factors which seem to be good predictors of gross sales for a new market. These factors or variables are

$X_2 =$ Traffic density on the road where the market is located

$X_3 =$ Number of supermarkets located in the same district as the Mess Express

$X_4 =$ Number of other convenience food markets located in the same district as the Mess Express

$X_5 =$ Population in the district

$X_6 =$ Mean family income in the district

The dependent variable is

X_1 = Gross annual sales of the Mess Express market

After identifying the dependent and independent variables, Mess Express Inc. collected information on each of these variables for each of its stores currently in operation. For example, one of the Mess Express markets located in Cincinnati can be described by X_1 = \$325,000, X_2 = 1,300 vehicles per day, X_3 = 2 supermarkets, X_4 = 1 convenience market, X_5 = 14,000 people, and X_6 = \$14,955 per family. Similar information is collected for each of the existing Mess Express markets. This information is then used to construct a regression model. Suppose that the resulting model turned out to be

$$X_1 = 60,000 + 40X_2 - 10,000X_3 - 20,000X_4 + 10X_5 + 5X_6$$

Furthermore, the multiple coefficient of determination proved to be R^2 = .82. This coefficient implies that 82 percent of the variation in gross sales X_1 is explained by the combined effects of the five independent variables.

With the multiple linear regression equation as determined above, Mess Express Inc. can evaluate the gross sales potential of a proposed site. For the site under consideration, Mess Express Inc. has determined that X_2 = 1,000 vehicles per day, X_3 = 3 supermarkets, X_4 = 1 convenience market, X_5 = 11,000 people, and X_6 = \$17,000 per family. Substituting these values into the multiple linear model given above, a point estimate for gross sales at the proposed new location is

$$X_1 = 60,000 + (40)(1,000) - (10,000)(3) - (20,000)(1)$$
$$+ (10)(11,000) + (5)(17,000)$$

$$= \$245,000$$

An interval estimate of X_1 could also be constructed if the various assumptions of the model were adequately satisfied.

Finally, it might be noted that through multiple correlation analysis the relationships between various pairs of variables from among the entire set of dependent and independent variables may be isolated. Such analysis often provides valuable insights into the workings of the situation being studied.

PROBLEMS

10.1

Name a variable which is directly related in each case to each of the following variables:
(a) Age of a person
(b) Distance a person can throw a softball
(c) Performance of blue chip stocks on the stock exchange
(d) Snowfall in Buffalo
(e) Rate of inflation in Kansas
(f) Amount of life insurance a person owns
(g) Number of automobiles a family owns
(h) Prime interest rate charged by a New York bank
(i) Gross sales tax collected in Richmond
(j) Price of a refrigerator

10.2

Draw a scatter diagram where an observation is a game such as a football game or a basketball game. Let X refer to the score of the winner and Y refer to the score of the loser in the game observed. Take a sample of at least ten games that took place in the last week or so. (The scatter diagram will therefore have at least ten points.) Comment on the nature of the relationship.

10.3

Draw a scatter diagram based on a sample of 20 stocks from the New York Stock Exchange. Let X equal the price of the stock and Y the dividend paid. Comment on the nature of the relationship.

10.4

Draw a scatter diagram based on a sample (it won't be a random sample) of eight families that you know. Let X equal the number of children in the family and let Y equal the number of years separating the youngest from the oldest child. Comment on the nature of the relationship.

10.5

Draw a scatter diagram based on a sample (it won't be a random sample) of ten adults that you know. Let X equal the age of the person and let Y equal the number of states which the person has not been in yet (out of the 50 states). Comment on the nature of the relationship.

10.6

Which of the following four lines is the regression line if the scatter diagram consists of the four given points?

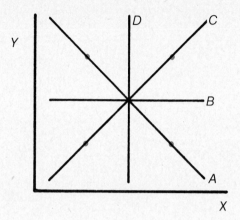

10.7

Gaier Inc. has done a study linking the maintenance expenses of its machines to the ages of the machines. Letting Y equal the annual maintenance expense and X equal the age, the following data have been obtained:

X	Y
2	$ 40
3	42
5	90
5	82
10	161

(a) Plot the scatter diagram.
(b) Determine the regression line.
(c) How much do maintenance costs increase for each year the machine ages?
(d) Plot the regression line on the scatter diagram of (a).
(e) What is the estimate of maintenance costs for a machine which is four years old?

10.8

An insurance company has done a study of six men linking life insurance in force to their salaries. The results of the study are given on page 314 where all figures are in thousands of dollars.

X	Y
Salary	Life Insurance
14	30
14	26
20	48
20	40
26	56
26	48

(a) Plot the scatter diagram.
(b) Compute the regression line and draw it on the scatter diagram.
(c) How much does the life insurance increase for each extra increment of a thousand dollars in salary?
(d) What is the estimate of life insurance in force for a man who makes $22,000 per year?
(e) What is the estimate of life insurance in force for a man who makes $88,000 per year?
(f) What is the estimate of life insurance in force for a woman who makes $25,000 per year?

10.9

A consumer testing agency has done a test linking the covering power Y of exterior home paints to their prices X. Fifty different paints were tested. From the test data the following were computed: $\Sigma X = 400$, $\Sigma Y = 1100$, $\Sigma XY = 9600$, $\Sigma X^2 = 3700$, and $\Sigma Y^2 = 42,000$
(a) Determine the regression equation.
(b) If the price of a given paint is $10 per gallon, estimate its covering power.
(c) How much extra covering power is achieved for every extra dollar spent per gallon on average?
(d) Construct a 90 percent prediction interval for the covering power of a $10 per gallon paint.

10.10

Describe the assumptions which must be satisfied before prediction intervals may be constructed in regression analysis.

10.11

In order to compute prediction intervals as described in Section 10.4, the data must be derived from a large sample. Working a problem with a large n would be too time consuming. Therefore, a small n is used in this problem. Use the large sample technique for constructing the prediction interval even though it is not really appropriate.

A political scientist has studied five middle-sized Eastern metropolitan areas in an attempt to link the percentage of votes received by Republicans to the percentage of residents receiving welfare payments. The results of the study are

Welfare Proportion X	Republican Proportion Y
2%	70%
8	30
6	50
4	50
5	40

(a) Determine the regression equation.
(b) If a city has 7 percent of its residents receiving welfare payments, find a 90 percent prediction interval for the proportion of votes the Republicans get.
(c) If a city has 14 percent receiving welfare, find a 90 percent prediction interval for Y.
(d) Compute the sample coefficient of determination and the sample correlation coefficient.

10.12

The introductory paragraph to Problem 10.11 applies here.

A railroad is interested in predicting how many meals will be demanded on a run of one of its trains from the Northeast to Florida. Four runs have been sampled yielding the following data:

Number of Passengers	Number of Meals Demanded
100	50
150	80
130	70
120	80

(a) Determine the regression equation.
(b) On the average, how many more meals are demanded for each extra passenger?
(c) If the train has 120 passengers, find a 95 percent prediction interval for the number of meals that will be demanded.
(d) Compute r^2 and r. Give an interpretation of the meaning of the coefficient of determination.

10.13

A sample of four companies taken from the American Stock Exchange revealed the following relationship between their current ratios and dividend yields:

Current Ratio	Dividend Yield
X	Y
2.4	6%
1.4	2%
1.8	3%
2.0	1%

(a) Determine the regression equation.
(b) On the average, by how much does the dividend yield increase for each unit increase in the current ratio?
(c) Find a point estimate for the yield when the current ratio of a company is 1.5.
(d) Compute r^2 and r. Give an interpretation as to the meaning of r^2.

10.14

A large meat packing company has done a study linking the number of cattle grazing and in feed lots as of May to the supermarket price of beef in November. From the last four years, the following has been found:

Number of Cattle	Price
X	Y
800	$1.60
1000	1.20
1200	1.10
1000	1.30

(a) Determine the regression equation.
(b) On the average, how much does the price change for every extra hundred cattle?
(c) It has been reported that this year there are 900 cattle in May. Find a point estimate for the price of beef in November.
(d) Compute r^2 and r.

10.15

State the conditions which must be met before a correlation coefficient can be tested for significance.

10.16

Compute the coefficient of determination for Problem 10.12 using the formula

$$r^2 = 1 - \frac{\Sigma(Y - Y_c)^2}{\Sigma(Y - \overline{Y})^2}$$

instead of the shortcut formula.

10.17

Compute the coefficient of determination and the correlation coefficient for Problem 10.7 using the shortcut formula.

10.18

Based on a study of 25 returns, the IRS has determined that the correlation between gross income and the number of dependents claimed is $+.2$. If the null hypothesis is $\rho = 0$ and the alternative hypothesis is $\rho \neq 0$, test the null hypothesis at the $\alpha = .02$ significance level. What can the IRS conclude concerning the relationship between gross income and the number of dependents?

10.19

A medical researcher is interested in determining if there is a significant relationship between salt intake, X, and high blood pressure, Y. A study of 40 persons yielded a correlation coefficient of $+.30$. Test the null hypothesis of no correlation against the one-sided alternate that $\rho > 0$ at the .10 significance level.

10.20

An electric company has noticed that there seems to be a relationship between wintertime average daily temperature X and electricity consumption Y in Richmond. Thirty-eight days were studied. The electric company found that the correlation between temperature and electricity consumption is $-.60$. Test the null hypothesis of no correlation against the one-sided hypothesis that $\rho < 0$ at the .04 significance level. What does a negative correlation imply in contrast to a positive correlation?

10.21

When traveling at speeds between 55 mph and 75 mph, a group of truckers claim that diesel fuel consumption on a per-mile basis is inversely related to speed. The federal government claims that there is a direct relationship. In order to determine what in fact is the case, a sample of 51 truck runs are made, yielding a correlation coefficient of $+.4$. Test the null hypothesis of no correlation against a two-sided alternative hypothesis at the .05 significance level. What does the sample evidence indicate concerning the relationship between speed and fuel consumption?

10.22

Why is the Spearman rank correlation often used instead of the correlation coefficient which was developed in this chapter?

10.23

A regression line has the equation given by

$$Y_c = 16.8 - .84X$$

Will the correlation coefficient be positive or negative? Why?

10.24

The regression line always passes through the point $(\overline{X}, \overline{Y})$. Take a look at the equations used for computing a and b in the regression equation. Why must the regression line pass through $(\overline{X}, \overline{Y})$?

10.25

A realtor has constructed a multiple regression model for the sake of predicting property values. The model is

$$X_1 = -4,000 + 24X_2 + 800X_3 + .1X_4$$

where X_1 equals the market value of the home, X_2 equals square feet of floor space, X_3 equals the condition of the home on a scale from 1 to 9, and X_4 equals the average income of the families in the neighborhood. Use this model to predict the value of a home where $X_2 = 2,000$ square feet, $X_3 = 7$, and $X_4 = \$24,000$.

10.26

You have been retained by Northern Arizona University to develop a model for the sake of predicting next year's enrollment. List at least four independent variables which might prove useful in a multiple regression model.

10.27

You wish to predict the amount of money families spend on food each year by means of a multiple regression model. List at least three independent variables which might be useful for the sake of predicting annual food expenditures.

CHAPTER 11

NONPARAMETRIC TESTS

11.1

INTRODUCTION

A number of hypothesis tests have been studied. Hypothesis testing has not only been considered in Chapter 8, where the subject was introduced, but has been used in the regression and correlation analysis of Chapter 10, as well as in the analysis of variance of Chapter 9. In this chapter several more hypothesis tests will be presented. The tests of this chapter are different from the previous tests in that they make few if any assumptions about the nature of the population which is being tested. These tests are called *nonparametric tests*; the tests of Chapters 8, 9, and 10, which can only be conducted if several requirements concerning the population are satisfied, are called *parametric tests*.

There are essentially three advantages and one disadvantage of nonparametric tests as compared to parametric tests. The first advantage is that the analyst using a nonparametric test does not have to satisfy a number of assumptions or conditions before the test can be used. Nonparametric tests make minimal demands in the way of prerequisites. Second, from the computational perspective, nonparametric tests are typically less complicated than corresponding parametric tests. This will become obvious in Section 11.4 where the nonparametric counterpart of the analysis of variance will be considered.

The third advantage of nonparametric tests is that they can be used with qualitative variables and with ranked data. A qualitative variable, for example, might be S, where S represents the state in which a customer was born. The possible "values" of S are

therefore Alabama, Alaska, Arkansas, ... Regression and correlation analysis, for instance, cannot use a variable like S. Nonparametric analysis can deal with such a variable. Another example of a qualitative variable is L, where L is the degree to which a
person likes tomato juice. The possible "values" for L could range
from "Dislike tomato juice very much" to "Like it very much."
Again, parametric tests are not designed to handle variables like
this.

   Data may also come in a ranked form. For example, in having
to choose between Pittsburgh, San Diego, Birmingham, and Houston as a place to live, you might say, "In order of preference, I
would like to live in San Diego, Birmingham, Houston, and Pitts-
burg." You can with relative ease rank the places from first
through fourth. However, it would be hard to attach a numerical
value to each of these cities in order to show exactly how much
you like them. In other words, it would be difficult to make a statement such as, "I like San Diego about 100, I like Birmingham
about 36, I like Houston about 32, and I like Pittsburgh about
-433." Parametric statistics needs actual numbers to work with,
whereas nonparametric tests can be used in cases where only
ranks are available. Thus, nonparametric tests can be applied to a
wider spectrum of problems.

   With the foregoing advantages of nonparametric statistics, one
might wonder why parametric tests are ever used. The advantage
of parametric tests is that if the assumptions are satisifed, parametric tests are more sensitive than nonparametric tests. For example, suppose we wish to test the null hypothesis that there is no
correlation between the age of a car and the age of its driver. If in
fact there were some small correlation between these two variables, a parametric test would be more likely to recognize the existence of the relationship. A nonparametric test applied to the
same data is more likely to miss the relationship and thus errone-
ously accept the null hypothesis. Therefore, if a parametric test
can be used, it should be used. But if the assumptions of the parametric test cannot be satisfied or if the form of the data prohibits
the use of a parametric test, then the analyst must use a nonparametric test.

11.2

CHI-SQUARE TEST FOR PROPORTIONS

   Universal Airlines (UAL) plans to begin a special advertising
program in the British Isles in an attempt to stimulate overseas
flights to the United States. Currently, UAL is uncertain about

whether the same advertising should be used in England, Scotland, and Ireland or if the advertising should differ. In an attempt to move toward an optimal advertising strategy, UAL has decided to question would-be English, Scottish, and Irish travelers about what sights in the United States appeal to them. Each of the sampled persons will be asked if he or she would prefer the Historic City Tour or the Wild West Tour. Each tour is described as follows:

Historic City Tour — Tourist visits Boston, Cape Cod, New York City, Hoboken, Philadelphia, Washington D.C., Richmond, Petersburg, Williamsburg, and Jamestown.

Wild West Tour — Tourist visits a variety of places between Phoenix and Denver, including the cactus deserts, Grand Canyon, Navajo Indian reservation, ghost towns, and the Rocky Mountains.

For the sake of being able to use one advertisement for the entire British Isles, UAL would hope that the proportion of English, Scottish, and Irish travelers who are interested in either of these tours as opposed to the other is about the same. Letting

p_e = Proportion of the English who would prefer the Historic City Tour over the Wild West Tour

p_s = Proportion of the Scots who would prefer the Historic City Tour

p_i = Proportion of the Irish who would prefer the Historic City Tour

UAL wants to test the hypothesis that these proportions are the same. The null hypothesis is therefore

$H_o: p_e = p_s = p_i$

If this hypothesis is accepted, it implies that the tourist tastes over the British Isles are the same, and thus UAL can use one advertisement instead of three separate advertising programs.

UAL proceeded to randomly sample 100 English, 50 Scots, and 50 Irish. Each person was asked for their preference between the two tours. Table 11.1 gives the sample results. Table 11.1 indicates that there were some differences among the people sampled. The sample proportion of English who prefer the Historic City Tour is $\bar{p}_e = 34/100 = .34$. The other two sample proportions are $\bar{p}_s = 12/50 = .24$ and $\bar{p}_i = 14/50 = .28$. Can UAL conclude from this evidence that the true proportions of the three groups are different? On the

TABLE 11.1

Tour Preferences of Sampled People

	English	Scots	Irish	
Prefer Historic City Tour	34	12	14	60
Prefer Wild West Tour	66	38	36	140
	100	50	50	200

face of it, it looks like the English prefer the Historic City Tour more than the Scots. However, this difference between $\bar{p}_e$ and $\bar{p}_s$ may not represent a real difference between p_e and p_s. In other words, the differences between $\bar{p}_e$, $\bar{p}_s$, and $\bar{p}_i$ may be due to pure chance; in reality there may be no difference between the English, Scots, and Irish.

Let us demonstrate that pure chance can yield different sample proportions when in fact no real differences exist. Suppose a penny, nickel, and dime are each flipped 20 times. Table 11.2 gives the results of this experiment. Notice that the sample proportions of heads for the penny, nickel, and dime are $\bar{p}_p = .40$, $\bar{p}_n = .65$, and $\bar{p}_d = .50$, respectively. Surely you would not argue that this proves that nickels have more of a tendency to produce heads than pennies. Rather, we say that the differences in the outcomes of Table 11.2 are due to the operation of pure chance. In reality, all three types of coins would, in the long run, produce the same proportion of heads. Nevertheless, sampling variations due to chance can still exist.

TABLE 11.2

Outcomes of Coin Flipping

	Penny	Nickel	Dime
Heads	8	13	10
Tails	12	7	10
	20	20	20

Thinking back to Table 11.1, we wonder if the differences observed in this table are attributable to pure chance. If the experiment of Table 11.1 had yielded $\bar{p}_e = .83$, $\bar{p}_s = .06$, and $\bar{p}_i = .42$, we would conclude without reservation that real differences exist between the English, Scots, and Irish. On the other hand, if the sample had yielded $\bar{p}_e = .31$, $\bar{p}_s = .28$, and $\bar{p}_i = .29$, then we would feel quite comfortable about accepting H_o, which means we believe that the English, Scots, and Irish are the same. These slight variations in the sample proportions could easily occur by pure chance when the three groups are the same in regard to their vacation preferences. The problem, however, is that the actual sample proportions proved to be $\bar{p}_e = .34$, $\bar{p}_s = .24$, and $\bar{p}_i = .28$. Could this have happened by pure chance, or could the only way these differences occur be because the three groups are in fact different? Chi-square analysis will be used to answer this question. If it turns out that these sample proportions could happen quite easily by pure chance when H_o is true, then there is no reason to reject H_o. However, if these sample proportions are very unlikely when H_o is true, then we will conclude that H_o is not true and will reject H_o.

Chi-square analysis begins by determining what the frequencies of Table 11.1 would be expected to look like if H_o were true. If H_o is true, this means that $p_e = p_s = p_i$. Out of the 200 people sampled, it is seen from Table 11.1 that a total of 60 preferred the Historic City Tour. This overall proportion of 60/200 or 30 percent would be a good estimate of the English, Scots, and Irish who would prefer the Historic City Tour *if* all three groups are identical with regard to their preferences. Therefore, if there are no real differences among the three groups (H_o is true), and since 30 percent is the overall estimate of those preferring the Historic City Tour, then we would expect 30 percent of the English, and 30 percent of the Scots, and 30 percent of the Irish to prefer the Historic City Tour. Since there were 100 English questioned, we would expect 30 to prefer the Historic City Tour if the English were no different from everybody else. Since there were 50 Scots questioned, we would expect 15, which is 30 percent of 50, to prefer the Historic City Tour. Likewise, if the Irish were the same as everybody else, we would expect 15 of the 50 Irish to prefer the Historic City Tour. Table 11.3 presents these expected frequencies, which are based on the assumption that everyone's preferences are the same, along with the original frequencies of Table 11.1.

Remembering the origin of the expected frequencies as given in Table 11.3, it should be apparent that if the observed frequencies, f_o, are close to the expected frequencies, f_e, then there is reason to believe that all three groups are the same with respect to their vacation preferences. In other words, if the f_o and f_e for each cell in Table 11.3 are roughly the same, then H_o can be accepted.

TABLE 11.3

Observed (upper left) and Expected (lower right) Frequencies

	English	Scots	Irish
Prefer Historic City Tour	$f_o = 34$ $f_e = 30$	12 15	14 15
Prefer Wild West Tour	66 70	38 35	36 35

However, if the observed and expected frequencies differ widely, then we would be prone to reject H_o and thus conclude that real differences exist among the English, Scots, and Irish.

Through a chi-square test, the analyst measures the amount of difference between the observed frequencies, f_o, and the corresponding expected frequencies, f_e. The chi-square statistic, which is represented by χ^2, is the statistic which measures these differences. If there is a large amount of difference between f_o and f_e as indicated by the value of χ^2, then H_o is rejected. On the other hand, if the statistic χ^2 shows that f_o and f_e are approximately the same, then H_o is accepted. The χ^2 statistic is computed according to

$$\chi^2 = \Sigma \left[\frac{(f_o - f_e)^2}{f_e} \right]$$

where the summation progresses cell by cell and where f_o and f_e are the observed and expected frequencies for a cell. For the UAL case of Table 11.3, the value of the χ^2 statistic is

$$\chi^2 = \frac{(34-30)^2}{30} + \frac{(12-15)^2}{15} + \frac{(14-15)^2}{15} + \frac{(66-70)^2}{70} + \frac{(38-35)^2}{35} + \frac{(36-35)^2}{35}$$

$$= \frac{16}{30} + \frac{9}{15} + \frac{1}{15} + \frac{16}{70} + \frac{9}{35} + \frac{1}{35}$$

$$= 1.71$$

Before attempting to reach a conclusion based on this χ^2 value of 1.71, let us think about the kinds of values that are possible for χ^2.

If the observed frequencies f_o in each cell of a table like Table 11.3 were to match the expected frequencies f_e perfectly, then χ^2 would have a value of 0. This is because the numerator of χ^2 which equals $(f_o - f_e)^2$ would equal 0 for every cell if f_o were always the same as f_e. As stated earlier, when the null hypothesis is true, then the observed frequencies will tend to be close to the expected frequencies. Therefore, it follows that when H_o is true, the value of χ^2 will tend to be close to 0. Now think of the case where H_o is false (i.e., the English, Scots, and Irish have different preferences about vacations), then the observed frequencies would differ substantially from the expected frequencies. This is because the expected frequencies were determined under the assumption that there are no differences among the English, Scots, and Irish. What happens to the χ^2 statistic if the observed frequencies differ substantially from the expected frequencies? If the difference, $f_o - f_e$, for a cell is great, then $(f_o - f_e)^2$ will be a positive number which is greater yet. Although these large positive numbers are divided by f_e, they will still yield a large value for χ^2 when they are added cell by cell. Therefore, if H_o is false, then the $(f_o - f_e)^2$ for each cell will tend to be large and finally χ^2 itself will be a large positive number. Let us summarize the discussion of this paragraph:

> If H_o is true, then the observed frequencies f_o will be close to the expected frequencies f_e, thus causing χ^2 to be close to 0. If H_o is false, then the observed frequencies will tend to substantially differ from the expected frequencies, thus yielding a large positive value for χ^2.

By reversing this,

> If χ^2 is near 0, then H_o is probably true and should be accepted. If χ^2 is a large positive number, then H_o is probably false and should be rejected.

In the Universal Airlines case the statistic χ^2 has a value of 1.71. Is this a small or a large positive number? We cannot answer this question since we need some basis of comparison. It's like asking, "Is a weight of 1.8 tons light or heavy?" The answer depends on whether we are talking about motorcycles or mountains.

In order to determine if a χ^2 of 1.71 is small (in which case H_o should be accepted) or large (in which case H_o should be rejected), the analyst must specify the probability of making a Type I error. (See Sections 8.3 and 8.4 of Chapter 8 for a discussion of Type I errors and fixing the level of α.) Typically the level of significance selected is in the range from .01 to .10. Suppose that Universal Airlines selects α to be .05. Next, the analyst takes a look at the chi-square distribution. The chi-square distribution is a sampling distribution which lists all of the possible χ^2 values which may occur when H_o is true. Figure 11.1 gives a picture of a chi-square distribution. The critical value C as shown serves to separate large χ^2 values from small χ^2 values in a manner which yields a probability of α of making a Type I error. If the χ^2 statistic which is computed from the sample data exceeds C, then H_o is rejected. If χ^2 is less than C, then the null hypothesis is accepted.

Appendix C gives the critical values for the chi-square distribution corresponding to different levels of significance α. The chi-square distribution has one parameter, which is the degrees of freedom d. There is a different chi-square distribution for various values of d. For a chi-square test of proportions as is being considered here, the degrees of freedom is computed by

$$d = (r - 1)(c - 1)$$

where r equals the number of rows in Table 11.1 and c equals the number of columns. In the case at hand,

$$d = (2 - 1)(3 - 1)$$
$$= 2$$

since there are $r = 2$ rows and $c = 3$ columns in Table 11.1. With $\alpha = .05$ we turn to Appendix C in order to find the critical value. From Appendix C it is seen that the critical value is $C = 5.99$. Let us now gather together all the loose ends and determine what Universal Airlines should conclude.

UAL has specified that the level of significance should be $\alpha = .05$ for testing the null hypothesis

$$H_o: p_e = p_s = p_i$$

which states that the English, Scots, and Irish are the same with respect to vacation preferences. UAL then sampled 100 English, 50 Scots, and 50 Irish. The observed frequencies f_o are presented in Table 11.3. Also, the expected frequencies based on the assumption that all three groups have identical preferences have been included in Table 11.3. Then the χ^2 statistic was computed according to

$$\chi^2 = \Sigma \left[\frac{(f_o - f_e)^2}{f_e} \right]$$

This χ^2, which measures the extent to which the observed frequencies differ from the expected frequencies, proved to have a value of 1.71. In order to determine if H_o should be rejected, this χ^2 value must be compared to the critical value as shown in Figure 11.1. The chi-square distribution that is appropriate has $d = 2$ degrees

FIGURE 11.1

Chi-Square Distribution with Critical Value

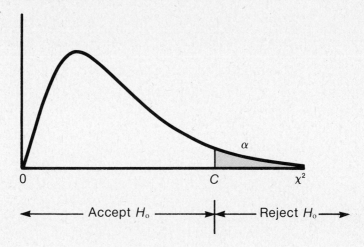

of freedom. With a significance level of .05, the critical value according to Appendix C is 5.99. Since the statistic χ^2 as computed from the sample equals 1.71, it follows that H_o should be accepted. The decision rule is

Accept H_o if $\chi^2 < 5.99$

Reject H_o if $\chi^2 \geq 5.99$

In accepting H_o, Universal Airlines concludes that the English, Scots, and Irish appear to have similar vacation interests. The differences between these three groups, as indicated by the sample data of Table 11.1, are most likely due to pure chance, just as the differences among the coins in Table 11.2 are due to chance. Therefore, UAL may go ahead and develop one advertisement for the entire British Isles rather than developing three different advertisements.

Since the chi-square test is a nonparametric test, we should not expect a long list of assumptions or conditions which must be met. However, there is one condition which must be satisfied. This condition does not regard the population but is rather a restriction that concerns the sample data. The expected frequency for each cell (there were six cells in Table 11.3) must equal at least five. That is, $f_e \geq 5$ for each cell. More will be said concerning this restriction in the next section, which deals with a generalization of the chi-square test for equal proportions.

11.3

CHI-SQUARE TEST FOR INDEPENDENCE

Sandra Scott is attempting to determine how women of different ages view three competing women's apparel shops in town. Scott has decided to ask a random sample of women the following question: "If you were to receive a $200 gift certificate, would you prefer to spend it at Sweetbriar's, LaVogue, or Continental?" A total of 100 women were randomly sampled and questioned. The results are presented in Table 11.4, which is called a *contingency table*. It is seen from this table, for example, that 12 of the 100 women were young women who preferred LaVogue.

Scott wishes to determine if age is related to the store which is preferred. As is usually the case, the null hypothesis states that there is no relationship between the variables:

H_o: Age and store are independent.

If the variables age and store are independent, this would mean that knowing the age of a woman does not give any information regarding the store which she is likely to prefer. (See Section 2.6 of Chapter 2, where the concept of independence was first introduced.) If age and store are not independent, then information about age is helpful in predicting the preferred store, and vice versa.

The reader should recognize that Table 11.4 is conceptually similar to Table 11.1, which showed the preferences of the various categories of British travelers. In Table 11.4 there are three types of women (young, middle-aged, and old); in Table 11.1 there were three types of British travelers. However, in Table 11.4 each

TABLE 11.4

Age and Store Preference of 100 Women

		STORE			
		Sweetbriar's	*LaVogue*	*Continental*	
	Young	13	12	3	28
AGE	*Middle*	13	23	11	47
	Old	6	10	9	25
		32	45	23	100

woman has three choices, whereas in Table 11.1 there were only two vacation choices. Therefore, it is not as convenient to talk about proportions in Table 11.4. Nevertheless, the situation is analogous. The null hypothesis in the case of Universal Airlines could have been stated as "Origin and vacation preference are independent." In other words, the test of proportions of the last section could have been conceived as a test of independence. By accepting the null hypothesis, Universal Airlines has concluded that there is no relationship between origin (English, Scottish, Irish) and where the person prefers to visit (Historic City vs. Wild West).

In order to determine if age and store are independent, Sandra Scott needs to compute the expected frequencies based on the assumption that H_o is true. She needs to see what the data could be expected to look like if H_o were true. If age and store preference are unrelated, then it follows that each store should get the same proportion of shoppers from each age group. Since 28 percent of all shoppers are young, as seen from Table 11.4, then 28 percent of Sweetbriar's, LaVogue's, and Continental's shoppers should be young. Since the number of shoppers for each of these stores is 32, 45, and 23, respectively, each of the stores should have $(32)(.28) = 9.0, (45)(.28) = 12.6$, and $(23)(.28) = 6.4$ young shoppers, respectively. These are the expected frequencies and are entered in the lower right of the cells in Table 11.5. Similarly, since 47 percent of all

TABLE 11.5_____

Observed (upper left) and Expected (lower right) Frequencies

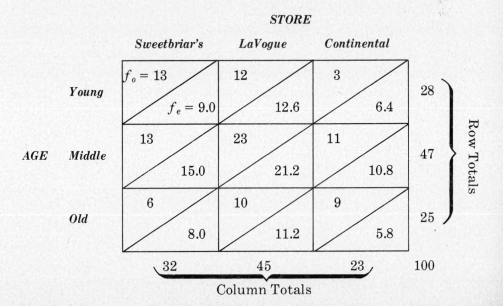

shoppers are middle-aged, then each store should find that 47 percent of its shoppers are middle-aged if age and store preference are independent. Thus, the expected frequencies for the second row in Table 11.5 are $(32)(.47) = 15.0$, $(45)(.47) = 21.2$, and $(23)(.47) = 10.8$, respectively. In like manner, the expected frequencies, if H_o is true, for the last row are $(32)(.25) = 8.0$, $(45)(.25) = 11.2$, and $(23)(9.25) = 5.8$. All of these expected frequencies are found in Table 11.5. Notice that the expected frequencies sum to the same row and column totals as the observed frequencies.

At this point, another way of computing the expected frequency for each cell should be noted. The expected frequency f_e for a cell can be determined according to

$$f_e = \frac{(\text{Row Total})(\text{Column Total})}{\text{Sample Size}}$$

where the row total is the sum of all the observed frequencies in the row which contains the cell and the column total is the sum of all the observed frequencies in the column where the cell is found. For example, the expected frequency for the cell in the northwest corner is nine, according to Table 11.5. This expected frequency could have been determined by the formula just given:

$$f_e = \frac{(28)(32)}{100}$$

$$= 9$$

Similarly, the expected frequency for the cell at the center of the contingency table could be found as

$$f_e = \frac{(47)(45)}{100}$$

$$= 21.2$$

This method of finding the expected frequencies is equivalent to the method first presented in this section and in Section 11.2.

As in the last section, if H_o is true then the observed frequencies f_o will be close to the expected frequencies f_e, thereby causing $(f_o - f_e)$ to be small. If the statistic χ^2 is computed according to

$$\chi^2 = \Sigma \left[\frac{(f_o - f_e)^2}{f_e} \right]$$

then this χ^2 will be small if H_o is true. On the other hand, if H_o is false (age and store are related), then the observed frequencies will substantially differ from the expected frequencies because the expected frequencies were computed under the assumption that age and store preference are independent. This in turn would yield a large positive value for the statistic χ^2. In general, the decision rule is

Accept H_o if $\chi^2 < C$

Reject H_o if $\chi^2 \geq C$

where the critical value C divides the small values of χ^2 from the large values as shown in Figure 11.1.

In the case at hand, Sandra Scott decided to use the .10 level of significance for the test. Next, she computed the value of the statistic:

$$\chi^2 = \frac{(13\text{-}9)^2}{9} + \frac{(12\text{-}12.6)^2}{12.6} + \frac{(3\text{-}6.4)^2}{6.4} + \frac{(13\text{-}15)^2}{15} + \ldots + \frac{(9\text{-}5.8)^2}{5.8}$$

$$= 6.44$$

This value of chi-square is also computed by means of a tableau format in Table 11.6.

TABLE 11.6
Computation of the Statistic χ^2

f_o	f_e	$f_o - f_e$	$(f_o - f_e)^2$	$\dfrac{(f_o - f_e)^2}{f_e}$
13	9.0	4.0	16.00	1.78
12	12.6	−.6	.36	.03
3	6.4	−3.4	11.56	1.81
13	15.0	−2.0	4.00	.27
23	21.2	1.8	3.24	.15
11	10.8	.2	.04	.00
6	8.0	−2.0	4.00	.50
10	11.2	−1.2	1.44	.13
9	5.8	3.2	10.24	1.77

$$\chi^2 = 6.44$$

The χ^2 value which has just been computed must now be compared to the critical value C in order to make a decision. The level of significance has already been set at $\alpha = .10$. The critical value is found in Appendix C as just described in Section 11.2. The degrees of freedom, which is the parameter of the chi-square distribution, is determined as before by

$$d = (r - 1)(c - 1)$$

Since there are $r = 3$ rows and $c = 3$ columns in Table 11.5, the degrees of freedom are

$$d = (3 - 1)(3 - 1)$$
$$= 4$$

According to Appendix C, the critical value for this test is $C = 7.78$ since $\alpha = .10$ and $d = 4$. Therefore, H_o must be accepted because the χ^2 statistic has a value of 6.44 as computed earlier. The evidence does not prove that age and store preference are related; thus, it will be assumed that these variables are independent until evidence otherwise is obtained.

In Section 11.2, it was stated that the expected frequency in each cell must equal at least five. This requirement must also be satisfied in tests of independence. If this condition is not satisfied, the contingency table containing the cells with the frequencies can sometimes be altered to satisfy this requirement. An example follows.

Dorothy Canova wishes to determine if the price of a stock is related to its dividend yield. The null hypothesis is

H_o: Stock price and dividend yield are independent.

Canova next sampled 200 stocks and categorized them as in the contingency table of Table 11.7a. The upper left corners of the cells hold the observed frequencies. The expected frequencies must next be determined. According to the formula

$$f_e = \frac{\text{(Row Total)(Column Total)}}{\text{Sample Size}}$$

the expected frequency for the cell in the southeast corner of the contingency table which represents stocks with 9–11.9 percent yields and $60.01–$1000 prices is

$$f_e = \frac{(42)(20)}{200}$$
$$= 4.2$$

Since this expected frequency falls below five, which is the required expected frequency for each cell, the chi-square test cannot be conducted. However, this difficulty can be overcome by either combining rows or columns appropriately. For example, the last

TABLE 11.7

Altering a Contingency Table

(a)

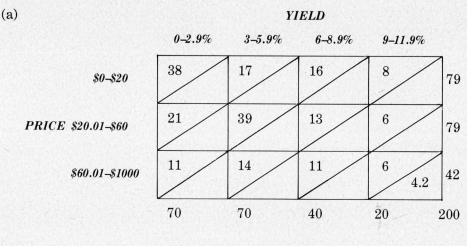

(b)

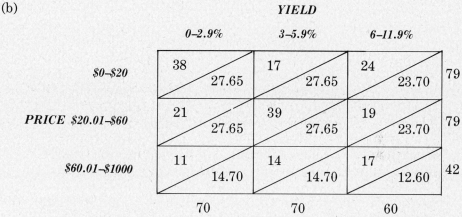

two columns of Table 11.7a have been combined to yield the contingency table of Table 11.7b, which has only three columns. Each of the expected frequencies for Table 11.7b equal at least five; therefore, the chi-square test can be conducted. The degrees of freedom would be $(3 - 1)(3 - 1) = 4$.

In concluding this section on the chi-square test for the independence of two variables, it should be noted that the variables may be qualitative or quantitative variables. An example of a qualitative variable is "store preference" as illustrated earlier. Examples of quantitative variables are "age" and "yield." Regardless of the type of variable, mutually exclusive and collectively exhaustive categories of each variable are always listed in the contingency table. The categories of one of the variables are listed along the top of the table and the categories of the other are listed down the left side. Then the random sample is taken and each sampled item is classified according to the categories of the two variables. The item is then included in the observed frequency for the cell in which it is classified.

11.4

KRUSKAL-WALLIS TEST

The analysis of variance was presented in Chapter 9. It was seen there that the analysis of variance deals with testing null hypotheses which state that the means of several populations are equal. Before analysis of variance can be used, the analyst must make sure that certain assumptions are satisfied. Two of the assumptions which are not always easily satisfied are the assumptions of normality and homoscedasticity. If such conditions do not prevail, then the analysis of variance cannot be used. Instead, the analyst will have to resort to a nonparametric test such as the Kruskal-Wallis test. The Kruskal-Wallis test will be studied and illustrated in this section.

It was not too many years ago that the East Coast Humane Society charged Minnie Clam with the cruel and unusual treatment of a great number of chickens. Minnie of course denied any knowledge of such. Nevertheless, the E.C.H. Society would not retract; the Society kept charging that Minnie had drowned a countless number of chickens in the waters of Chesapeake Bay. As a result of the charges brought against Minnie Clam, a federal judge ordered the Army Corps of Engineers to dredge a large area of the bay in search of the aquafied fryers.

Contrary to what some people might think, dredging something like a 100 square mile section of the Chesapeake Bay is no easy task. One of the major difficulties concerns the matter of keeping the path of the dredging vessel true so that it does not overlap or miss certain areas. In fact, electronic companies have developed sophisticated guidance systems to accomplish this task. Before the Army Corps of Engineers would begin the dredging, it was decided that several dredging systems would be tested. The three systems to be tested were the M system, and A system, and the J system.

Since field testing these systems is quite expensive, the first two systems were each tested only five times and the J system was tested six times. Table 11.8 presents the test results. The "scores" for the systems are composite values which measure the overall

TABLE 11.8

Dredging System Test Results

M	A	J
$i = 1$	$i = 2$	$i = 3$
27.2	30.0	34.1
26.3	27.4	28.3
27.0	28.0	32.2
29.1	31.7	29.5
30.9	31.6	30.3
		32.5

efficiency of the system as tested. A low score is good; a high score indicates a poor dredging performance.

The Army Corps of Engineers suspected that the requirements of the analysis of variance might not be satisfied in this situation. Therefore, the Kruskal-Wallis test was chosen. The null hypothesis for this situation where the Kruskal-Wallis test is to be used is

> H_o: There are no differences in the effectiveness of the three dredging systems.

In Kruskal-Wallis tests, the null hypothesis states that the populations being tested are identical.

In order to conduct the Kruskal-Wallis test of the foregoing hypothesis, all the scores from Table 11.8 must be pooled and then arranged according to size and ranked. The scores, origins, and ranks are

Score: 26.3, 27.0, 27.2, 27.4, 28.0, 28.3, 29.1, 29.5,
Origin: M M M A A J M J
Rank: 1 2 3 4 5 6 7 8

30.0, 30.3, 30.9, 31.6, 31.7, 32.2, 32.5, 34.1
A J M A A J J J
9 10 11 12 13 14 15 16

After this ranking is accomplished, the following are computed:

S_i = Sum of all the ranks for the ith group

n_i = Sample size of the ith group

n = Total sample size

g = Number of groups (systems)

In the case at hand, the following are the values for the M system, which is the $i = 1$ group or system:

$$S_1 = 1 + 2 + 3 + 7 + 11$$
$$= 24$$
$$n_1 = 5$$

Notice that from the ranked data above, M's scores are ranked 1, 2, 3, 7, and 11. Therefore, $S_1 = 24$. Since the M system was tested five times, n_1 equals five. For the A system, which is the $i = 2$ system:

$$S_2 = 4 + 5 + 9 + 12 + 13$$
$$= 43$$
$$n_2 = 5$$

For the J system which is the $i = 3$ system:

$$S_3 = 6 + 8 + 10 + 14 + 15 + 16$$
$$= 69$$
$$n_3 = 6$$

For the entire test the total number of observations or scores is

$$n = 5 + 5 + 6$$
$$= 16$$

and the total number of groups or populations being tested is

$$g = 3$$

Before going further with the mechanics of the Kruskal-Wallis test, notice that if the systems are all about equally efficient, then each system will have some low, some medium, and some high scores (ranks). In other words, the S_i will be about the same for each system if the n_i were the same. However, if one system is better than the others, then its scores (ranks) will tend to be lower, thus yielding a lower S_i. At the same time, the other systems would have higher ranks, thus yielding greater S_i's. The Kruskal-Wallis test puts all this kind of reasoning concerning the sizes of the S_i together in order to devise a statistic which will enable the analyst to either accept or reject H_o.

In a Kruskal-Wallis test the statistic K is computed according to the following equation:

$$K = \left(\frac{12}{n(n+1)}\right)\left(\Sigma\frac{S_i^2}{n_i}\right) - 3(n+1)$$

This test statistic is then compared to a critical value which is derived from the chi-square distribution which has $g - 1$ degrees of freedom. Of course, the level of significance must be specified before the critical value C can be determined. If the statistic K equals or exceeds the critical value, then H_o is rejected. Otherwise, H_o is accepted. The decision rule is

Accept H_o if $K < C$

Reject H_o if $K \geq C$

This will now be illustrated as we continue the Army Corps of Engineers case.

The Army Corps of Engineers began by stipulating that the level of significance α should be .10. The Kruskal-Wallis for this case where there are 3 systems or groups is

$$K = \left(\frac{12}{n(n+1)}\right)\left(\frac{S_1^2}{n_1} + \frac{S_2^2}{n_2} + \frac{S_3^2}{n_3}\right) - 3(n+1)$$

It has already been shown that $n = 16, n_1 = 5, n_2 = 5, n_3 = 6, S_1 = 24, S_2 = 43$, and $S_3 = 69$. These values are now substituted into the equation for the statistic K.

$$K = \left(\frac{12}{16(16+1)}\right)\left(\frac{24^2}{5} + \frac{43^2}{5} + \frac{69^2}{6}\right) - 3(16+1)$$
$$= 5.40$$

The Army Corps of Engineers next goes to Appendix C in order to find the critical value C when $\alpha = .10$ and the degrees of freedom are $g - 1$ or $3 - 1 = 2$. The critical value is seen to be $C = 4.61$. Therefore, H_o should be rejected. The Army Corps of Engineers should conclude that the three dredging systems are not the same.

Subsequently, the Army Corps of Engineers decided to employ the M system and began the multimillion dollar dredging project. As a result of the extensive dredging, a total of three water-logged chickens were found.

A couple of comments should be made before leaving the Kruskal-Wallis test. Sometimes two of the scores are identical. Suppose, for example, that the first two scores in the set of pooled scores were identical and originated from different populations (systems). In such a case each score is assigned a rank of 1.5. Hence, there are two ranks of 1.5 which replace the ranks of one and two. As long as there are not a great number of ties, the Kruskal-Wallis test can be conducted in the manner described in this section.

One condition that should be met if the Kruskal-Wallis test is used is that there should be at least five observations or scores for each population. There need not be the same number of observations in each group or population, however.

11.5

RANK CORRELATION

In Chapter 10 correlation analysis was introduced. It was seen that the coefficient of determination and the correlation coefficient measure the strength of the relationship between two variables. It was pointed out in Section 10.6, however, that correlation analysis is only proper when certain requirements are satisfied. If these requirements cannot be satisfied, then another method of measuring the strength of the relationship must be used. The Spearman rank correlation is a method which is commonly used in cases where the correlation analysis of Chapter 10 is inappropriate. Spearman rank correlation will be explained in this section through two examples.

A panel of physicians who practice in western United States has ranked the seven far western states according to the overall quality of the medical care provided to the residents of the respective states. The first column of Table 11.9 gives these ranks. For example, medical care was rated the highest (rank of one) in California and the lowest (rank of seven) in Idaho. Similarly, a panel of dentists ranked the overall dental care provided in these same

TABLE 11.9

Ranks for Medical and Dental Care

State	Medical Care	Dental Care	d	d^2
Arizona	4	7	−3	9
California	1	3	−2	4
Idaho	7	5	2	4
Nevada	6	6	0	0
Oregon	3	1	2	4
Utah	5	4	1	1
Washington	2	2	0	0
				22

seven states. The second column of Table 11.9 gives these ranks. According to the dentistry panel, for example, Oregon was ranked first and Arizona was ranked the lowest.

In view of the judgments of the two panels, the Health, Education, and Welfare Department wishes to determine the extent to which medical care and dental care are related. It is apparent from Table 11.9 that there does appear to be a relationship between these two variables since the states with the higher medical care ranks tend to have the higher dental care ranks, and the states with the lower medical care ranks tend to have the lower dental care ranks.

The Spearman rank correlation, r_s, is capable of measuring the strength of the relationship between two variables when the data for the variables are presented in ranked form. The rank correlation is computed by

$$r_s = 1 - \frac{6\Sigma d^2}{n(n^2 - 1)}$$

where n is the number of items (states) being considered and d is the difference in the ranks for a given item (state). This definition will become clear as we apply it to the panel judgments of Table 11.9.

To begin, the number of items or states being considered is seven, hence $n = 7$ for the situation of Table 11.9. The third column of Table 11.9 gives the difference d between the medical and dental ranks for each state. For example, Arizona is ranked fourth for medical care and seventh for dental care; therefore, $d = 4 - 7 = -3$. Similarly, for California $d = 1 - 3 = -2$ and for Idaho $d = 7 - 5 = 2$. These differences are next squared as shown in the fourth column. Finally, the squared differences of the fourth column are summed, which yields 22. Symbolically, this is expressed by $\Sigma d^2 = 22$. The rank correlation can now be computed:

$$
\begin{aligned}
r_s &= 1 - \frac{6\Sigma d^2}{n(n^2 - 1)} \\
&= 1 - \frac{(6)(22)}{(7)(7^2 - 1)} \\
&= 1 - .39 \\
&= +.61
\end{aligned}
$$

HEW can therefore state that the rank correlation between medical care and dental care for the seven far western states is +.61.

The Spearman rank correlation will always be a value between −1 and +1. If $r_s = -1$, then a perfect inverse correlation among the ranks exists. If $r_s = 1$, then a perfect positive or direct correlation exists. If $r_s = 0$, then no correlation exists between the two variables. A rank correlation of .61 in the case above indicates that there is a moderate positive (direct) relationship between the quality of medical and dental care in the far western states.

In the foregoing example the rank correlation was found to be .61. Since this correlation was based on a census of the entire population of the seven far western states, it is not a statistic but rather a parameter of the population. Since every far western state was considered in this study, we know with certainty that the true rank correlation between medical and dental care is .61. No hypothesis testing is involved if a census is taken. In the next example, however, a sample will be drawn from a population. Based on the sample rank correlation, which is a statistic, we will make an inference about the population rank correlation. Therefore, hypothesis testing will be used.

The over-the-counter securities market is a very extensive market in which various sorts of securities are bought and sold. The over-the-counter market encompasses all of the business in securities that is not transacted on an organized exchange. At the heart of the over-the-counter securities market is the wholesale dealer or market maker. The wholesale dealer maintains a market in a particular security by offering to buy quantities of that security at a price called the "bid" price and by standing ready to sell quantities of the security in question at the "asked" price. Therefore, because of the presence of and operation of the market maker or wholesale dealer, there is a market for certain securities. The difference between the asked and bid prices is called the "spread." This spread represents the wholesale dealer's gross profit margin.

According to the theory of how a market maker operates, if the price of a particular stock is quite variable, then the market maker will operate with a larger spread. On the other hand, the spreads will tend to be small for stocks which are stable. An analyst for the Securities and Exchange Commission wishes to determine if there is in fact a relationship between the spread size and price variability for the thousands of stocks which are traded over-the-counter. The analyst begins by formulating the following hypotheses:

> H_o: There is no relationship between spread size and price variability for over-the-counter stocks. (The true rank correlation is 0.)

> H_a: There is a positive relationship between spread size and price variability. (The true rank correlation exceeds 0.)

If H_o is rejected, then the analyst has shown that a positive relationship between these two variables exists.

The SEC analyst randomly sampled $n = 10$ over-the-counter stocks. Table 11.10 presents the spread size and price variability data for the ten stocks that were sampled. The analyst used the coefficient of dispersion (see Section 5.8 of Chapter 5) in order to measure the spread size and price variability for each stock that was sampled. The analyst then ranked each of the price variability percentages from the greatest (a rank of one) to the least (a rank of ten). Similarly, the spread size percentages are ranked. For example, the Dayspring stock has the greatest spread size and thus gets a rank of one. The Green stock has the least spread size and thus gets ranked tenth. (It should be noted that the stocks could have been ranked starting with the lowest percentage receiving a rank of one, and so on; the result would be the same.) Once the ranks are determined, the Spearman rank correlation for this sample data is computed as earlier. Table 11.10 shows the differences d between the ranks for each stock, the d^2, and Σd^2. Therefore,

$$r_s = 1 - \frac{6\Sigma d^2}{n(n^2 - 1)}$$

$$= 1 - \frac{(6)(22)}{(10)(10^2 - 1)}$$

$$= +.87$$

Though the sample data shows a strong positive (direct) rank correlation, the analyst needs to determine if the sample evidence, being based on a rather small sample, is sufficient to warrant the

TABLE 11.10

Over-the-Counter Stocks

Stock	Price Variability	Rank	Spread Size	Rank	d	d$_2$
Abus	8.3%	5	3.81%	5	0	0
Brindley	4.5	10	1.41	9	1	1
Casey	8.2	6	5.22	3	3	9
Dayspring	17.6	1	6.14	1	0	0
Ellis	7.5	7	2.99	6	1	1
Franklin	7.2	8	1.50	8	0	0
Green	6.1	9	1.20	10	−1	1
Heizer	14.6	2	5.50	2	0	0
Ileo	12.2	3	4.96	4	−1	1
Jay	9.3	4	2.86	7	−3	9
						22

rejection of H_o. In order to test H_o, the analyst begins by stipulating the level of significance. Suppose $\alpha = .05$ is selected. Then the test statistic Z is computed according to

$$Z = r_s \sqrt{n - 1}$$

where the sample size n must be at least 10. The alternate hypothesis in the case at hand states that the true rank correlation exceeds 0; thus, it is an upper-tailed test. The critical value is represented by Z_c as in Chapter 8 and the decision rule is

Accept H_o if $Z < Z_c$

Reject H_o if $Z \geq Z_c$

The critical values Z_c for several levels of significance are given in Table 11.11a. If the alternate hypothesis had stated that the true correlation is not 0, then it would be a two-tailed test and the decision rule would be

Accept H_o if $-Z_c < Z < Z_c$

Reject H_o if $Z \leq -Z_c$ or $Z \geq Z_c$

The critical values, $-Z_c$ and Z_c, for two-tailed tests are shown in Table 11.11b.

TABLE 11.11
Critical Values of Z

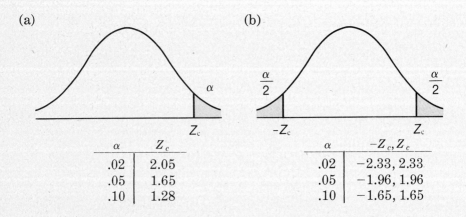

(a)			(b)		
α	Z_c		α	$-Z_c, Z_c$	
.02	2.05		.02	$-2.33, 2.33$	
.05	1.65		.05	$-1.96, 1.96$	
.10	1.28		.10	$-1.65, 1.65$	

Since the SEC analyst is using a .05 significance level and since this is a one-tailed test, the decision rule is

Accept H_o if $Z < 1.65$

Reject H_o if $Z \geq 1.65$

where the test statistic Z is computed by $Z = r_s\sqrt{n-1}$. The analyst has already found that r_s equals .87 based on a sample of size $n = 10$; therefore,

$$Z = .87\sqrt{10-1}$$
$$= +2.61$$

Accordingly, H_o should be rejected. The analyst has shown that it can be concluded that price variability and spread size are related for the entire population of over-the-counter stocks.

11.6
OTHER NONPARAMETRIC TESTS

There are a great number of nonparametric tests which enable the analyst to test all sorts of hypotheses in a wide variety of situations. Two of the standard works which are entirely addressed to describing many of these tests are

Siegel, S. *Nonparametric Statistics for the Behavioral Sciences*, New York: McGraw-Hill Book Company, 1956.

Gibbons, J. *Nonparametric Methods for Quantitative Analysis*, New York: Holt, Rinehart, & Winston, 1976.

These references are easy to read and are quite comprehensive.

PROBLEMS

11.1

How do nonparametric tests differ from parametric tests?

11.2

What are the advantages and disadvantages of nonparametric tests in comparison to parametric tests?

11.3

A large chemical company has nonunion chemical plants in various locations around the country. A sample of 50 employees is taken from each plant, revealing the following attitudes toward unionization.

	Plant A	Plant B	Plant C
Favor Union	12	14	19
Against Union	38	36	31

Can the company conclude that attitudes toward unionization are uniform across the three plants? Use a .10 level of significance.

11.4

Koduck wishes to determine if the proportion of people owning an instamatic camera varies by region around the country. A sample of 30 Westerners shows that 10 own an instamatic. Fifty Easterners are sampled and 10 own an instamatic. Finally 20 Southerners are sampled and 10 of them own an instamatic. At the .05 significance level, should Koduck conclude that the proportion varies by region?

11.5

Flores, an actuary, has sampled 40 life insurance insurees from each of companies A, B, and C. Four of the Company A insurees had made their most recent premium payment during the grace period, eight of the Company B and seven of the Company C insurees also had made their premium payments during the grace period. At the .10 level of significance, can Flores conclude that the proportion of insurees making grace period payments is the same for the three companies?

11.6

Patsy Green, a marketing analyst, wishes to determine if the proportion of older people who own three different makes of American cars, C, F, and P, is the same. One hundred owners of each type of automobile were randomly selected. Thirty-five percent of the car C owners were older people, 30 percent of the car F owners were older, and 44 percent of the car P owners were older. Should the analyst conclude that the proportion of older owners is the same for each type of automobile? Let $\alpha = .05$.

11.7

The Lighting Institute wishes to determine if the light bulb brand is related to the purchaser's income. A study of 80 light bulb purchases reveals the following.

		Brand		
		W	*G*	*S*
	High	10	5	5
Income	*Middle*	11	20	9
	Low	4	10	6

At the .10 significance level, can it be concluded that these two variables are related?

11.8

A food canning company wants to determine if the residents of Phoenix vary in their preferences for vegetables according to the place of their birth. A sample of 200 Phoenicians resulted in the following.

	Birthplace			
	North	*East*	*West*	*South*
Green Beans	8	16	4	4
Spinach	12	40	10	42
Carrots	18	10	20	16

Can the company, at the $\alpha = .05$ significance level, conclude that vegetable preference and birthplace are related?

11.9

Sandra Lynn, a health insurance executive, suspects that the extent of health insurance maternity benefits affects the length of stay in the hospital of mothers who have just given birth to a child. A sample of 200 cases yielded the following results.

		0–3	*4*	*5*	*6*	*7*	*8–*
Maternity	*Poor*	2	15	15	7	5	1
Benefits	*Good*	1	30	40	18	5	2
	Excellent	0	12	20	17	6	4

Does the evidence support the executive's suspicion? Let the level of significance be .10.

11.10

A large farm equipment company has advertised in three different news magazines. Thirty readers of each magazine were asked how much they remembered of the advertisement. The table below shows the results of this survey. Can the company conclude that reader awareness of their ad is the same for each magazine? Use α = .05.

	Magazine		
	U	N	T
Don't Remember Ad	20	25	27
Remember Slightly	6	3	3
Remember Well	4	2	0

11.11

Frank Besnette, a management consultant, is interested in determining if the leadership style of a manager is related to the performance rating the manager receives. A survey of 60 managers revealed the following. Of the 23 managers who received a high performance rating, 10 were autocratic, 8 were participative, and 5 were free-rein. Of the 21 who received good performance ratings, 4 were autocratic, 10 were participative, and 7 were free-rein. Of the 16 managers who received a low performance rating, 6 were autocratic, 2 were participative, and 8 were free-rein. At the .10 significance level, are leadership style and performance rating related?

11.12

(A one-dimensional chi-square test) Torres Tortillas is attempting to determine if shoppers are indifferent between three different package designs for their corn tortillas. A sample of 90 shoppers showed that 22 preferred the Puerto Rican design, 30 preferred the Mexican design, and 38 preferred the Japanese design. The table below presents the observed frequencies.

	Design	
Puerto Rican	Mexican	Japanese
22	30	38

If the null hypothesis is that each design is equally preferred, what would be the expected frequencies for the table above? Use the chi-square test in order to accept or reject the null hypothesis.

Use the .05 significance level. In this type of test which was not discussed in the text, the degrees of freedom equal $c - 1$, where c equals the number of columns.

11.13

In Problem 9.10 of Chapter 9 it was indicated that the analysis of variance cannot be used. Use the Kruskal-Wallis test on this data to determine if the three systems differ. Assume that the same flyer is involved in all the tests and that all of the tests are conducted at the same place. Use a level of significance of .10.

11.14

Fifteen new employees of Wilhelm & Weber of Germany were given formal job training and 15 were given only on-the-job training. A year later the productivity of these 30 workers was checked. Can Wilhelm & Weber assume that the type of training makes no difference with regard to productivity? Use $\alpha = .10$.

Productivity Ratings

Formal: 18, 42, 16, 51, 19, 40, 38, 29, 27, 32, 48, 26, 28, 20, 31
O-J-T: 17, 54, 25, 34, 36, 45, 41, 24, 49, 47, 33, 23, 37, 47, 21

11.15

A chemical company is testing two chemical pesticides and a biological pest control method. Eighteen separate plots of tomatoes are tested where six of the plots receive each method of pest control. The results of this experiment are shown below where the yields of each plot are recorded.

LSDWHAP	*DDTNT*	*Cannibal Aphids*
46.2	41.9	33.3
36.5	28.5	31.2
26.3	47.3	26.9
34.9	48.1	35.0
35.2	44.3	36.0
27.9	35.6	35.4

At the .10 significance level, can the company conclude that the three methods vary in effectiveness?

11.16

The New York Department of Motor Vehicles has received a number of complaints that certain service stations, which perform the state inspections, require the motorists to have unnecessary minor repairs before the inspection sticker is issued. Samples of the bills of inspected autos at four service stations are taken. The sizes of the sampled bills are shown below. At the .10 significance level, can the NYDMV conclude that there are differences among these four stations?

Station

A	B	C	D
$4.68	$ 3.85	$2.00	$1.45
0	0	8.40	1.17
2.20	14.36	.50	.95
.80	4.50	5.15	.82
1.50	7.26	5.12	6.84
	8.10	5.45	

11.17

The Metropolitan Museum of Art has eight modern paintings on display. Two well-known art critics have been asked to rank the eight according to their values as works of art. The artists names, however, are covered so that the critics will not be influenced by this information. The judgments of the critics are given below. Determine the rank correlation. Comment on the critics and/or the nature of modern art.

Painting:	A	B	C	D	E	F	G	H
Critic Goya:	8	1	7	2	3	5	4	6
Critic Tooloose:	6	3	7	8	2	5	1	4

11.18

The National Association of Managers has ranked nine companies according to their corporate social involvement and according to their profitability. A low rank indicates low social involvement and low profitability. Compute the rank correlation between these two variables.

Company	Social Involvement	Profitability
A	1	1
B	3	2
C	5	4
D	6	7
E	2	8
F	9	9
G	8	6
H	4	5
I	7	3

11.19

The realty firm of Zen & Company has information on 12 homes that have recently been sold in Flagstaff. All of the homes have about 2,000 square feet of floor space. The ages of the homes and their selling prices are given below. At the .10 significance level, is there evidence to indicate that age and price are related?

Home	Age	Price
A	2.3 years	$71,500
B	14.5	64,300
C	6.3	80,000
D	9.1	72,000
E	3.8	78,400
F	5.1	76,000
G	26.3	68,900
H	1.1	70,000
I	.8	71,200
J	17.9	72,300
K	11.0	69,750
L	6.2	75,600

11.20

Fuji Appliance is wondering if the amount of newspaper advertising is related to appliance sales. For ten weeks the dealer recorded advertising expenditures and gross appliance sales. These values are given below.

Week	Newspaper Advertising	Gross Sales
1	$100	$4,000
2	346	8,000
3	42	2,900
4	79	4,300
5	220	5,700
6	840	8,900
7	652	7,600
8	145	3,500
9	0	3,120
10	95	3,860

Can the appliance dealer conclude that advertising and sales are positively correlated? Let $\alpha = .20$.

11.21

A financial analyst wishes to determine if the price-earnings ratio of a stock is related in any way to dividend yield. A sample of 14 American Stock Exchange stocks reveals the following.

Stock	P-E Ratio	Yield
A	6.2	6.1%
B	12.5	0
C	9.8	2.4
D	4.1	3.8
E	4.2	6.5
F	6.3	4.8
G	8.4	1.3
H	15.1	1.1
I	7.9	5.3
J	9.1	2.6
K	4.5	6.7
L	5.2	6.0
M	8.7	5.2
N	8.9	4.1

Using a two-tailed test at the .05 significance level, can it be concluded that the price-earnings ratio and yield are dependent variables?

CHAPTER 12   DECISION THEORY

12.1
INTRODUCTION

Through *decision theory* economic quantities like costs, revenues, and profits are joined with probability for the sake of making a decision. The analyst constructs a decision model which sets forth the various relationships between the economic consequences and the probabilities. This model becomes an abstract representation of a real-world decision situation which the decision maker faces. After constructing an adequate model, the decision maker proceeds to solve the model. Solving the model consists of determining the best decision in view of the decision maker's objectives. In this chapter the basic principles of constructing and solving simple decision models will be studied.

12.2
DECISION MODEL

A decision model is an abstract representation of a real-world decision situation. Typically, a decision model is comprised of four parts. The four parts of a decision model are

1. Acts
2. States
3. Probabilities of the states
4. Payoffs

The *acts* consist of the several alternative actions the decision maker faces. Ultimately, the decision maker must decide which act to implement. The act to be selected should be the act which contributes the most toward the achievement of the decision maker's objectives. A production manager, for example, might be faced with the following three acts:

a_1: Build a large factory

a_2: Build a small factory

a_3: Do not build another factory

The manager then wishes to select the act which will maximize the company's profits.

The second part of a decision model consists of the *states of nature*. The states of nature refer to the possible occurrences which have direct implications for the situation at hand. For example, the states which might be of concern to the production manager above are

S_1: High demand for the company's product

S_2: Moderate demand

S_3: Low demand

These states of nature are always mutually exclusive and collectively exhaustive.

The third part of a decision model is composed of the *probabilities* of the various states of nature. These probabilities may be subjectively or empirically determined. (See Section 2.2 of Chapter 2.) In the case at hand, the probabilities of the states might be

$P(S_1) = .15$

$P(S_2) = .50$

$P(S_3) = .35$

Thus, the decision maker believes, for example, that there is a 15 percent chance that the demand for the company's product will be high. Since the states of nature are mutually exclusive and collectively exhaustive, the probabilities of the states will add to one. These probabilities form a probability distribution where the random variable is the state.

The fourth part of a decision model consists of the *payoffs*. The payoffs are the economic consequences of various combinations of the acts and states. For example, if a large factory is built, a_1, and the demand for the product proves to be moderate, S_2, the resulting profit might be $20,000,000. Table 12.1 presents a decision model for the decision situation being discussed. Notice that there are a total of nine payoffs displayed in the model. There is a payoff for each combination of a_i and S_j. We shall now consider another decision model where the payoffs will be deliberately calculated.

TABLE 12.1

A Decision Model

		a_1: Large Factory	a_2: Small Factory	a_3: No New Factory
$P(S_1) = .15$	S_1: High Demand	$45,000,000	$35,000,000	$10,000,000
$P(S_2) = .50$	S_2: Moderate Demand	20,000,000	25,000,000	10,000,000
$P(S_3) = .35$	S_3: Low Demand	0	5,000,000	10,000,000

The leadership of the MORONs has just finished a brainstorming session where this year's big outdoor adventure has been planned. This year the Masochistic Order of Roaming Outdoor Neophytes has decided to sponsor a float down the Amazon. The plans call for the MORONs to dive from a low flying jet airliner into the headwaters of the Amazon. After hitting the water, the MORONs will each inflate a nickel balloon and ride it down the river to the sea where they will be picked up for their return flight to Detroit. The leaders of the MORONs have decided that they will promote the trip among their membership at a price of $1,200 for the round-trip flight to the Amazon from Detroit. At this price it is uncertain as to how many members will make the trip. Based on past experience, the MORON leaders believe that 100, 150, or 200 members will make the trip at $1,200 per ticket; the subjectively assessed probabilities of these events or states are .5, .3, and .2, respectively.

The MORON leaders next contacted several airlines to see what kind of charter deals could be negotiated. Only two airlines offered charter arrangements which seemed competitive. Amazon Airways said that they would fly 100 to 200 people at the rate of $950 per person. World Airlines offered a somewhat more complex arrangement. WA stated that they would charge the MORONs $1,000 per ticket if 100 people make the trip. However, for every person over 100 that goes, everyone's ticket would be reduced by

$2. For example, if 103 people went, then each ticket of the 103 passengers would cost $994. This represents a $6 discount from $1,000; this discount applies since there were three people in excess of 100. Similarly, if 200 people went, the discount for each passenger's ticket would be (200-100)($2) which equals $200. The MORON leaders must decide which airline to use. Regardless of the airline chosen, the leaders are charging their members $1,200 per person. The difference between $1,200 and the actual cost of the ticket will be deposited in Davy Jones National Bank in order to fund future activities.

In the decision situation described, there are two acts:

a_1: Charter Amazon Airways

a_2: Charter World Airlines

The three states of nature are

S_1: 100 MORONs make the Amazon trip

S_2: 150 make the trip

S_3: 200 make the trip

The probabilities of these states are

$P(S_1) = .5$

$P(S_2) = .3$

$P(S_3) = .2$

Finally, the payoffs are shown in Table 12.2. These payoffs are profits. Let us consider how each is computed.

If a_1 is selected, each ticket costs $950. Since the MORON leadership charges $1,200 per ticket, a profit of $1,200 - 950$ or $250 is made for each ticket that is sold. If 100 tickets are sold, S_1, then

TABLE 12.2_____

Decision Model for the MORONs

Probability	State	a_1: Amazon Airways	a_2: World Airlines
.5	S_1: 100	$25,000	$20,000
.3	S_2: 150	37,500	45,000
.2	S_3: 200	50,000	80,000

the profit is (100)($250) = $25,000. If 150 tickets are sold, S_2, then the profit is (150)($250) = $37,500. If 200 passengers make the trip, S_3, then the profit is (200)($250) = $50,000. These three profits or payoffs are recorded under a_1 in Table 12.2. If a_2 is selected, the cost of a ticket varies depending on how many members make the trip. The total cost of 100 tickets is (100)($1,000) = $100,000. When the leaders sell these 100 tickets at $1,200 each, the gross revenue will be (100)($1,200) = $120,000. Therefore, the profit when S_1 occurs is $120,000 − 100,000 = $20,000. If S_2 occurs, then the leaders will collect a total of (150)($1,200) = $180,000. In this case where 150 MORONs make the trip, WA will charge $900 per person. This is because 50 people more than 100 go and WA gives a discount of $2 for every person in excess of 100 who goes. Therefore, WA's bill will be (150)($900) = $135,000. Hence, the profit to the leaders will be $180,000 − 135,000 = $45,000. Similarly, the profit for (a_2, S_3) can be found to equal $80,000.

With the decision model of Table 12.2 constructed, the MORON leaders have a concise, abstract representation of the decision situation that is being faced. This model may now be solved by selecting the act which is optimal from a profits perspective.

12.3

EXPECTATION PRINCIPLE

The most widely accepted method of solving a decision model is through the application of the *expectation principle*. According to the expectation principle, the act which has the greatest expected profit (or least expected cost) is the optimal act.

The concept of an expected value was introduced in Section 3.4 of Chapter 3. It was shown there that the expected value of the random variable X is defined as

$$E(X) = \Sigma X P(X)$$

Expected values of a function of a random variable were considered in Section 3.7. Analogous to this material in Chapter 3, the expected profit of an act is determined by

$$E(P) = \Sigma \text{ (Profit) (Probability)}$$

where the summation extends over each state of nature. Therefore, the expected profit of a_1 in Table 12.2 is

$$E(P_1) = (\$25,000)(.5) + (\$37,500)(.3) + (\$50,000)(.2)$$
$$= \$33,750$$

The expected profit for a_2 is

$$E(P_2) = (\$20{,}000)(.5) + (\$45{,}000)(.3) + (\$80{,}000)(.2)$$
$$= \$39{,}500$$

Since a_2 has the greater expected profit, a_2 is optimal. The MORON leaders should select World Airlines rather than Amazon Airways.

12.4

EXPECTED VALUE OF PERFECT INFORMATION

It has just been shown that, according to the expectation principle, the MORON leaders should select a_2. The fact that a_2 is optimal before the fact does not mean that it will ultimately prove to have been the best choice. If S_1 were to occur (see Table 12.2), then with a_2, the leaders would make \$20,000 but could have made \$25,000 if a_1 had instead been selected. Furthermore, there is a 50 percent chance that S_1 will occur. Thus, it is evident that the leaders, after it is all over, might have wished that they had selected a_1 instead of a_2. This does not mean, however, that a_1 is better than a_2. It merely means that a_2 is not always better than a_1. On an overall basis, a_2 is better than a_1 according to the expectation principle. Forced to make a decision between a_1 and a_2 at the present time (before the trip), the leaders should select a_2.

Though the Amazon Airways plan would be better if S_1 occurs, the MORON leaders, in accord with the expectation principle, were ready to sign the charter contract with World Airlines. Just then Marquette Research appeared. Marquette told the leaders to wait before signing anything. She then told them that she was gifted with extrasensory perception and that her specialty was fortune telling. At first the MORON leaders doubted Marquette's claim. However, after a few demonstrations they decided that Marquette could indeed see into the future. Marquette then told the leaders that she could tell them exactly how many MORONs would make the Amazon trip. She further stated that this perfect information about which state will occur would cost them \$1,000. The MORON leaders were convinced that Marquette could accurately tell how many MORONs would take the flight, and so they began to wonder if this information was worth \$1,000.

The leaders began to evaluate the situation as follows. They reasoned that if Marquette says S_1 will occur (i.e., 100 persons make the trip), then a_1 is the best act since it yields a profit of \$25,000 as compared to \$20,000 for a_2. If instead Marquette were to say that S_2 will occur, then a_2 should be selected yielding \$45,000.

Likewise, if Marquette says that S_3 will occur, then a_2 is the best act yielding a profit of $80,000. Table 12.3 displays these choices in view of the range of Marquette's possible predictions. It is therefore not difficult to decide which act should be selected if Marquette tells the leaders which state will occur. However, what will be Marquette's prediction? As of now (before Marquette is hired) the leaders believe there is a 50 percent chance that S_1 will occur, and since Marquette's predictions are always perfectly accurate, it can be concluded that there is a 50 percent chance that Marquette will predict S_1. Likewise there is a .30 probability that Marquette will predict S_2 and a .20 probability that Marquette will say that S_3 will occur. In other words, since Marquette's predictions are in perfect harmony with reality, the probabilities of her predictions equal the probabilities of reality (the states). These probabilities are entered in Table 12.3.

The leaders are now close to evaluating the worth of Marquette's services. If Marquette is hired for $1,000, then there is a .50 chance that she will say "S_1 will occur" and then the leaders will choose a_1 and make a profit of $25,000. There is a .30 chance that Marquette will say "S_2 is sure to occur" and then the leaders will choose a_2 and make $45,000. Finally, there is a .20 chance that she will say "S_3 will occur" and then the leaders will select a_3 and make $80,000. Putting all of this together, the Expected Value with Forthcoming Perfect Information is

$$EVFPI = (\$25,000)(.5) + (\$45,000)(.3) + (\$80,000)(.2)$$
$$= \$42,000$$

In other words, with Marquette's forthcoming perfect information (perfect prediction), the leaders have an expected profit of $42,000. The EVFPI is the expected profit which is based on the assumption that perfect information with regard to the state will become available before an act must be selected.

TABLE 12.3
Finding the EVFPI

Marquette Predicts	Best Act Based on Perfect Information	Profit	Probability
S_1	a_1	$25,000	.5
S_2	a_2	45,000	.3
S_3	a_3	80,000	.2

$$EVFPI = (25,000)(.5) + (45,000)(.3) + (80,000)(.2)$$
$$= \$42,000$$

Without Marquette the leaders would have selected a_2 which has an expected profit of $E(P_2) = \$39,500$. This expected profit was computed in Section 12.3. It has just been shown that with Marquette (that is, with forthcoming perfect information), the expected profit is EVFPI = $42,000. Therefore, by using this perfect information, the leaders can increase their expected gain by $2,500. Hence, the value of the information is called the Expected Value of Perfect Information and is found according to

$$\text{EVPI} = \text{EVFPI} - (\text{Expected Value of the Optimal Act})$$
$$= \$42,000 - \$39,500$$
$$= \$2,500$$

If the expected value of perfect information is $2,500 and if this information can be purchased for $1,000, should it be bought? Quite obviously the leaders should be willing to pay $1,000 for $2,500 worth of information. Therefore, the leaders hired Marquette.

Once the decision maker has determined the EVPI for a decision situation, an upper bound has been established on the amount of money that might be spent to acquire further information regarding the state which will occur. If the EVPI equals $2,500, then the decision maker should not spend any more than $2,500 for perfect information regarding the state which will occur. If the information is imperfect, then the decision maker should pay at most some figure below $2,500 for it, depending on how good the information is. Finding the precise value of imperfect information is relatively more difficult than finding the EVPI. More advanced methods of decision theory do exist for determining the value of various sorts of imperfect information. Typically, this imperfect information consists of sample information. Therefore, finding the expected value of sample information, EVSI, is an important consideration in advanced decision theory.

In concluding this section on the value of information, it should be noted that information serves to alter the probabilities of the states in the decision model. In the MORON case, the states and their subjective probabilities as initially given were

State	Probability
S_1: 100 passengers	.5
S_2: 150 passengers	.3
S_3: 200 passengers	.2

Now suppose that instead of hiring Marquette Research, the leaders decide to do some market research on their own. In particular, they randomly sample 25 MORONs in order to get their reactions to the proposed Amazon trip. Suppose that 20 of the 25 people responded enthusiastically to the proposal. With such sample evidence, the leadership would want to change the probabilities of the states. The *prior* probabilities of .5, .3, and .2 might become .3, .3, and .4, respectively. These new probabilities are called *posterior probabilities* of the states, since they come after and are based on the sample information. These posterior probabilities would then replace the prior probabilities in the decision model. The act to be chosen would then be based on the expected profits where the posterior probabilities are used.

It has just been indicated that sample information serves to alter the probabilities of the states of nature. The actual mathematical method by which this is accomplished was not explained. A theorem in probability theory known as *Bayes Theorem* is the vehicle by which the posterior probabilities are found. Bayes Theorem takes the prior probabilities (.5, .3, and .2) and modifies them on the basis of sample evidence (enthusiastic response of 20 of the 25 sampled people) to yield posterior probabilities (.3, .3, and .4) of the states. Being based on the sample evidence, the posterior probabilities should be used to make the decision. Of course, if sample information is not collected, then the decision maker bases the decision on the original decision model with the prior probabilities.

The actual method of applying Bayes Theorem for revising the probabilities of the states is not presented here, as it is a somewhat involved technique. The reader who is interested in Bayes Theorem might refer to Chapter 4 of David Heinze, *Management Science: Introductory Concepts and Applications*, which is published by South-Western Publishing Company. Also, many other elementary management science texts as well as statistics texts cover the application of Bayes Theorem.

12.5

DECISION DIAGRAMS

The decision model, as constructed earlier in the chapter, is the simplest way of representing a decision situation which confronts the decision maker. Such a model is not designed, however, to represent situations where there is a series of decisions to be made. In situations where more than one decision is to be made, a *decision diagram* is often a useful modeling technique. A decision diagram is quite similar to a probability tree. It would be a good idea to review Section 2.7 of Chapter 2 before continuing this discussion of decision diagrams.

A decision diagram is an orderly, logical diagram of the sequence of events (or states) and decisions that the decision maker faces. An example will be given to illustrate the nature of a decision diagram.

Cali Rose is a Texas company which is involved in the exploration for natural gas. After sinking several exploratory wells in Zacatecas, Mexico, Cali Rose hit a large field of gas which has an estimated market value of 500 megapesos. Having found the gas field, Cali Rose has three alternatives which are denoted by a_1, a_2, and a_3. The first alternative is to relinquish all rights to the gas field. If Cali Rose were to do this, the Mexican government would make a payment to Cali Rose equal to 5 percent of the market value of the gas. Thus, Cali Rose would receive $(.05)(500) = 25$ megapesos. The second alternative, a_2, is for Cali Rose to construct a gas pipeline from the gas field to Laredo, Texas. The third alternative, a_3, is to build the gas pipeline jointly with Mexico. The pipeline in this case would be known as the Mexicali Rose Pipeline.

Figure 12.1 presents the decision diagram for the situation which Cali Rose faces. The diagram begins with a square; this square is an *act fork*. The decision maker may select any of the branches emanating from an act fork. On top of the branches several words of identification are given. Below the branches, any monetary consequences precipitated by selecting the branch in question are shown. Under a_1 is "+25" which indicates that Cali Rose would receive 25 megapesos if a_1 is selected. If a_2 is selected, Cali Rose will have to pay 20 megapesos to the Mexican Tax and Regulation Comission; this payment is a pipeline proposal filing fee. Therefore, "−20" appears under this branch. If a_3 is selected there is no filing fee, since the Mexican government does not require a filing fee if it is a party to the pipeline.

Only the events and acts emanating from a_2 will be described. Once this description is given, the branches proceeding from a_3 will be self-explanatory. After the Cali Rose pipeline proposal is filed, a_2, the Mexican Tax and Regulatory Commission will decide whether the gas will be taxed at 10 percent or 20 percent of its market value. Cali Rose figures that the probability is .4 that the tax will be 10 percent and that there is a .6 probability that the tax will be 20 percent. These two possibilities (branches) emanate from a circle. A circle represents a *chance fork* in a decision diagram. In a chance fork, the decision maker does not control the branch that occurs. Rather, it is said that chance determines the branch. Therefore, the probability of each branch is placed on the branch; typically, the probability is placed in parentheses above the branch. The branches (events or states) emanating from a chance fork must always be mutually exclusive and collectively exhaustive. Therefore, their probabilities add to one.

If a 10 percent tax ruling occurs, Cali Rose will go ahead with the construction of the pipeline. It will cost either 200 or 400 megapesos to build. However, if a 20 percent tax ruling occurs, Cali Rose may decide to abandon the pipeline. Because Cali Rose must decide whether to go ahead or abandon if a 20 percent tax ruling occurs, these two alternatives flow from a square which is an act fork. If Cali Rose goes ahead with the pipeline, then there would be either a low construction cost of 200 megapesos or a high cost of 400 megapesos. The probabilities of these, as Cali Rose sees it, are .5 and .5. After construction of the pipeline is completed, there will be a 500 megapeso revenue less the tax. Such is the nature of a decision diagram.

Before the decision diagram is solved, it is necessary to add all the costs and revenues along each path from the beginning to the end of the diagram. This yields a net gain for each end position on the diagram. For example, for the sequence of

a_2 — 20 percent Tax — Go Ahead — Low Cost — Gas Revenue less Taxes

the net gain is $-20 - 200 + 500 - 100$ or 180 megapesos. If Cali Rose were to follow the sequence of

a_3 — 10 percent Tax — High Cost — Gas Revenue less Taxes

then the net gain would be $-150 + 250 - 25$, which equals 125 megapesos. The net gains corresponding to each of the end positions are shown in Figure 12.1.

We shall now consider the method of determining the optimal act.

12.6

BACKWARD INDUCTION

Decision diagrams are solved by the expectation principle, just as the simpler model of Section 12.2 was solved. The act with the greatest expected gain (or least expected cost) is the act which is optimal.

The process of applying the expectation principle to a decision diagram is known as *backward induction*. To begin, all the intermediate costs and revenues attached to the branches are erased; only the net gains at the end positions are used. Figure 12.2 presents the Cali Rose decision diagram with only the end position net gains shown.

FIGURE 12.1

Decision Diagram for Cali Rose (Payoffs in Megapesos)

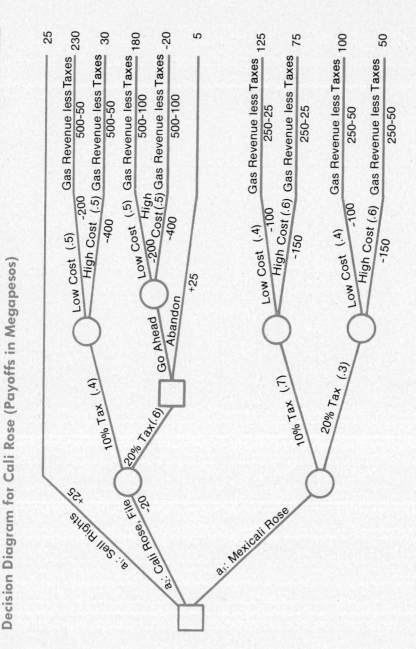

FIGURE 12.2

Decision Diagram with Payoffs at End Positions

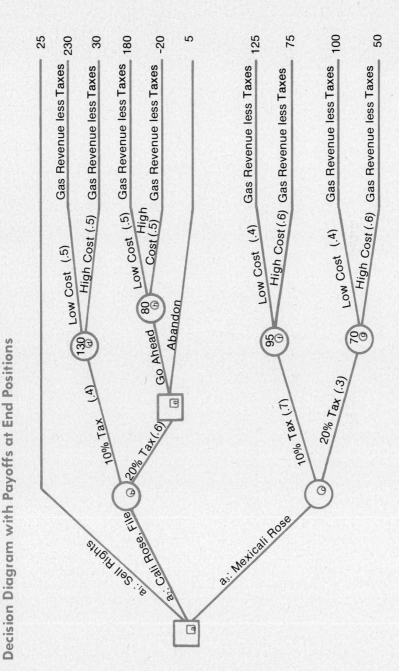

To begin the actual solution process, the analyst finds a fork which has all of its branches leading directly to an end position. Chance fork ⓗ is such a fork. Since fork ⓗ is a chance fork, the expected value of the gains at the ends of its branches is computed using the respective probabilities on the branches. For chance fork ⓗ the expected value is

$$\text{Expected Gain for } ⓗ = (.5)(180) + (.5)(-20)$$
$$= 80$$

This expected gain of 80 megapesos is then placed inside the circle of fork ⓗ. Since 80 megapesos is the expected value of chance fork ⓗ, it can be said that this particular chance situation with its two branches is equivalent to 80 megapesos. This means that fork ⓗ, with its two branches, can be replaced by a single value of 80 megapesos.

Now another fork is sought which has all of its branches leading directly to an end position. Chance fork ⓓ is such a fork. The expected value of chance fork ⓓ is computed according to

$$\text{Expected Gain for } ⓓ = (.5)(230) + (.5)(30)$$
$$= 130$$

This expected gain is entered in the circle of fork ⓓ. The expected gain will replace this fork with its two branches in a later part of this analysis.

Another fork is sought which has all of its branches leading directly to end positions. Chance fork ⓕ is such a fork. Its expected value is

$$\text{Expected Gain for } ⓕ = (.4)(125) + (.6)(75)$$
$$= 95$$

This expected value of 95 megapesos, which is equivalent to fork ⓕ, is placed in the circle of fork ⓕ.

Another fork is sought which has all of its branches leading directly to end positions. Chance fork ⓖ is the last such fork remaining in Figure 12.2. Its expected value is

$$\text{Expected Gain for } ⓖ = (.4)(100) + (.6)(50)$$
$$= 70$$

This expected gain is then placed inside the circle of fork ⓖ to indicate that fork ⓖ is equivalent to a single payment of 70 megapesos.

The analyst, in applying backward induction, next reduces the decision diagram of Figure 12.2 to that of Figure 12.3. All the

FIGURE 12.3

A Reduced Decison Diagram

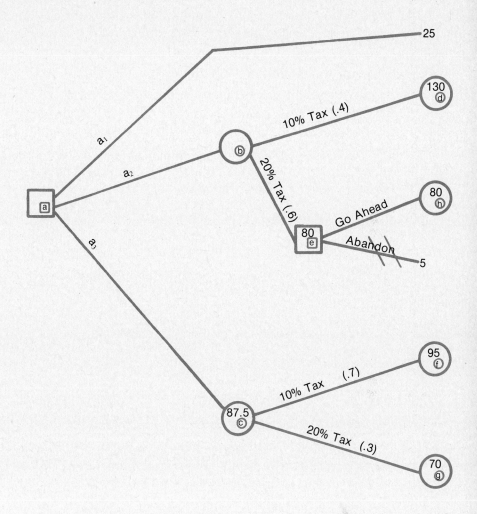

branches that were used to find expected values are deleted; only the equivalent expected values in the forks are preserved. These expected values, which are equivalent to the branches from which they were derived, are now considered to be end position values in the diagram of Figure 12.3. Then the process continues as before.

In Figure 12.3 a fork is now sought which has all of its branches leading directly to end positions. Chance fork ⓒ is such a fork. Its expected value is

$$\text{Expected Gain for } ⓒ = (.7)(95) + (.3)(70)$$
$$= 87.5$$

Thus, the expected profit of 87.5 megapesos is placed in the circle of fork ⓒ. Fork ⓒ, with its two branches, is monetarily equivalent to 87.5 megapesos.

Another fork is sought which has all of its branches leading directly to end positions. Act fork [e] is such a fork. Since fork [e] is an act fork, the decision maker gets to select the branch. If Cali Rose were at [e], the company would have a choice between "Go Ahead" and "Abandon." Since "Go Ahead" offers an expected gain of 80 megapesos as compared to 5 megapesos for "Abandon," Cali Rose should select "Go Ahead." Therefore, 80 is placed in the square of act fork [e] and the "Abandon" act is crossed off, since Cali Rose should not take that act if ever given the choice at [e]. This has already been done in Figure 12.3.

There are no longer any forks in Figure 12.3 whose branches all lead directly to end positions. All the branches emanating from the forks that have just been evaluated are now deleted. The result is the diagram of Figure 12.4. The diagram of Figure 12.4 is equivalent to that of Figure 12.3. Only chance fork ⓑ in Figure 12.4 has all of its branches leading directly to an end position. The expected value of fork ⓑ is

$$\text{Expected Gain for } ⓑ = (.4)(130) + (.6)(80)$$
$$= 100$$

Thus 100 megapesos is entered in circle ⓑ. It is the value of this chance fork.

The decision diagram of Figure 12.4 is now reduced to that of Figure 12.5 by deleting all the branches used to compute the expected value of ⓑ. From Figure 12.5 it is seen that the expected gain for a_1 is 25 megapesos, the expected gain for a_2 is 100 megapesos, and the expected gain for a_3 is 87.5 megapesos. Therefore, by the expectation princple, a_2 is the optimal act. After selecting a_2, Cali Rose should select "Go Ahead" if the company ever comes to act fork [e] in real life.

By following the procedure of backward induction as illustrated, the reader can analyze a decision diagram in order to determine the optimal act(s). Always be sure that the decision diagram mirrors the real world sequence of acts and events. After constructing the decision diagram, discard all the intermediate revenues and costs and keep only the end position values. Then by backward induction, analyze the forks leading directly to end positions. Replace chance forks with their equivalent expected values, and replace act forks with the best act (branch). In this fashion the decision diagram is decomposed in order to arrive at the optimal initial decision.

FIGURE 12.4_____

A Reduced Decision Diagram

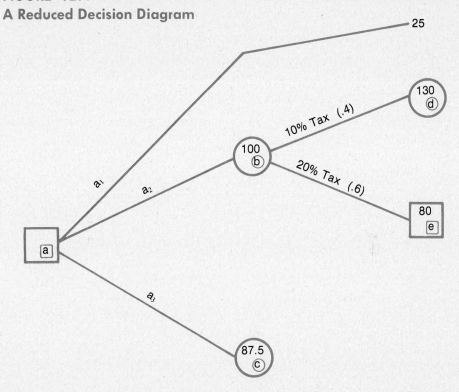

FIGURE 12.5_____

Final Reduced Decision Diagram (a₂ is Optimal)

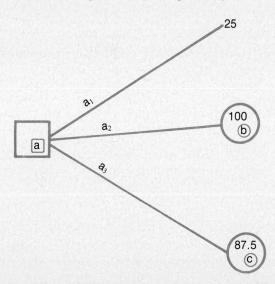

PROBLEMS

12.1

What are the four parts of a decision model? Briefly describe each part.

12.2

In the following decision model, the payoffs are expressed in terms of profits. Use the expectation principle to select the optimal act.

		a_1	a_2	a_3
.2	S_1	800	300	900
.4	S_2	400	600	100
.3	S_3	500	500	400
.1	S_4	700	200	900

12.3

If the payoffs of Problem 12.2 are costs, use the expectation principle to determine the optimal act.

12.4

If the payoffs in the following decision model are costs, use the expectation principle to determine the optimal act.

		a_1	a_2	a_3	a_4
.4	S_1	80	90	0	50
.4	S_2	60	10	90	40
.2	S_3	20	0	70	80

12.5

(a) You are offered a choice between a_1 and a_2 where the payoffs in gains are described in the decision model below. Which act should you select according to the expectation principle? Is this the act that you would in fact select if given the choice?

		a_1	a_2
.5	Heads	$1	$50
.5	Tails	$1	0

(b) Answer the two questions asked in part (a) for the decision model below. Is the expectation principle always an appropriate method of selecting an act?

		a_1	a_2
.5	*Heads*	$1,000,000	$50,000,000
.5	*Tails*	$1,000,000	0

12.6

A production manager is aware of two possible layout designs for a machine shop. The monthly cost of layout A is given by

$$C_A = 20 + 4X$$

and the monthly cost of layout B is given by

$$C_B = 60 + 2X$$

In both instances X represents the monthly number of jobs handled by the machine shop. X may be 15, 20, or 30 jobs; the probabilities of these values are .2, .5, and .3, respectively. Set up a decision model for the production manager and then solve it using the expectation principle.

12.7

An insurance company is designing a fire insurance policy for a certain small business. The probability of a $1,000 fire is .013, the probability of a $40,000 fire is .0015, and the probability of no fire is .9855. What is the expected fire loss if the insurance company insures the small business? The insurance company computes the premium according to

$$\text{Premium} = (1.1)\,[E(FL)] + 50$$

where $E(FL)$ is the expected fire loss. What will the premium be?

12.8

Dr. Osvaldo has invented a new machine for use in testing blood. Osvaldo has three alternatives regarding the manufacture and sale of the machine. The alternatives are

a_1: Osvaldo manufactures and sells

a_2: Sell patent to Medi-Manu Company

a_3: Selling patent to Canter Medical Ltd.

With a_1 Osvaldo can make a profit equal to

$$P = 500X - 50,000$$

where X represents the number of machines that are sold. With a_2 Osvaldo will receive $10,000 for the patent and a royalty of $50 for each machine that Medi-Manu sells. With a_3 Osvaldo would receive $14,000 for the patent and would receive no royalty payments. Osvaldo figures that either 50, 100, or 200 of the machines will be sold. The respective probabilities are .10, .30, and .60.
(a) Use the expectation principle to select the optimal act.
(b) Find the EVPI. Why is the EVPI important to Osvaldo?

12.9

Bethany & Kramer is a large department store chain which is considering the possibility of selling through a catalog in addition to through its retail outlets. If the catalog idea were implemented, Bethany & Kramer would give away catalogs to any customer desiring one. The cost of giving away a catalog is $2.00. The annual average purchase from the catalog per person receiving the catalog will be either $5, $10, or $15 with probabilities of .3, .5, and .2, respectively. The markup, based on selling price, on all the items in the catalog is 25 percent. Should Bethany & Kramer get into the catalog sales business?
(a) Set up a decision model.
(b) Use the expectation principle to make a decision.

12.10

High Country Farms has leased an alpine meadow in Arizona for the sake of grazing sheep this summer. High Country must decide whether to purchase 1,000 or 2,000 sheep. The condition of the grazing land is dependent on summer rainfall. If there are 12 inches of rainfall, High Country will make $7 per sheep if 2,000 are grazing and $9 per sheep if 1,000 are grazing. If there are 8 inches of rainfall, the respective profits per sheep will be $5 and $9. If there are 4 inches of rainfall, the respective profits per sheep for 2,000 and 1,000 sheep are $1 and $6. The probability of 12 inches of rain is .2, the probability of 8 inches is .6, and the probability of 4 inches is .2.
(a) Set up the decision model for High Country.
(b) Solve the model using the expectation principle.
(c) Determine the EVPI.

12.11

Legend City is a bankrupt regional resort. The bankruptcy trustees are willing to lease Legend City for $500,000 per year. Naomi

Brooks, Jane Jestila, and Tommy Buck are three wealthy investors who wish to lease Legend City. The investors believe that either 60,000, 70,000, or 80,000 people will visit Legend City in a year if the admission price is $10. The probabilities of these numbers of visitors are .1, .5, and .4, respectively. The investors also figure that it would cost an additional $200,000 per year to keep Legend City open.

(a) Set up the decision model.
(b) Use the expectation principle to determine if Legend City should be leased.
(c) Find the EVPI.
(d) If the admission fee were reduced to $7 per person, then the number of visitors would increase by 30 percent. Should $7 or $10 be the admission fee?

12.12

Gook Appliance has been offered the opportunity to purchase four microwave ovens at $100 each from a local wholesaler who has declared bankruptcy. The wholesaler has 1,000 of these ovens and it is known that 20 percent of them are damaged. The four ovens that Gook would get would be randomly selected from the stock of 1,000 ovens. Gook Appliance can sell a damaged oven for $20 and can sell an undamaged oven for $140. Should the four ovens be purchased?

(a) Set up the decision model. (Hint: the states will be "0 damaged ovens," "1 damaged oven," and so on. The probabilities of the states must be determined by the binomial distribution.)
(b) Use the expectation principle to select the optimal act.

12.13

Ponderosa Concession Company provides cola at the NAU basketball games. PCC purchases cola for $.50 per liter and sells it to the fans for $1.50 per liter. Any cola which is not sold at the end of the game can be returned to the supplier, who pays $.20 per liter for it. The demand, X, for the cola at a game has the following distribution:

X	$P(X)$
10 liters	.1
12	.5
14	.4

In order to maximize the expected profit, should PCC buy 10, 12, or 14 liters?

(a) Set up the decision model with the three acts.
(b) Use the expectation principle to select an act.
(c) Determine the EVPI.

12.14

Determine the EVPI for Problem 12.2.

12.15

Determine the EVPI for Problem 12.4. Remember that the payoffs are in costs; this will change your method of finding the EVPI somewhat.

12.16

Why is a decision maker often interested in determining the EVPI?

12.17

How is Bayes Theorem used in decision theory?

12.18

Use backward induction to determine the optimal acts for the following decision diagram.

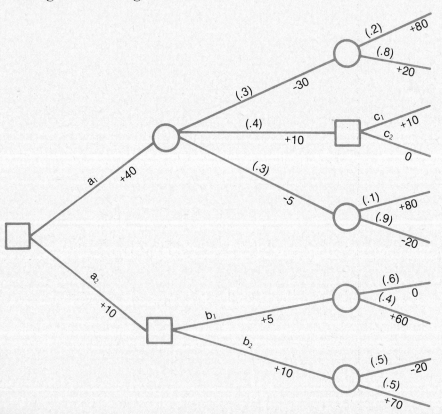

12.19

Use backward induction to determine the optimal acts for the following decision diagram.

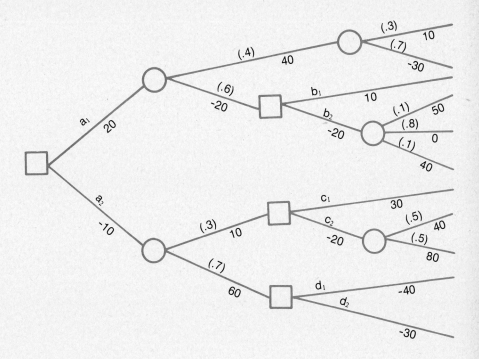

12.20

Draw a decision diagram for the decision situation of Problem 12.10.

12.21

You are offered either a_1 or a_2. With a_1 you will receive a payment of \$50. If you should select a_2, then a coin will be flipped and you will receive \$100 if heads appears but lose \$20 if tails occurs. If heads occurred, you must flip the coin again receiving \$200 for heads on this flip and losing \$40 if tails occurs. In either case the game is over. However, if on the first flip you got tails, then a die is rolled and you get a monetary reward equal to ten times the number of dots which turn up. Then the game is over.

(a) Draw a decision diagram for the situation given.
(b) Use backward induction to choose the best act.

12.22

The Electric and Power Company must decide whether its next electricity generating plant should be a nuclear facility or a coal facility. A nuclear plant would cost $310,000,000 to construct. Nuclear fuel would cost either $20,000,000 or $50,000,000 depending on whether breeder reactors are developed or not. The probability that breeder reactors will be developed (thus producing relatively cheap nuclear fuel) is .50. If a coal plant is constructed it will cost $100,000,000. If there is labor unrest among coal miners, this will cost EPCO about $60,000,000 because of the various costs which are precipitated due to an uncertain supply of coal. EPCO sees a 70 percent chance of labor unrest. If labor unrest prevails, there is an .80 probability of high coal costs of $300,000,000, and there is a .20 chance of moderate coal costs of $200,000,000. If there is no labor unrest (the probability of this is .3), then there is a 50 percent chance of high coal costs of $300,000,000 and a 50 percent chance of moderate coal costs of $200,000,000. Draw a decision diagram for EPCO and use backward induction to determine whether EPCO should build a nuclear plant or a coal-fired plant.

CHAPTER 13

TIME SERIES

13.1

INTRODUCTION

What would you answer if someone asked you, "How much did you weigh?" Chances are you would answer with another question like "When?" The reason, of course, is that you were several weights in the past and to answer specifically you need to know the specific time to which the questioner is referring. If you were then asked, "How much did you weigh in 1970?" you would be able to give a specific answer. Obviously, a person's weight is related to time.

In Chapter 10 it was shown that if two variables are correlated, then one of the variables can be used to estimate the other. In this chapter we will use time as the independent variable to estimate some other variable such as sales. Thus, we will be able to estimate or forecast a company's sales in two years, in five years, and so on based on the pattern of sales over the past years.

To determine the relationship of time to a variable like sales, a set of observations of the variable is taken over time. This set of data is called a *time series*. The observations in a time series will be denoted by $Y_1, Y_2, Y_3, \ldots, Y_t, Y_{t+1}, \ldots, Y_n$. Here Y refers to some variable like sales, and the subscripts refer to the various times. For example, if the annual sales of Northwest Forest Industries were recorded for the past five years, the time series would consist of $Y_1 = \$12,000,000$, $Y_2 = \$14,250,000$, $Y_3 = \$13,766,000$, $Y_4 = \$18,997,000$, and $Y_5 = \$19,780,000$. It is assumed that the time interval which separates observations is always the same. In the example just given, the time interval was a year.

*This chapter was written by Daniel G. Brooks of Arizona State University.

This set of observations consisting of $Y_1, Y_2, \ldots, Y_n$ is different from the data collected in other chapters because the order of the observations is very important now. The values of the observations are still important, but the order in which these values appeared is crucial to answering questions about how this variable (sales) acted in the past or how it will act in the future. This, in fact, is what makes time series very important in statistics. If the specific form of the relationship of the variable to time can be determined, then not only can past fluctuations in the variable be explained, but future behavior can be predicted.

Examples of time series appear everywhere: in economics, the Dow-Jones daily closing averages, the Consumer Price Index, the yearly GNP; in sports, a player's batting average each year, a team's yearly won-lost record; in personal calculations, a student's grade average each year, an employee's annual income, and so forth. Examples of time series data are graphed in Figures 13.1 and 13.2 by connecting adjacent observations or points with straight lines. Some differences between these two time series can be seen by looking at them, but to say anything more specific would require that some analysis be done. This analysis is broken into two major parts in this chapter: first, to use the observed data to estimate the true relationship between time and the variable under study, and second, to use this estimate of the relationship to forecast future values of the variable.

FIGURE 13.1

Net Annual Change in Business Inventories for the Tribe of Benjamin

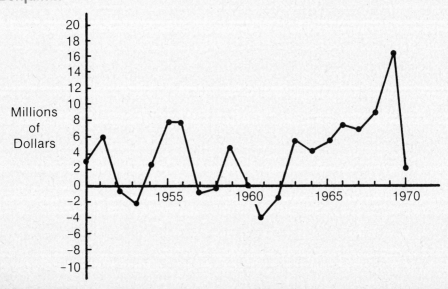

FIGURE 13.2_____

Gross National Product for the Tribe of Benjamin

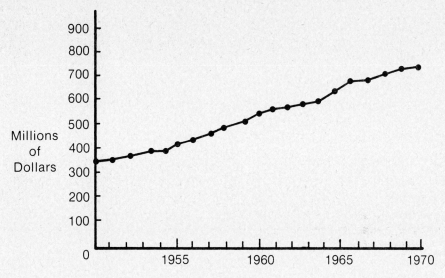

13.2_____

ESTIMATING THE RELATIONSHIP TO TIME

It is often difficult for a person to determine to what extent a variable is related to time. Sometimes a person sees a pattern in a time series when the time series in actuality is only a string of random numbers. Figure 13.3 presents a time series which has been generated by 17 rolls of a die. The number of spots turning up on each roll is denoted by Y. Any patterns you might see in this time series are illusory since they cannot be expected to be repeated. In other cases a person rightly discerns a pattern in the time series. For example, in Figure 13.2, it can be concluded that the GNP is steadily rising. In such a case the observed values of the time series are related to the passage of time in a fairly predictable manner. There are many time series, however, which are in between these two extremes of no relationship to time and a strong relationship to time. For annual rainfall, common-stock yield, or the annual inflation rate measured over the past 30 years, the relationship to time is not always easy to discern.

We now consider the cases where the observed values of the time series are related to the passage of time. In these cases the major influences on the time series data are called *components*. These components which may influence the pattern in a time series are isolated so that each can be analyzed separately to see

FIGURE 13.3_____

Randomly Generated Time Series

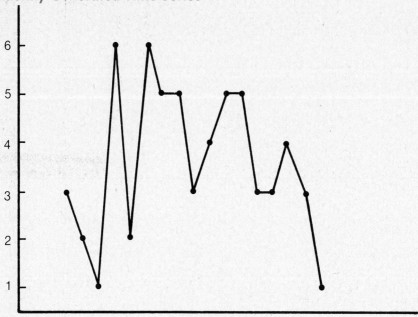

its particular effect on the time series. Once these components are formulated, they can be used not only to explain past observations but also to predict future values.

The *classical approach* to analyzing a time series is to separate the influences into four components, which are:

1. Trend (T)

2. Cyclical (C)

3. Seasonal (S)

4. Random or Irregular (I)

A brief overview of these components will be given before considering each in more detail.

Trend

St. Clair Penitentiary, a privately owned institution, absorbs some of the overflow from local public jails. Conrad Flit, who has always run the prison store, notices that he seems to be continually out of stock lately on everything. Checking enrollment figures at St. Clair for the past 30 years, he comes up with the time series graph of Figure 13.4. This time series indicates that the stock outages may be due to the increased number of prisoners staying at St. Clair.

FIGURE 13.4

Enrollment at St. Clair Penitentiary

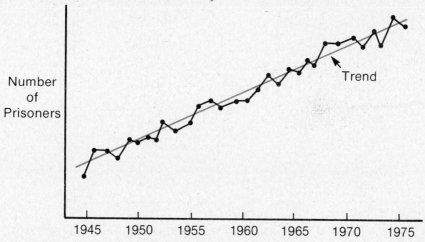

Although there are small fluctuations from year to year, the number of prisoners seems to be steadily increasing. *Trend* is the "long-term" direction or movement of the time series. In this case the number of prisoners reflects population growth in the St. Clair area. The result is the linear trend as shown in Figure 13.4. Sometimes the trend is nonlinear and is thus represented by a smooth, gentle, curved line. Annual operating costs at St. Clair are shown in Figure 13.5; notice that this time series follows a nonlinear trend. In this chapter only linear trends, however, will be considered. Whether linear or nonlinear, the trend is the general, gradual tendency or direction of the time series.

Cycle

If sales at the St. Clair store are plotted against time, as shown in Figure 13.6, it is seen that the trend is linear. It should also be noticed that the time series fluctuates above and then below the trend according to a somewhat repeating pattern. This might be due to the cyclical influence. Cycles in economic time series are quite common as the economy moves from recession to boom and back to recession. Typically we think of a cycle as lasting anywhere from a year or two up to eight years or more. Besides being evident in many economic time series, cycles also appear in time series involving weather and such things as the performance of a football team over the years.

FIGURE 13.5
Operating Costs at St. Clair Penitentiary

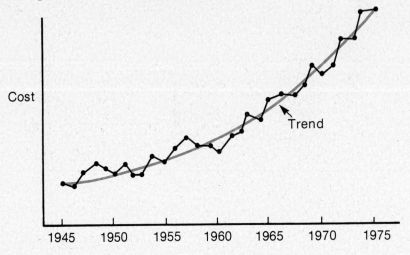

FIGURE 13.6
Store Sales at St. Clair (Dotted Line Follows the Cycles)

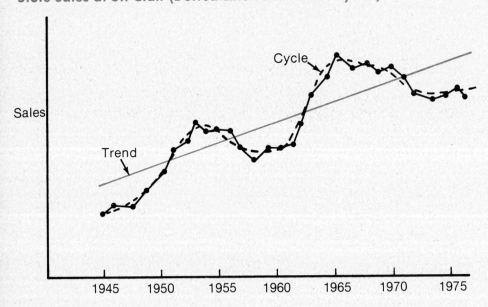

Seasonal

By selecting 5 years from the past 30 and plotting quarterly curio sales, the graph of Figure 13.7 is obtained. A regular fluctuation is observable in that sales rise in the latter part of each year. This, Conrad reasons, reflects the fact that most releases from

FIGURE 13.7

Quarterly Curio Sales at St. Clair Penitentiary

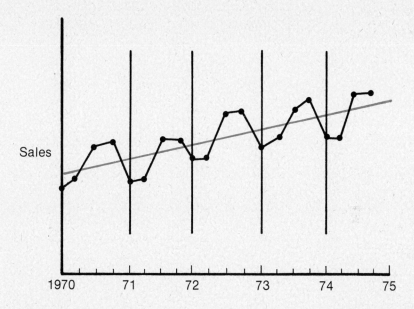

prison occur in the autumn as the squeeze of the year's budget begins to be felt. Those leaving usually buy items to take with them since the prison store is cheaper; therefore, business enjoys a spurt in the third and fourth quarters of each year. *Seasonal fluctuation* is a systematic change in the time series which keeps repeating itself over some fixed time period like a year or a month. The time period is never longer than a year in the case of seasonal fluctuations. High sales at stores on Fridays, long lines at banks on the 15th and 30th of each month, big sales of clothing in March and September, and heavy traffic in the morning and evening are all examples of seasonal fluctuations, as are the cases of high ski rentals in the winter and high turkey sales in November.

Irregular and Random

The small, erratic, unpredictable short-term changes in the time series are attributed to irregular or random influences. These can be one-of-a-kind influences like a strike or a flood or a prison riot, or these changes can be just random fluctuations. Irregular movements in the time series will not be formally considered in the model in this chapter because of their totally unpredictable character.

Figure 13.8 illustrates these four components. The next section presents the classical time series model which shows how these four components can be combined to explain variation in observed time series data.

FIGURE 13.8
Time Series Components

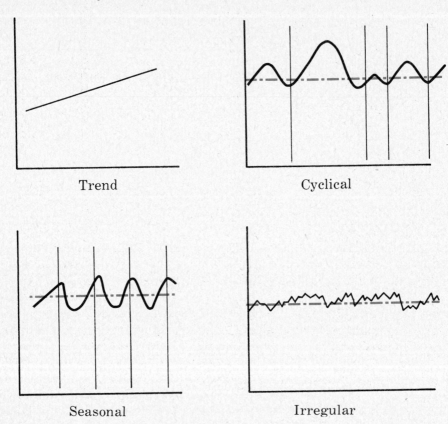

Trend

Cyclical

Seasonal

Irregular

13.3
CLASSICAL TIME SERIES MODEL

Now that the four different components or influences on the observed time series data have been identified, how can they be combined to give the series itself? The most common method of blending the effects of the four components in order to yield a time series is called the *multiplicative model* and is written

$$Y = T \cdot C \cdot S \cdot I$$

Does this model make sense? If the individual terms are thought of in the correct way it does. Think of T as the unadjusted amount of sales at a specified point in time. Thus T, the trend value, is some dollar amount like $200. Then think of C, S, and I as percentage adjustments of this dollar amount. For example, if due to a slump in the business cycle sales are at this time 20 percent below normal, then $C = .8$. The component C functions as a cyclical "deflator." If, in addition, it is the third quarter of the year and sales are 10 percent above normal because of the season, then the seasonal adjustment or multiplier is $S = 1.10$. This seasonal multiplier will "inflate" sales for the third quarter. When the trend, cycle, and seasonal effects are combined, it yields a third quarter sales figure of ($200)(.8)(1.10) or $176. Finally, I reflects the percentage difference between the sales predicted, $176, and the sales actually observed. That is, if actual sales were $Y = \$185$, then I would be found by

$$Y = T \cdot C \cdot S \cdot I$$
$$185 = (176)(I)$$
$$I = 1.05$$

The next two sections show how to estimate the three components T, C, and S in order to model a set of observed data. Since there is no way to predict the irregular influence I, I will not form a part of the analysis. To facilitate the explanation of the use of the classical model, consider the following business problem.

Don Diego Cutter-Bridgework, originally from Britain, worked in the early 1920's in the headquarters office of British Petroleum in Mexico, mostly swatting flies. He had a small house and a small family in Tobasco, a small, hot town at the foot of the Sierra Madre mountains. Wanting to get a little business of his own going on the side, Don Diego considered his meager talents. He wanted a business that was not too mentally taxing, but was primarily inside work with no heavy lifting. He did have a way with animals, but cattle were too much work and there was not much money in smaller animals. Then it came to him: a tribble farm. He would raise tribbles — only a few to start — and then skin them and sell their pelts, which are well known for their quality as well as their beauty.

Although Cutter-Bridgework could not skin tribbles himself, good tribble-skinners could be had quite reasonably, so he started the tribble farm. Tribbles, as it turned out, were cheaper than even Don had expected, so he started with approximately one million of them. The tribbles multiplied nicely. Don Diego sold as many pelts as there were tribbles produced, and what had started out as a sideline became one of the largest known tribble farms in the free world. The pelts seemed to sell briskly, and the loosely run but happy business venture grew over the next several years.

Then, in 1938, something changed which greatly increased Don Diego's interest in his farm. Mexico nationalized foreign petroleum holdings, the headquarters of British Petroleum moved, and Don Diego's financial well-being suddenly rested entirely on the tribble ranch. Sales had been recorded for each quarter of the past four years, and annual sales records were available back to 1929. This data is released here for the first time in Tables 13.1 and 13.2. Although gross sales were respectable, costs were high. A tribble ranch is different from your ordinary ranch. One does not string barbed wire, brand the tribbles, and then just set them loose to graze for their food. Tribbles must be fed, and tribble food is not always cheap. In fact, if food was not found soon, the tribbles would begin to eat each other.

TABLE 13.1_____

Annual Sales in Thousands of Pesos for Cutter-Bridgework

Year		Sales
1929	1	102
1930	2	124
1931	3	175
1932	4	153
1933	5	181
1934	6	228
1935	7	195
1936	8	235
1937	9	231
1938	10	264

TABLE 13.2_____

Quarterly Sales in Thousands of Pesos for Cutter-Bridgework

Quarter	Year			
	1935	1936	1937	1938
1	54	67	71	69
2	39	44	46	54
3	48	60	54	66
4	54	64	60	75
Annual:	195	235	231	264

It was at this point that Don Diego conceived of a brilliant plan: a rat ranch. Now, of course, rats must eat also, but Don Diego had thought of this too: the tribbles would eat the rats and the rats, while they were growing fat for the tribbles, would eat the carcasses of the skinned tribbles. So the tribbles would eat the rats, the rats would eat the tribbles, and Don Diego would get the pelts. However, breeding the number of rats necessary to run the operation would take far too many years. This meant he must import these rats, and that would require a sizeable loan.

With a sizeable loan to be paid off in quarterly installments over the next two years and with the escalating costs of operating his ranches, Don Diego realized that he needed to be able to forecast future sales of the pelts. Gross sales must be sufficient to cover the loan payments and operating costs if Don were to remain in business. So Don then decided to use the classical model for the sake of predicting quarterly sales over the next two years. Through this analysis, Don was ultimately able to determine the financial viability of his business. We shall now consider this analysis.

13.4

TREND ANALYSIS

Before future patterns in sales can be predicted, past patterns of changes in sales must be understood. To be able to more clearly see the past patterns of change, it is helpful to get rid of random fluctuations and consider the long-term, gradual change (trend) in Y. Figure 13.9 is the graph of the time series of Cutter-Bridgework annual sales; these sales figures come from Table 13.1. We will now consider the determination of the trend of this time series.

Past data from a series or past experience with a time series may indicate that the trend follows a straight line; that is, it is a linear trend. In such a case we treat Y as a linear function of time, t. By visual inspection of the Cutter-Bridgework time series of Figure 13.9 it is seen that the observations follow an upward, linear trend. This trend is indicated by the dotted line in Figure 13.9. This linear trend is determined by using the regression formulas given in Section 10.3 of Chapter 10. The independent variable is t, the number of years since 1928. The dependent variable is Y, the observed annual sales. The resulting linear regression model will be of the form

$$Y = a + bt$$

or we may replace the Y with T since it is the trend line which is being estimated. Therefore, the linear regression equation is

$$T = a + bt$$

where T is the trend value expressing annual sales in thousands of pesos. The values for a and b are determined in Table 13.3 and are

$$b = \frac{\Sigma tY - n\bar{t}\,\bar{Y}}{\Sigma t^2 - n\bar{t}^2} = \frac{11{,}724 - (10)(5.5)(188.8)}{385 - (10)(5.5)^2}$$

$$= 16.24$$

$$a = \bar{Y} - b\bar{t} = 188.8 - (16.24)(5.5)$$

$$= 99.48$$

Therefore, the linear trend in sales based on annual sales data for the past ten years is estimated by the line

$$T = 99.48 + 16.24t$$

This trend line is the dotted line which is graphed in Figure 13.9 along with the time series data. This regression line has a coefficient of determination, r^2, of .89 which indicates that the effect of time on sales accounts for about 89 percent of the variation.

FIGURE 13.9

Time Series Graph of Cutter-Bridgework Sales Based on Table 13.1

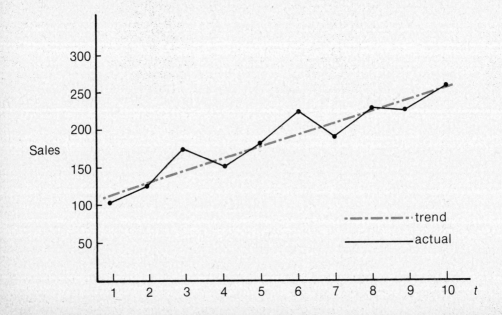

TABLE 13.3_____

Computation of the Linear Regression Trend Line for
Cutter-Bridgework

Year, t	Sales, Y	tY	t^2
1	102	102	1
2	124	248	4
3	175	525	9
4	153	612	16
5	181	905	25
6	228	1368	36
7	195	1365	49
8	235	1880	64
9	231	2079	81
10	264	2640	100
55	1888	11724	385

$$\bar{t} = \frac{55}{10} = 5.5 \qquad\qquad \bar{Y} = \frac{1888}{10} = 188.8$$

$$b = \frac{\Sigma tY - n\bar{t}\,\bar{Y}}{\Sigma t^2 - n\bar{t}^2} = \frac{11724 - (10)(5.5)(188.8)}{385 - (10)(5.5)^2}$$

$$= 16.24$$

$$a = \bar{Y} - b\bar{t} = 188.8 - (16.24)(5.5) = 99.48$$

Since Don Diego is going to perform a quarterly analysis, it is
desirable to break the trend into quarterly figures. The annual
trend can be applied to the quarters by dividing the predicted
sales, T, for the year t by 4:

$$\text{Quarterly Trend Value} = \frac{T}{4}$$

For example, using the trend equation just determined, the predicted annual sales for year 14, which is 1942, would be

$$T = 99.48 + (16.24)(14)$$
$$= 327$$

The trend value for each quarter of year $t = 14$ would be 327/4 or
81.75. This gives a sales prediction for each quarter which takes
into account changes in sales due to the trend. Having determined
the trend of sales, we will now turn to an analysis of the seasonal
and cyclical components.

13.5

SEASONAL AND CYCLICAL FLUCTUATIONS

Suppose the owner of a new ski rental business wonders if his business has died. Rental revenue has fallen way off. In January he grossed $70,000 and this month, June, he barely cleared $500. Does this harrowing evidence seem conclusive that people don't like his business and have taken their trade elsewhere? Probably not. It merely indicates that the endeavor he has chosen is subject to large seasonal fluctuations in business. It is clear that to compare any one month this year with any different month last year to see if business is increasing or not requires that seasonal variation be taken into account before the absolute sales figures are compared. In addition, to be able to see short-term trend effects, for instance over three or four months, the fluctuations due to seasonal change must be eliminated.

Don Diego Cutter-Bridgework can appreciate this need for separating out seasonal fluctuations. He anticipated potential cash flow problems during some quarters and also anticipated having extra cash in other quarters because of seasonally high sales. For example, Don Diego noticed that sales were always high in the October-November-December quarter due to annual potlatch festivities. Sales also seemed to be especially brisk in the winter quarter (first quarter) probably due to consumer interest in winter coverings. It was Don's desire to be able to accurately measure the extent of the seasonal change in sales for the sake of predicting future sales on a quarterly basis. One of the simpler approaches to determining the seasonal influence in a time series will now be considered.

Recall that for the multiplicative model

$$Y = T \cdot C \cdot S \cdot I$$

the trend component has already been determined using a linear regression model. The component S is a multiplier which either inflates or deflates the current trend estimate according to whether it falls in a seasonally high sales period or low sales period.

In order to determine the value of the component S for a given quarter, the time series must be smoothed. It will be shown that the smoothed time series is devoid of the seasonal movements which are apparent in the time series of quarterly sales values. (Table 13.2 presents the quarterly observed values for Cutter-Bridgework.) This smoothed series is therefore composed of trend and cyclical movements. Before considering the reason why a smoothed time series is needed in order to determine the seasonal influence, let us consider a method for smoothing a time series.

Figure 13.10 a presents the quarterly Cutter-Bridgework sales for 1935 through 1938; these data are taken from Table 13.2. It is apparent from this time series that sales are depressed in the second quarter of each year and seem to be exceptionally strong in the first and fourth quarters. The graph of the time series is quite jagged, showing these seasonal fluctuations. The *moving average method* is a technique of smoothing such a time series, thereby eliminating the seasonal influence. Through the moving average method, successive groups of observations are averaged and then these averages are plotted. In particular, the first four observations are averaged yielding

$$\frac{54 + 39 + 48 + 54}{4} = 49$$

It should be noticed that this average is based on data from each quarter of the year; hence, it is essentially based on annual data. This average is plotted in Figure 13.10b above the third quarter mark of 1935. Since the average is composed of values from the first, second, third, and fourth quarters of 1935, the average date of the data is July 1, which is the beginning of the third quarter. This is why the average of 49 is related to the third quarter of 1935.

FIGURE 13.10

Quarterly Sales Figures and Smoothed Time Series for Cutter-Bridgework

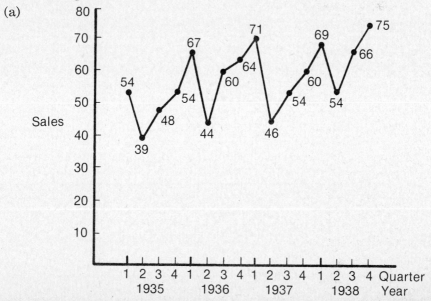

(b)

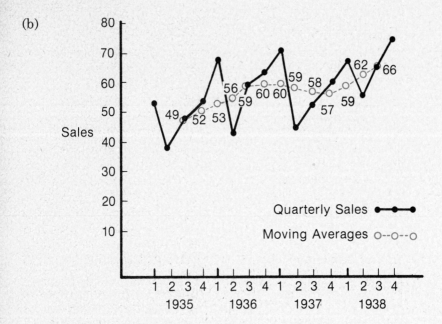

The next average is based on the sales values from the second, third, and fourth quarters of 1935 and the first quarter of 1936, that is,

$$\frac{39 + 48 + 54 + 67}{4} = 52$$

This average is plotted above the fourth quarter of 1935 since its average date is October 1, 1935. By moving one more quarter forward, the next moving average is

$$\frac{48 + 54 + 67 + 44}{4} = 53$$

This average is associated with the center of the four quarters from which it is derived, which extends from the third quarter of 1935 through the second quarter of 1976, namely, the beginning of the first quarter of 1976 (January 1). Thus, it is so plotted above the first quarter of 1976 in the graph of Figure 13.10b. Succeeding moving averages, where a new quarterly sales figure is added while dropping the oldest quarterly figure from the previous average, are

$$\frac{54 + 67 + 44 + 60}{4} = 56 \qquad \text{(Centered on Second Quarter of 1936)}$$

$$\frac{67 + 44 + 60 + 64}{4} = 59 \qquad \text{(Centered on Third Quarter of 1936)}$$

$$\frac{44 + 60 + 64 + 71}{4} = 60 \qquad \text{(Centered on Fourth Quarter of 1936)}$$

and so on. The complete set of moving averages are plotted in Figure 13.10 and are also given, along with the original sales values, in Table 13.4 which will soon be presented. When all these moving averages are plotted and connected with a dotted line, the result is a smoothed time series which is devoid of seasonal fluctuations. The time series when smoothed reveals the underlying trend and cyclical movements.

Now let us return to considering how the smoothed series of moving averages can be of use in determining quarterly values for S, the seasonal multiplier. The smoothed time series forms a benchmark to which actual quarterly sales figures are compared. Since this smoothed series is devoid of seasonal influences because each moving average is composed of data from each quarter, it is therefore influenced solely by the trend and cyclical components. Thus, it is possible to determine the extent of the seasonal influences by comparing the actual quarterly sales values to the corresponding moving average. In particular, if a smoothed value (moving average) is only trend and cycle, then we can say

$$\text{Moving Average} = T \cdot C$$

An actual quarterly sales figure, however, is composed of the trend, cyclical, and seasonal components; that is,

$$\text{Actual Quarterly Value} = T \cdot C \cdot S$$

(Recall that I, being totally unpredictable, is not formally included in this analysis.) If, as will be done shortly, the actual quarterly sales value is divided by the moving average, this results in the isolation of the seasonal component:

$$\frac{\text{Actual Quarterly Value}}{\text{Moving Average}} = \frac{T \cdot C \cdot S}{T \cdot C} = S$$

Let us see how this all works for the sake of determining the seasonal multiplier S.

TABLE 13.4

Determination of Seasonal Indexes for Cutter-Bridgework

Year	Quarter	Sales TCS	Moving Average TC	Historical Seasonal Multiplier TCS/TC = S
1935	1	54		
	2	39		
	3	48	49	.98
	4	54	52	1.04
1936	1	67	53	1.26
	2	44	56	.79
	3	60	59	1.02
	4	64	60	1.07
1937	1	71	60	1.18
	2	46	59	.78
	3	54	58	.93
	4	60	57	1.05
1938	1	69	59	1.17
	2	54	62	.87
	3	66	66	1.00
	4	75		

QUARTERLY SUMMARY OF HISTORICAL SEASONAL MULTIPLIERS

	1	2	3	4
	1.26	.79	.98	1.04
	1.18	.78	1.02	1.07
	1.17	.87	.93	1.05
			1.00	
Mean	1.20	.81	.98	1.05

Sum of Means = 1.20 + .81 + .98 + 1.05 = 4.04
Adjustment Ratio = 4.00/4.04 = .99
Multiplying each Mean by .99 yields Seasonal Indexes

Quarter	1	2	3	4
Seasonal Index	1.19	.80	.98	1.05

The first step for Don Diego is to list all of the quarterly sales figures for the past four years. Don has done this in Table 13.4. Only four years of past data are used because this is how long Don has kept quarterly records. Next he computes moving averages based on successive sales figures over a four-quarter period. Earlier the method of computing moving averages was demonstrated. To repeat, the first moving average of 49 in Table 13.4 was computed by (54 + 39 + 48 + 54)/4. The second moving average of 52 was computed by (39 + 48 + 54 + 67)/4, and the last moving average in the column which is 66 was computed by (69 + 54 + 66 + 75)/4.

After computing the moving averages, Don divides each quarterly sales figure by the corresponding moving average. For example, 48/49 = .98, 54/52 = 1.04, 67/53 = 1.26, and so on. These values which are recorded in the next column of Table 13.4 represent the pure seasonal influence present in the quarterly sales figures over the past four years. For example, the .98 indicates that the 1935 third quarter sales are 2 percent below what sales would have been if no seasonality existed. In the fourth quarter of 1935 the seasonal influence increased sales 4 percent above normal. In the first quarter of 1936 the sales figure was greatly inflated by seasonal pressures; the sales of 67 were 26 percent above normal because of the seasonal influence working in that quarter.

Looking down the column of historical seasonal multipliers, as they may be called, it is seen that sales were 126 percent of normal in the first quarter of 1936, 118 percent of normal in the first quarter of 1937, and 117 percent of trend-cycle in the first quarter of 1938. Thus, it appears that sales are about 120 percent of normal, on average, for the first quarter since

$$\frac{1.26 + 1.18 + 1.17}{3} = 1.20$$

The historical seasonal multipliers for each quarter are thus averaged in Table 13.4. This indicates that first quarter sales appear to be 120 percent of trend-cycle, second quarter sales appear to be 81 percent of normal, third quarter sales are about 98 percent of normal, and fourth quarter sales have historically been 105 percent of normal. A small problem exists here, however. When these four percentages are added together they yield 404 percent; and when 404 percent is divided by four (as in four quarters) the result is 101 percent. This implies that on average the sales are 101 percent of normal for each quarter. That can't be! the multipliers must average to 100 percent. To rectify this situation, the four quarterly means of 1.20, .81, .98, and 1.05 are added yielding 4.04. Then the following adjustment ratio is formed

$$\frac{\text{What They Should Sum To}}{\text{What They Do Sum To}} = \frac{4.00}{4.04} = \frac{400\%}{404\%} = .99$$

Each quarterly mean is then multiplied by this adjustment ratio of .99:

Quarter 1   (1.20)(.99) = 1.19

Quarter 2   (.81)(.99) = .80

Quarter 3   (.98)(.99) = .97

Quarter 4   (1.05)(.99) = 1.04
                         ‾‾‾‾
                         4.00

Now the quarterly means sum to 400 percent. These resulting quarterly mean values of S are called the *seasonal indexes* or seasonal multipliers. The first quarter seasonal index of 1.19 or 119 percent indicates that first quarter sales are typically about 19 percent above normal because of seasonal pressures. The other indexes are similarly interpreted.

Now we consider how these seasonal indexes may be used. Seasonal indexes may be used to deseasonalize (seasonally adjust) the actual quarterly sales figures. When an actual quarterly sales figure is divided by the appropriate seasonal index, the seasonal influence is removed from the sales figure. This is because an actual sales figure, Y, is composed of $T \cdot C \cdot S$, and when it is divided by S, the result is $T \cdot C$. Therefore, a seasonally adjusted sales figure is not influenced by the seasonal component. The seasonally adjusted figures for Don Diego are given in Table 13.5. The deseasonalized figure of 45, for example, was found by dividing the actual first quarter sales of 1935 by the first quarter index, namely, $54/1.19 = 45$. The seasonally adjusted sales for the second quarter of 1935 is found by $39/.80 = 49$. In a similar manner, the remaining seasonally adjusted figures of Table 13.5 are determined. By examining these deseasonalized figures it is possible to more clearly see the underlying movement in sales due to trend and cyclical influences. Another use of these seasonal indexes is in forecasting. In a later section Don Diego will use these indexes in forecasting sales over the next eight quarters covering 1939–1940.

Before considering the cyclical component, it should be noted that if seasonal indexes were desired for each month of the year rather than for each quarter, the procedure of finding these would be analogous to that already set forth. In the monthly case, the moving average would be composed of sales figures for 12 successive months and this moving average would be centered at the (beginning of the) seventh month.

Fluctuations in the data due to cycles in the underlying series are much more difficult to analyze because the cycles are of unknown and varying lengths. Due to combinations of several different influencing factors at different times, the series takes upturns and downturns. Even discovering these upturns and

TABLE 13.5_____

Seasonally Adjusted (Deseasonalized) Sales for Cutter-Bridgework

Year	Quarter	Sales, Y	Seasonal Index, S	Seasonally Adjusted Sales
1935	1	54	1.19	45
	2	39	.80	49
	3	48	.97	49
	4	54	1.04	52
1936	1	67	1.19	56
	2	44	.80	55
	3	60	.97	62
	4	64	1.04	62
1937	1	71	1.19	60
	2	46	.80	58
	3	54	.97	56
	4	60	1.04	58
1938	1	69	1.19	58
	2	54	.80	67
	3	66	.97	68
	4	75	1.04	72

downturns for cycles in past data is difficult. Looking for cycles usually reduces to looking for a general change in the direction of the cyclical part of the time series. For an economic series like one explaining business cycles, this means observing "leading indicators" which economists feel change directions before a general change in the business cycle occurs. Changes or reversals in the observed series of values of indicators, such as the number of houses being built, the money supply, or the amount of investment nationally in new equipment, would indicate that a change in the direction of the business cycle (whether to recession or growth) may be imminent. There are certain techniques for detecting cycles which quickly become rather involved due to the subtlety of the underlying causes; therefore, these will not be considered here. However, if it seems desirable to isolate the cyclical effect on past data such as sales for the Cutter-Bridgework ranches, the original sales figures, Y, can be divided by the trend component for each quarter and also by the corresponding seasonal index, yielding

$$\frac{Y}{T \cdot S} = \frac{T \cdot C \cdot S \cdot I}{T \cdot S} = C \cdot I$$

The remaining values, $C \cdot I$, will reflect the changes in the time series due to cyclical and random-irregular effects. Then a time series composed solely of these $C \cdot I$ values could be plotted. The analyst might then attempt to see if any useful pattern in the cyclical movements is apparent. (For example, the time series of the $C \cdot I$ values might appear something like the cyclical graph of Figure 13.8.) In this manner, a rough approximation of where the cycle will be in the next few periods can be made. This estimate of C could then be incorporated into the forecast. For the purposes here, however, we will assume that $C = 1.0$ and thus base our forecasts on T and S only.

To summarize, this section shows how the magnitude of fluctuations in time series data can be determined when the fluctuations are caused by seasonal factors. For the Cutter-Bridgework tribble ranch, quarterly sales were compared to an average of the year (four-quarter moving average) to determine if the sales in that quarter were above or below average. Doing this quarter by quarter and then averaging the findings, we derived a set of seasonal indexes which shows the manner in which seasonal factors influence the time series.

13.6
ANALYSIS AND FORECASTING WITH THE CLASSICAL MODEL

Forecasting has been defined as being like driving a car blindfolded by following the directions of someone looking out the back window. At its best, forecasting is not quite completely safe. However, it is safer than following no directions at all. The directions that are given are in the form of a model which has been built to describe past observations of series data and which will then be used to predict future values of the series for any specified month and year t.

By combining what is known about past sales, Don Diego is prepared to make some assertions about sales in the future. In particular, Don is primarily interested in predicting sales for the next two years, beginning in the first quarter of 1939 on through the last quarter of 1940.

The time series model for sales has been found to be

$$Y = T \cdot C \cdot S \cdot I$$

where T is the predicted trend value of annual sales for t, the number of years since 1928. T is found by the regression equation which was derived in Section 13.3:

$$T = 99.48 + 16.24t$$

The quarterly trend is $T/4$. For this short-run period of two years it is assumed that C has no influence; thus, $C = 1.0$. The seasonal fluctuations for Cutter-Bridgework are given by the seasonal multipliers S of Table 13.4. For the respective quarters they are 1.19, .80, .97, and 1.04. Since I is unobservable and random, it cannot be predicted and is ignored in forecasting. Based on this introduction, let us now move forward to forecast sales over the next two years for the Cutter-Bridgework tribble ranch.

Each quarter's sales is forecasted by taking 1/4 of the annual sales forecast for that year and multiplying that value by the seasonal index for the quarter. For the first quarter of 1939 that would be

$$Y = (T/4)(S)$$

$$Y = \left[\frac{99.48 + 16.24t}{4} \right] (1.19)$$

$$Y = \left[\frac{99.48 + (16.24)(11)}{4} \right] (1.19)$$

$$= (69.53)(1.19)$$
$$= 82.7$$

where $t = 11$, because 1939 is 11 years after 1928. The forecasted sales for the next two years are listed in Table 13.6. It is seen from Table 13.6 that the forecasted sales for the second quarter of 1939

TABLE 13.6

Sales Forecasts for Cutter-Bridgework

Year	Quarter	Trend $\frac{99.48 + 16.24t}{4}$	Seasonal, S	Quarterly Sales Forecast $(T/4)(S)$
1939	1	69.53	1.19	82.7
(t = 11)	2	69.53	.80	55.6
	3	69.53	.97	67.4
	4	69.53	1.04	72.3
1940	1	73.59	1.19	87.6
(t = 12)	2	73.59	.80	58.9
	3	73.59	.97	71.4
	4	73.59	1.04	76.5

Figures are in thousands of pesos

is 55.6 thousand pesos, and the respective forecast for the third and fourth quarters of 1939 are 67.4 and 72.3 thousand pesos. The respective forecasts for the quarters of 1940 are 87.6, 58.9, 71.4, and 76.5 thousand pesos.

Based on the forecasted sales over the next two years, Don Diego felt that his business would continue without any major financial difficulties. Furthermore, Don was also able to predict profits over the next two years based on his sales forecasts.

Some of the dangers of forecasting are the same as those associated with extrapolation using linear regression. It must be remembered that the model was constructed as an estimate of the underlying components of series behavior in the past. This model is then used to predict values in the future — a new time frame. This assumes that the trend and seasonal components remain unchanged. If, for some reason, either of these seems to be an unrealistic assumption, the model should not be used.

13.7

EXPONENTIAL SMOOTHING

We have now completed a discussion of forecasting by means of the classical time series model. Such a forecasting procedure can be lengthy but is worth the effort expended if the forecast concerns an important item to our business. However, suppose that a manufacturer of automobile parts wishes to forecast demand for each of the hundreds of parts it manufactures. No single part is of crucial importance to the manufacturer, and because there are so many parts, the manufacturer would be reluctant to allocate the resources required to do a full-blown time series analysis for each manufactured part. Furthermore, only a short-term forecast is needed for each part. Therefore, a forecasting technique is needed which can be used quickly and which is relatively inexpensive.

In this section a simple smoothing technique known as *exponential smoothing* is presented which can be used to get point estimates or forecasts. It is widely used because it is easy to apply. Exponential smoothing needs only a few data points to be able to predict future values; it is easily programmed, and it requires little computer time to calculate. Furthermore, it is primarily suited for short-term forecasting. Such a technique would be ideal for the automobile parts manufacturer noted above. An example will now be presented to illustrate exponential smoothing.

In the early 1900's there were several places to buy clothes on the lower east side of New York. The good stores were on Canal Street and Stanton Street. The clip joints were on the Bowery.

They bought the rejects and throw-aways from the other stores and usually bought in bulk at the end of each month for the next month's sales. Rachel Buck had a little place, Buck's Bowery Boutique, and one thing she did not want was a lot of money tied up in inventory. But she was in the business of palming off suits, so she didn't have a lot of time to be fiddling with trends and cycles and "seasonal index numbers." The number of suits sold in each of the 12 months is given in Table 13.7. Based on this pattern of sales, how many suits should she buy for next month?

TABLE 13.7_____

Monthly Sales of Suits at Buck's Bowery Boutique

Month t	Sales Y_t
1	200
2	180
3	170
4	220
5	260
6	200
7	190
8	230
9	250
10	210
11	260
12	220

Exponential smoothing gives a method of combining past and present information into a weighted average to predict the next value of the series. The next question is how to weight past information. Looking at the record of past sales, it appears that they are starting to increase during the last few months. Should she take this as a general increase, ignore earlier data, and start buying more or should she view it only as a temporary shift and keep buying as she did before? Exponential smoothing is a simple means by which this weighting is given. For each time period (each month for this example) an average or smoothed value, S_t, is calculated. Begin by making $S_1 = Y_1$, where Y_t represents actual sales in month t. Each subsequent smoothed value is a weighted average of the actual value observed that period and the smoothed value from the previous period. For the second month,

$$S_2 = \alpha Y_2 + (1 - \alpha)S_1$$

For the third month the smoothed value is

$$S_3 = \alpha Y_3 + (1 - \alpha)S_2$$

The constant α is a number between zero and one and is called the *smoothing constant* or the *tracking constant*. In general, the smoothed value for month t is

$$S_t = \alpha Y_t + (1 - \alpha)S_{t-1}$$

In exponential smoothing, the smoothed value for period t, which is a weighted average of that period's actual value and the smoothed value or average from the previous period, becomes the forecast for the next period. Letting F_{t+1} denote the forecast for period $t + 1$, it follows that

$$F_{t+1} = S_t = \alpha Y_t + (1 - \alpha)S_{t-1}$$

If $\alpha = 1$, then the forecast for next month's sales is exactly equal to the number of sales this month. This means that whoever decides that α should equal one thinks every change in sales portends a future exactly like the present; hence, all past data about sales are not considered. Analogously, if $\alpha = 0$, current sales are ignored and only past sales are considered.

Obviously, the crucial step in making this model an accurate forecasting tool is selecting the correct value for the smoothing constant. As α gets larger, the forecasts bounce around nearly as randomly as current sales following every up and down. As α gets smaller, the forecasts become more dependent on past sales, ignoring random fluctuations; this yields a series of "smooth" forecasts. Because the use of a small α causes the forecast to ignore random fluctuations, exponential smoothing models are good at forecasting series with a lot of irregular fluctuations about a gentle trend.

Let us now return to the Buck's Bowery Boutique case. Along with the actual monthly sales figures, Table 13.8 presents the forecasted sales for each of the past twelve months. First are listed the forecasts resulting from the use of $\alpha = .1$; then the forecasts based on $\alpha = .5$ are given. The actual sales are plotted along with the smoothed values (forecasts) in Figure 13.11. Let us see how these forecasts were determined.

The first smoothed value, S_1, is set equal to Y_1 in order to start the process:

$$S_1 = Y_1 = 200$$

Using $\alpha = .1$, the second smoothed value is

$$S_2 = \alpha Y_2 + (1 - \alpha)S_1$$
$$= (.1)(180) + (.9)(200)$$
$$= 198$$

This smoothed value of $S_2 = 198$ may be considered as the forecast for the third period, namely, $F_3 = 198$. The third smoothed value when $\alpha = .1$ is

$$S_3 = \alpha Y_3 + (1 - \alpha)S_2$$
$$= (.1)(170) + (.9)(198)$$
$$= 195.2$$

Alternately, S_3 may be considered as F_4, the forecast for the fourth period.

In a similar manner, the smoothed values of Table 13.11 based on $\alpha = .5$ may be computed. Continuing the process of computing the S values for both alphas, $S_{12} = 215.1$ when $\alpha = .1$ is used and

TABLE 13.8

Exponential Smoothing for Buck's Bowery Boutique Sales

Month	Sales	Smoothed Values $S_t = F_{t+1}$	
t	Y_t	$\alpha = .1$	$\alpha = .5$
1	200	200	200
2	180	198	190
3	170	195.2	180
4	220	197.7	200
5	260	203.9	230
6	200	203.5	215
7	190	202.2	202.5
8	230	205.0	216.3
9	250	209.5	233.1
10	210	209.5	221.6
11	260	214.6	241.8
12	220	215.1	230.4
Forecast 13		215.1	230.4
		215 suits	230 suits

Note: The smoothed value for month t is the forecast for month $t + 1$. For example, the smoothed value (when $\alpha = .1$) for month 3 is $S_3 = 195.2$ which becomes the forecast for month 4; that is, $F_4 = 195.2$. The actual sales in month 4 turned out to be $Y_4 = 220$.

FIGURE 13.11

Exponential Smoothing for Buck's Bowery Boutique

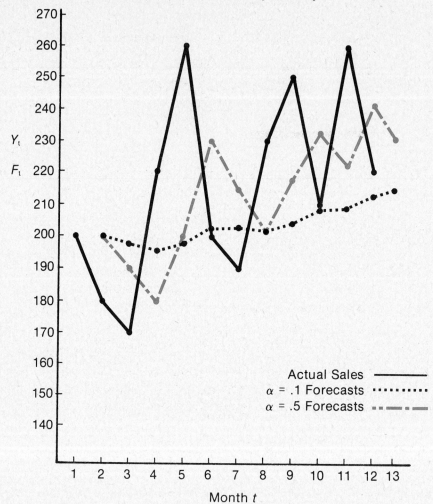

$S_{12} = 230.4$ when $\alpha = .5$ is used. As stated earlier, the two respective forecasts for period 13 are therefore $F_{13} = 215.1$ and $F_{13} = 230.4$, depending on which smoothing constant is used. Which of these two forecasts should be believed?

One way to compare the two forecasts is to see which value of α has done the best in the past in forecasting and use that one now. In order to do this, the forecast deviation for month (period) t is defined as

$$\text{Forecast Deviation for Period } t = \text{Forecasted Sales} - \text{Actual Sales}$$

For example, the forecast (using α = .1) for Month 2 is 200, whereas the actual sales for Month 2 turned out to be 180; therefore, the forecast deviation is 200 − 180 or 20. Likewise, the forecast deviation for Month 3 is 198 − 170 and for Month 4 it is 195.2 − 220. Squaring these deviations for each month, adding them, and then dividing by n − 1 gives an estimate of forecast variance. The *standard forecast deviation* (SFD) is then calculated by taking the square root of the forecast variance:

$$SFD = \sqrt{\frac{\Sigma(\text{Forecast} - \text{Actual})^2}{n - 1}}$$

where n is the number of periods being considered. The alpha which yields the least *SFD* is the preferred alpha.

In the case at hand, the *SFD* for α = .1 is

$$SFD = \sqrt{\frac{(200 - 180)^2 + (198 - 170)^2 + \ldots + (214.6 - 220)^2}{10}}$$
$$= 32.6$$

For α = .5, the *SFD* is calculated in a similar manner yielding 37.2. Since α = .1 has done a better job of forecasting in the past as evidenced by the lower SFD, we would conclude that the forecast of 215 suits should be selected over the 230 suit forecast.

Another benefit of exponential smoothing is that smoothing out erratic fluctuations in past data can often make otherwise hidden trends more visible. In summary, exponential smoothing is an easy-to-use method of short-term forecasting. By changing the value of the smoothing constant, the user can adapt exponential smoothing to the purpose at hand. This makes it a versatile forecasting technique.

13.8

SUMMARY

While the need for accurate forecasting is plain enough, the means by which it is to be accomplished is not always so clear. This chapter has presented a couple of elementary ways in which models such as the classical model or exponential smoothing model can be built to fit past data and then used to project this past pattern of a time series into the future. But what about cases in which there is no past data? If a new product is being introduced or a new investment undertaken, what methods are there for forecasting? This is the area of *qualitative forecasting* and it includes such approaches as panel discussions, market research, and the Delphi method. Panel discussions involve getting several experts together and letting them discuss the matter until they come to some kind of a consensus about how the new product or investment will perform in the future. Market research involves forming hypotheses about future performance and then testing these hypotheses by carefully collecting market data. The Delphi method is a well-known technique which employs a series of questions put to a group of experts individually and designed to elicit all the relevant information necessary for a forecast. This technique is more selective than simple majority voting because it avoids some of the bandwagon effect.

PROBLEMS

13.1

What is the difference between regression analysis and time series analysis?

13.2

Name the four components in the classical approach to the analysis of time series.

13.3

Name three products which experience a seasonal pattern of sales.

13.4

If computer sales have increased at a rate of 10 percent per year, will the trend be linear or nonlinear? (Hint: assume sales were $100,000 in 1970, and then plot annual sales over the decade of the 70's in order to answer the question.)

13.5

For the Gnome Company, the trend value for next year's sales is $400. Due to a business slowdown sales are expected to be 20 percent below normal. Based on the given information, predict Gnome's sales for next year.

13.6

The data below gives the union shepherd pay scale for the years 1961–1966.

Year	Monthly Pay
1961	160
1962	190
1963	205
1964	220
1965	245
1966	250

(a) Find the equation of the trend line.
(b) Predict monthly pay for 1967 and 1968.

13.7

Clifford Gifford Landford runs the Fort Commanche blood bank. It is crucial that the bank maintain the required reserves of blood. Lanford has determined the seasonal indexes for blood demand for May, June, July, and August to be 70, 96, 180, and 160, respectively. Blood demand over these past four months has been, in pints, 600, 900, 1900, and 1825. Is the increased demand due to seasonal variation or is there a cyclical-trend upswing in progress? (Hint: deseasonalize the actual demand figures in order to answer the question.)

13.8

Margy Bee is a manufacturer of clothes. Margy Bee has found the seasonal index for clothes sales to be 120 in February and 145 in March. Next year's trend prediction for sales is $2.4 million. Because of a cyclical boom in clothing sales, the cyclical influence is expected to boost sales 15 percent above normal next year. Based on this information, predict February and March sales for next year.

13.9

Which of the following, trend, cycle, or seasonal, is typically the most difficult to determine for forecasting?

13.10

Betsy Jestila, an analyst for Paterson Tile, has studied the pattern of Paterson Tile sales over the past ten years. Betsy found the trend to be given by the equation

$$T = 100,000 + 5,000t$$

where t represents the number of years since 1970. From this information, determine what the cyclical pattern has been over the

past ten years; the following are the actual sales figures for Paterson Tile. (Hint: detrend the sales figures.)

Year	Sales
1970	$100,000
1971	101,000
1972	102,000
1973	111,000
1974	123,000
1975	136,000
1976	144,000
1977	148,000
1978	149,000
1979	150,000

13.11

The Missouri River brought many trappers and hunters into St.
Louis in the mid 1800's. In those days a trapper's life insurance in
the wilds was his body: the better fit he was, the longer he lived.
One of the burliest trappers was the burly Big Barn O'Casey. At
age forty he quit trapping and set up Big Barn's Body Building
Center. The trappers came in during the winter months when the
river was frozen and worked on building their bodies. They paid
their bills in pelts usually. The monthly returns in number of pelts
is given below for Big Barn's first three years of operation.

Month	1841	1842	1843
January	87	95	112
February	75	91	102
March	69	86	94
April	67	73	85
May	42	67	73
June	30	48	69
July	32	46	64
August	27	42	57
September	35	49	64
October	56	67	79
November	67	79	91
December	88	91	103

From these data, determine the monthly seasonal indexes for Big
Barn's business. What is Big Barn's worst month? best month? In
November business is what percent of normal? If annual sales, in
pelts, for 1844 were expected to be 1,000, what is Big Barn's forecast for sales in the month of March?

13.12

Edgar vonBarrington-Cosworth is a newly enfranchised partner in the prestigious advertising agency Clark, Clark, Clark, Clark, and vonBarrington-Cosworth. His first major appointment is as new account manager for Groom, the revolutionary new hair dressing that comes frozen on a stick. He used heavy TV advertising for the first time for the product and sales reached a new high. The product was introduced three years ago and Edgar feels that the TV advertising should be increased because of its sudden impact on sales for the product. The other partners (the Clarks) feel the jump may be due only to trend and seasonal variation in sales and not to the advertising. Quarterly sales data are given below in thousands of dollars.

Quarter	1976 Year 1	1977 Year 2	1978 Year 3	1979 Year 4
1	36	45	51	60
2	28	37	45	
3	26	39	42	
4	38	43	54	
Annual	128	164	192	

Assuming that there is no cyclical variation, is it likely that TV advertising has caused the record-high sales for the first quarter of 1979? Would you recommend that more money be put into TV advertising? Support your conclusions. (Hint: use the annual sales figures for the trend projection.) Finally, forecast quarterly sales for 1980.

13.13

Is exponential smoothing primarily suited to long-term or short-term forecasting?

13.14

How does the value of the smoothing constant influence the forecasts derived from exponential smoothing?

13.15

Goose & Dors is a wholesaler of photo chemicals which wishes to use exponential smoothing to predict June sales of a particular photo chemical. Sales over the past few months are recorded on the top of page 408.

	Photo Chemical
Month	*Sales*
January	620
February	540
March	610
April	650
May	635

(a) Use exponential smoothing with a smoothing constant of .1 to forecast June sales.

(b) Use exponential smoothing with a smoothing constant of .3 to forecast June sales.

(c) Compute the standard forecast deviation for each of the forecasting procedures in (a) and (b) to determine which has done the better job of forecasting in the past.

13.16

Genghis and Sylvia Khan are having trouble with roaches in the kingdom. In order to determine how many anti-roach spices should be purchased, the Khans need to predict the degree of roach infestation for next year, 1210. Infestation figures over the past several years have been collected; they are given below.

Year	1205	1206	1207	1208	1209
Infestation	430	420	440	580	550

(a) Use exponential smoothing with $\alpha = .1$ to predict roach infestation in 1210.

(b) Use exponential smoothing with $\alpha = .4$ to predict roach infestation in 1210.

(c) Comment on the relative merits of the two foregoing forecasts.

(d) Use trend analysis to forecast infestation in the year 1210.

(e) Might there be the cyclical influence at work? Explain.

CHAPTER 14

INDEX NUMBERS

14.1

INTRODUCTION

Most of us are familiar with *index numbers*. Perhaps the index which receives the greatest attention is the Consumer Price Index. Changes in this index indicate relative price changes of a broad spectrum of goods and services which are of importance to many consumers. If the index were 100 last year and 105 this year, we would conclude that the average price of the goods and services represented by the index has increased by 5 percent. In general, it is the purpose of index numbers to describe changes in such things as prices over a period of time.

Index numbers may be constructed with reference to prices, quantities, or values. A price index shows the relative changes in the price of a product. For example, Table 14.1 gives a price index for the price of a certain model of semiconductor. From this index, it can be seen that the price in 1978 was 8 percent greater than the price of the semiconductor in 1976. Also, the price in 1979 is 16.67 percent higher than it was in 1975. That is,

$$\text{The 1979 Price as a Proportion of the 1975 Price} = \frac{\text{1979 Price Index Number}}{\text{1975 Price Index Number}}$$

$$= \frac{112}{96}$$

$$= 1.1667$$

TABLE 14.1_____

Indexes

Year	Price Index for Semiconductor	Quantity Index for Electricity Usage	Value Index for Pea Soup Sales
1975	96	88	60
1976	100	100	100
1977	102	106	102
1978	108	109	115
1979	112	118	116
1980	114	125	122

Therefore, the 1979 price is 116.67 percent of the 1975 price, thus indicating a 16.67 percent price increase over this period.

A quantity index shows relative changes in the quantity produced or sold of some item. For example, Table 14.1 shows a quantity index for the annual electricity used by the town of Essex Fells over the past few years. From this it is seen that electricity usage has increased by 9 percent from 1976 to 1978. The increase in electricity usage from 1975 to 1980 is 42 percent as indicated by the ratio 125/88 = 1.42.

Finally, an index may be based on changes in values. A value is influenced by both price and quantity. Table 14.1 gives an index for the value of the pea soup sold in Kansas. Suppose that 100 cans of pea soup were sold in Kansas at $.20 per can in 1975. This would mean that the total value of pea soup sold in 1975 is (100 cans)($.20) = $20.00. The value may increase or decrease year by year as either the price changes, or the quantity changes, or both change. According to Table 14.1 the value of pea soup sold increased by 67 percent from 1975 to 1976 as indicated by the ratio 100/60 = 1.67. It follows that if $20.00 was spent on pea soup in 1975, then ($20.00)(1.67) = $33.40 was spent on pea soup in 1976.

Indexes have been categorized by what they measure, that is, whether they measure changes in price, quantity, or value. Another method of categorizing indexes is by the number of items which the index encompasses. All of the indexes of Table 14.1 are *simple indexes* since each deals with precisely one item. The first deals with the price of a semiconductor, the second with electricity usage in a given town, and the third with only pea soup sales. A *composite index*, on the other hand, deals with several items. For example, the Consumer Price Index measures the aggregate change in the prices of a number of goods and services. We shall now consider the construction of both simple and composite indexes.

14.2

SIMPLE INDEX NUMBERS

A *simple index* concerns the changes in the price, quantity, or value of a single entity. As mentioned already, the three indexes of Table 14.1 are simple indexes. The construction of simple index numbers is easy. Table 14.2 gives price, quantity, and value data for ski lift tickets to Sugar Beet, a famous ski resort. Sugar Beet indexes will be constructed in a moment.

In order to construct an index, one of the years must be chosen as a base year. The base year is the year to which all the other years in the time series are compared. In Table 14.1, for example, the base year is 1976. The index always has a value of 100 in the base year. The base year should not be one of the very last years for which data has been accumulated. It also should not be too far in the past. For example, a base year of 1960 would not be suitable for indexes extending into the 1980's. The base year should also be a year which was more or less normal. The owners of Sugar Beet decided that 1977 should not be the base year, since there was very little snow that year and therefore it was not a normal year. Furthermore, it was the first year of operation, making it atypical. Therefore, 1978 was chosen as the base year for the various Sugar Beet indexes.

TABLE 14.2

Sugar Beet Lift Ticket Sales

Year	Lift Ticket Price, p	Price Index	Quantity of Tickets Sold, q	Quantity Index	Value of Sales, pq	Value Index
1977	$4.00	89	200	33	$ 800	30
1978	4.50	100	600	100	2700	100
1979	5.00	111	800	133	4000	148
1980	6.00	133	900	150	5400	200

To compute a price index for lift tickets, each price is compared to the price for the base year. The price index, I_n, for year n is computed according to

$$I_n = \frac{p_n}{p_o} (100)$$

where p_n is the price of the item in year n, and p_o is the price in the base year. Therefore, the price index numbers for the lift tickets are

$$I_{1977} = \frac{p_{1977}}{p_{1978}}(100) = \frac{4.00}{4.50}(100) = 89$$

$$I_{1978} = \frac{p_{1978}}{p_{1978}}(100) = \frac{4.50}{4.50}(100) = 100$$

$$I_{1979} = \frac{p_{1979}}{p_{1978}}(100) = \frac{5.00}{4.50}(100) = 111$$

$$I_{1980} = \frac{p_{1980}}{p_{1978}}(100) = \frac{6.00}{4.50}(100) = 133$$

These index numbers are recorded in Table 14.2.

The quantity index number for year n is computed according to

$$I_n = \frac{q_n}{q_o}(100)$$

where q_n equals the quantity sold in year n and q_o equals the quantity for the base year. Therefore, the quantity index numbers for Table 14.2 are found by

$$I_{1977} = \frac{200}{600}(100) = 33$$

$$I_{1978} = \frac{600}{600}(100) = 100$$

$$I_{1979} = \frac{800}{600}(100) = 133$$

$$I_{1980} = \frac{900}{600}(100) = 150$$

Finally, the value index for year n is determined according to

$$I_n = \frac{p_n q_n}{p_o q_o}(100) = \frac{v_n}{v_o}(100)$$

where v_n refers to the value of the product sold in year n and v_o is the value for the base year. The value index numbers for Sugar Beet are computed according to

$$I_{1977} = \frac{(4.00)(200)}{(4.50)(600)}(100) = \frac{\$800}{\$2700}(100) = 30$$

$$I_{1978} = \frac{2700}{2700}(100) = 100$$

$$I_{1979} = \frac{4000}{2700}(100) = 148$$

$$I_{1980} = \frac{5400}{2700}(100) = 200$$

These index numbers, like the price and quantity indexes, are presented in Table 14.2.

14.3

COMPOSITE INDEX NUMBERS

Susan Brindley, the president of Industrial Reporting, is seeking to develop an index which will be of use to the manufacturers of wooden pallets. Brindley's Wooden Pallet Index is to be a composite index in that it will measure the changes in prices of the several materials or resources which are used by pallet manufacturers. The three primary resources used in the production of wooden pallets are rough hardwood lumber, pallet nails, and electric power. Table 14.3 presents the prices of these resources over a recent five-year period.

TABLE 14.3

Prices for the Wooden Pallet Index

Year	Lumber Price per Board Foot	Nails Price per Pound	Electricity Price per Kilowatt Hour
1	$.17	$.36	$.035
2	.17	.42	.040
3	.16	.48	.042
4	.19	.48	.045
5	.21	.52	.050

In constructing the Wooden Pallet Index, Brindley was careful to give appropriate weights to each of the three resources used in the manufacturing of a wooden pallet. Since the primary resource or material used is lumber, lumber price changes are the most important price changes to a pallet manufacturer. Therefore, the index should be constructed in such a way that lumber prices are most influential. Brindley found that most wooden pallets use about 20 board feet of lumber, 1 pound of pallet nails, and 1.5 kilowatt hours of electricity. Therefore, the cost of a pallet in year 2, for example, was about

$$(\$.17)(20) + (\$.42)(1) + (\$.040)(1.5) = \$3.88$$

The prices of the lumber, nails, and electricity are given in Table 14.3.

Suppose that year 2 is the base year for the Wooden Pallet Index. The composite price index for year n can be computed according to

$$I_n = \frac{\Sigma p_n q_o}{\Sigma p_o q_o}(100)$$

where p_n is the price of a material in year n, p_o is the price in the base year, and q_o is the quantity of the respective materials which are used. The q_o values become the weights for each material or resource. The summation extends over all the materials or resources that are to be included in the composite index. This type of index is called a *weighted aggregate index* or sometimes a *Laspeyres index*. Using this method to compute a composite index, the Wooden Pallet Index for each year when year 2 is the base is

$$I_1 = \frac{\begin{array}{c}(\$.17 \text{ per bd.ft.}) (20 \text{ bd.ft.}) + (\$.36 \text{ per lb.}) (1 \text{ lb.}) \\ + (\$.035 \text{ per KWH}) (1.5 \text{ KWH})\end{array}}{\begin{array}{c}(\$.17 \text{ per bd.ft.}) (20 \text{ bd.ft.}) + (\$.42 \text{ per lb.}) (1 \text{ lb.}) \\ + (\$.040 \text{ per KWH}) (1.5 \text{ KWH})\end{array}} (100)$$

$$= 98$$

$$I_2 = \frac{(.17)(20) + (.42)(1) + (.040)(1.5)}{(.17)(20) + (.42)(1) + (.040)(1.5)} (100) = 100$$

$$I_3 = \frac{(.16)(20) + (.48)(1) + (.042)(1.5)}{(.17)(20) + (.42)(1) + (.040)(1.5)} (100) = 96$$

$$I_4 = \frac{(.19)(20) + (.48)(1) + (.045)(1.5)}{(.17)(20) + (.42)(1) + (.040)(1.5)} (100) = 112$$

$$I_5 = \frac{(.21)(20) + (.52)(1) + (.050)(1.5)}{(.17)(20) + (.42)(1) + (.040)(1.5)} (100) = 124$$

A composite quantity index can be constructed in a similar fashion according to

$$I_n = \frac{\Sigma q_n p_o}{\Sigma q_o p_o}(100)$$

where q_n is the quantity produced or sold in year n, q_o is the quantity for the base year, and p_o is the price of the product in the base year. The summation extends over all the products to be included in the index. The base year prices, p_o, serve as the weights.

Table 14.4 shows turquoise and red coral prices and the respective quantities of these two over a three-year period. Letting year 1 be the base year, the composite quantity index for turquoise and red coral production for each year is

$$I_1 = \frac{(60,000)(2.00) + (4,000)(.80)}{(60,000)(2.00) + (4,000)(.80)}(100) = 100$$

$$I_2 = \frac{(74,000)(2.00) + (4,700)(.80)}{(60,000)(2.00) + (4,000)(.80)}(100) = 123$$

$$I_3 = \frac{(76,000)(2.00) + (7,800)(.80)}{(60,000)(2.00) + (4,000)(.80)}(100) = 128$$

Notice that the weights are the base year prices of the turquoise and red coral.

TABLE 14.4

Data for Turquoise and Red Coral

Year	Turquoise Price per Carat	Turquoise Production in Carats, q	Coral Price per Carat	Coral Production in Carats, q
1	$2.00	60,000	$.80	4,000
2	2.48	74,000	.88	4,700
3	2.63	76,000	.97	7,800

A composite value index can be computed by

$$I_n = \frac{\Sigma p_n q_n}{\Sigma p_o q_o}(100)$$

For the turquoise and red coral of Table 14.4, the composite value index for these two materials which are used in Indian jewelry is

$$I_1 = \frac{(60,000)(2.00) + (4,000)(.80)}{(60,000)(2.00) + (4,000)(.80)}(100) = 100$$

$$I_2 = \frac{(74,000)(2.48) + (4,700)(.88)}{(60,000)(2.00) + (4,000)(.80)}(100) = 152$$

$$I_3 = \frac{(76,000)(2.63) + (7,800)(.97)}{(60,000)(2.00) + (4,000)(.80)}(100) = 168$$

where year 1 is the base year. Since value is affected by both price and quantity, neither is held constant in determining the index numbers for later years.

14.4

IMPORTANT INDEXES

The most widely known index is the *Consumer Price Index*, which is prepared by the Bureau of Labor Statistics. In 1978, the Bureau of Labor Statistics began reporting two consumer price indexes. One is called the *Consumer Price Index for Urban Wage Earners and Clerical Workers* and the other is the *Consumer Price Index for All Urban Consumers*. In both cases, the composite index reflects monthly changes in prices of a representative market basket of goods and services which consumers purchase. The composition of the market basket of goods and services for the CPI for Urban Wage Earners and Clerical Workers is based on the buying habits of urban blue-collar and clerical families and singles. This group comprises about 50 percent of the urban population of the United States. The All Urban CPI, on the other hand, is based on price changes of goods and services which are on the average representative of the spending patterns of 80 percent of all Americans. In both indexes the major categories of expenditures are housing, food, transportation, apparel, medical, goods and services, and entertainment. Roughly speaking, the housing category is given a weight of 40 percent, food is given a weight of 20 percent, and transportation is given a weight of 20 percent. The nature of the consumer price indexes will be discussed further in Section 14.5.

The Consumer Price Index is used for several purposes. First, it is used as an escalator. The wages of close to nine million workers are tied to the CPI. Sometimes pensions, alimony, royalties, and child support payments are also tied to changes in the CPI. The CPI is also valuable as an economic indicator which measures inflation. Government fiscal and monetary policymakers carefully consider changes in the CPI. One might be tempted to say that another use of the CPI is to show the change in the cost of living. Though in a sense this is true, the CPI is not actually a cost-of-living index. The reasons why it does not actually measure changes in the cost of living will be explained in the next section.

Another important composite price index is the *Producers Price Index*, which has also been known as the *Wholesale Price Index*. The Producers Price Index measures the price changes of about 2,800 commodities sold in primary markets. The prices measured are the prices the producers of the commodities receive. The commodities in this index include finished goods (automobiles, bread, etc.), intermediate goods (sheet metal, flour, etc.), and crude materials (iron, wheat, etc.). The PPI is of considerable importance to businesses who are tracking price changes at the producer level. Besides giving an overall picture of price changes, changes in the prices of special categories of goods such as lumber and wood products can be determined from Bureau of Labor Statistics publications. This permits a business to trace price changes within a limited group of commodities.

Among composite quantity indexes, the *Federal Reserve Board Index of Industrial Production* is an important index which measures changes in the physical output of factories, mines, and utilities. An example of a value index is the construction contracts index published by the F. W. Dodge Corporation. This index measures changes in the value of construction contracts that are awarded.

14.5

PROBLEMS OF CONSTRUCTION AND APPLICATION

There are certain difficulties which crop up in the construction of indexes. One of these difficulties relates to handling quality changes in the case of price indexes. For example, suppose you are constructing a price index for a full-sized car. Over the years the price of that particular model has increased, yielding an increasing price index. Suppose the index were 100 in 1950 and 300 in 1980; this would indicate that the price of the car has tripled. We should not, however, be too hasty in stating that the price has tripled over this period. The reason is that the 1980 model is considerably more sophisticated than the 1950 model. Some of the price increase is attributable to an overall increase in the quality and sophistication of the vehicle. The big problem is determining how much of the price increase is due to quality changes in the product. Statisticians attempt to estimate how much of the price change is due to quality changes. However, many times the attempts are not entirely adequate; this remains a real difficulty in constructing many indexes.

Another problem that must be considered in the case of certain indexes like the Consumer Price Index is that of the changing buying habits of consumers. It might be that in 1960 the average American spent 30 percent of his/her income on housing, but in

1980 housing accounted for 40 percent of the consumer's expenditures. This means that the relative importance of housing is increasing. The problem for the statistician concerns how much weight housing should be given over a series of consumer price index numbers which extends from 1960 to 1980. If the index is a composite price index, a fixed set of weights is necessary. Determining what the appropriate weights should be for a composite index extending over many years is not an easy task. It is a problem for which there often is no good solution. Recall that in Section 14.3 the composite price indexes were based on the weights, q_o, of the base year. This is the most common approach.

Another problem associated with the construction of an index like the CPI deals with determining the appropriate weights for the categories of expenditures for some particular year like the base year. Selecting the items which represent the various categories can also be a problem. To begin, the statistician asks, "Whose buying habits are of importance for the index?" An answer to this question will give considerable guidance in determining the categories (like housing, food, transportation, . . .) and their appropriate weights for the composite index. The All Urban CPI attempts to reflect, in an average way, the spending patterns of all urban persons whether they be unemployed, accountants, teachers, bus drivers, plumbers, lawyers, or taxidermists. These urban people spend an average of 20 percent of their budgets on food; therefore, the food category is given a 20 percent weight in the CPI. It should be apparent, however, that very few people are in fact average. Therefore, the index is not perfectly suited to many people, even if they live in an urban setting.

Once the weights for the various categories (like housing, food, transportation, . . .) are established, then actual items in each of these categories must be sampled to chart price changes. Selecting the items to be incorporated into the index is a considerable problem if only a few items from each general category can go into the representative market basket. For example, if only four foods were allowed in an index like the CPI, what four should they be? Black pepper, oranges, frozen chicken livers, and Idaho potatoes, or skim milk, sirloin steak, whole wheat bread, and tomato soup? Obviously, much care must go into the selection of the representative items in the market basket.

Some of the problems in constructing an index like the Consumer Price Index have been briefly considered. In view of these kinds of problems, indexes should be used and applied with considerable discernment. As a case in point, it was stated in Section 14.4 that strictly speaking the CPI is not a cost-of-living index. That is, it does not measure the change in your or my cost of living. Let us consider why this is so.

The CPI does not accurately reflect changes in your cost of living for several reasons. First of all, you don't spend exactly 40 percent of your budget on housing, 20 percent on food, 20 percent on transportation, and so on. However, these are the assumptions of the CPI. Since the CPI does not reflect *your* particular spending pattern, it is obviously going to be somewhat in error as a measure of the change in *your* cost of living. For example, if you only spend 10 percent on food, and if food has rapidly increased in price in comparison to other products and services, then the CPI will go up more quickly than your cost of living because the CPI gives a 20 percent weight on food. But suppose that you do spend 20 percent on food, 40 percent on housing, 20 percent on transportation, and so on. Will the CPI reflect your cost of living changes then? The answer is still no. One reason is that you will switch the products you purchase in an attempt to minimize your costs. A composite price index might include eight pounds of chuck roast, three pounds of ham, and two pounds of chicken in every market basket. You might purchase the meats in these exact proportions this month, but if beef prices rapidly rise, you will substitute chicken or pork or fish. Therefore, next month you might buy four pounds of chuck roast, five pounds of pork, and four pounds of chicken. You will still satisfy your needs but at a lower cost than the eight, three, two combination. The price index, however, does not account for such substitutions. Since consumers subsitute relatively inexpensive items for the more expensive ones, their cost of living is typically not as high as the consumer price index. For such reasons, the CPI is not actually a cost-of-living index; it is a price index.

14.6

SHIFTING THE BASE

In order to compare two indexes, it is helpful to have a common base year. Suppose that the two quantity indexes representing the tortilla consumption in a Texas town and the town's population are as given in Table 14.5a for 1951–1954. In order to compare the growth of tortilla consumption and population, we wish to restate the tortilla index so that it has a base year of 1951 like the population index. In order to shift the base, the analyst must divide each index number in the old index by the index number corresponding to the year which is to be the new base, and then multiply by 100. For example,

| | Old Tortilla Index
(Base = 1946) | New Tortilla Index
(Base = 1951) |
Year		
1951	158	$\frac{158}{158}(100) = 100$
1952	169	$\frac{169}{158}(100) = 107$
1953	183	$\frac{183}{158}(100) = 116$
1954	197	$\frac{197}{158}(100) = 125$

Since 158 was the index number corresponding to 1951 which was to become the new base year, each index number was divided by 158 in order to get the new index.

The new tortilla index with a 1951 base is given in Table 14.5b. It is seen by comparing it to the population index that the tortilla consumption rose more rapidly than the population in the Texas town.

TABLE 14.5

Tortilla and Population Indexes

(a) With Different Bases

Year	Tortilla Index (Base = 1946)	Population Index (Base = 1951)
1951	158	100
1952	169	104
1953	183	109
1954	197	112

(b) With a Common Base

Year	Tortilla Index (Base = 1951)	Population Index (Base = 1951)
1951	100	100
1952	107	104
1953	116	109
1954	125	112

14.7

DEFLATING A TIME SERIES

An Asian country reports that the average wages of its workers has increased over a recent five-year period from 17 yokosaki per hour to 31 yokosaki per hour. The actual time series of wages is given in Table 14.6. This increase represents an 82 percent increase in hourly wages (31/17 = 1.82).

Before concluding that the standard of living for Asian workers of this country is rapidly increasing, we must ask how prices have changed over the same period. A glance at the Asian Consumer Price Index for this country, which is given in Table 14.6, shows that prices have risen by 70 percent over the same period of time. In other words, the Asian workers are not faring as well as first thought.

TABLE 14.6

Wages and a Price Index

Year	Average Wages (Yokosaki/Hour)	Asian Consumer Price Index
1976	17	100
1977	19	110
1978	23	130
1979	27	150
1980	31	170

In cases where prices are increasing as well as wages, it is useful to adjust the wages for the price increases in order to show the changes in the real wage. This process whereby the time series of wages is adjusted for price changes is called *deflating the time series*. The wages are deflated by dividing each wage figure by the corresponding price index number and then multiplying by 100. For example, if it is desired to express wages in terms of constant 1976 prices and money (1976 is the base year), then the deflated time series is

Year	Wages	Deflated Wages
1976	17	$\frac{17}{100}(100) = 17.00$
1977	19	$\frac{19}{110}(100) = 17.27$
1978	23	$\frac{23}{130}(100) = 17.69$
1979	27	$\frac{27}{150}(100) = 18.00$
1980	31	$\frac{31}{170}(100) = 18.24$

This means that in terms of increased purchasing power, wages over the five years have gone up by only 7 percent since

18.24/17.00 = 1.07. Most of the advance in wages from 17 yokosaki per hour to 31 is in fact illusory since prices have risen almost as fast.

The price index has proven to be useful for deflating wages to determine the real changes. Other examples where an index is used to adjust a time series are given in the problems at the end of this chapter.

PROBLEMS

14.1

Distinguish between a simple index and a composite index.

14.2

The annual football attendance figures at the Athens Stadium and the gross annual revenue figures are given below. Compute a simple index for each series with year 2 as the base year. Identify each index as being either a price, quantity, or value index.

Year	Attendance	Gross Revenue
1	610,000	$3,000,000
2	700,000	3,400,000
3	680,000	3,300,000
4	790,000	3,800,000
5	840,000	4,100,000

14.3

Tuition costs and enrollment figures for a university are given below. Using year 1 as the base year, construct a simple index for tuition costs and an index for enrollment.

Year	Tuition	Enrollment
1	$3,000	8,000
2	3,400	8,420
3	3,600	9,600
4	3,800	10,200

14.4

The number of copies of theological books sold each year and the average price per copy are given below. Construct a value index for sales letting year 2 be the base.

Year	Copies	Average Price
1	14,000	$5.40
2	17,000	6.00
3	18,000	6.60
4	20,000	7.20

14.5

The price index for 1/2″ steel cable over the past three years is 100, 102, and 109. If the cable sold for $1.50 per foot in the first year, what was its selling price in the third year?

14.6

The price index for cement over the past three years is 114, 125, and 136. If cement sold for $3.00 per sack in the third year, what was its selling price in the first year?

14.7

A computer company has increased sales by 10 percent each year since 1975. If 1975 were the base year, give the index number for each year since 1975.

14.8

The number of homes constructed in Coconino County and their average price for the past four years is given below. With year 2 as the base, construct a value index for home construction, a price index for homes, and a quantity index for the number of homes constructed.

Year	Number of Homes	Average Price
1	400	$50,000
2	450	53,000
3	390	56,000
4	480	60,000

14.9

America's dogs eat dry dog food, canned dog food, and raw meat. In year 1 there were 2 million kilograms of dry dog food sold, 8 million kilograms of canned dog food, and 1 million kilograms of raw meat sold for dogs. The average prices of these dog foods over a four-year period are given below. Construct a composite price index for dog food.

| | *Prices per Kilogram* | | |
Year	Dry	Canned	Raw Meat
1	$.27	$.36	$.51
2	.30	.39	.58
3	.33	.41	.69
4	.36	.44	.78

14.10

In Problem 14.9 the quantity of each type of dog food sold increased by 10 percent each year. Construct a value index for dog food sales.

14.11

The Dow-Smith Stock Index is composed on three stocks: IBX, General Mechanics, and du Punt. In particular, there is one IBX share, five General Mechanics shares, and three shares of du Punt which compose the stocks for the index. The December 31 prices of these stocks over the past four years are given below. With year 2 as the base year, construct the Dow-Smith Stock Index.

Year	IBX	GM	dP
1	$280	$40	$120
2	250	50	130
3	260	45	110
4	250	60	100

14.12

In year 1 there were 200 tons of steel produced at a price of $120 per ton, 30 tons of copper produced at a price of $500 per ton, and 90 tons of aluminum produced at $300 per ton. In year 2 the quantities of these three metals were 300, 40, and 100, respectively. In year 3 the respective quantities were 300, 60, and 140 tons. With year 1 as the base year, construct a composite quantity index for metal production.

14.13

The American Vacation Society wishes to construct a composite price index for the cost of a typical two-week vacation taken by the average American family of size four. As of year 1, the base year, the expenditure categories of lodging, food, gasoline, and entertainment received weights of .30, .40, .10, and .20, respectively. Simple price indexes for each of the categories are given below.

Construct a composite vacation price index. (Comment: The construction of a composite index from simple indexes was not discussed in the text. However, you should be able to determine how to do it.)

Simple Price Indexes

Year	Lodging	Food	Gasoline	Entertainment
1	100	100	100	100
2	108	110	120	102
3	111	118	121	104
4	115	129	121	106

14.14

Briefly describe the two Consumer Price Indexes.

14.15

For what purposes is the Consumer Price Index used?

14.16

Briefly describe the Producers Price Index.

14.17

Discuss three problems which are often encountered in the construction of a composite index like the CPI.

14.18

Why is it not accurate to state that the CPI is a cost-of-living index?

14.19

For the index below shift the base so that year 3 is the base year.

Year	Index
1	110
2	130
3	150
4	180
5	187

14.20

Three indexes for the Spurgeon Company, publisher of the *Sword and Trowel* magazine, are given below. Put the indexes on a common base and then make a speculative statement regarding the financial health of the company.

Year	Labor Cost	Material Cost	Gross Sales Revenues
1	100	230	500
2	110	246	510
3	120	261	530
4	135	284	540
5	146	299	545

14.21

The number of automobile fatalities over the past five years is given below. Also, an index showing the number of vehicle miles traveled from year to year is given. Use the index to deflate the auto fatalities time series. Is automobile travel getting safer?

Year	Fatalities	Index for Vehicle Miles Traveled
1	70,000	100
2	74,000	106
3	75,000	114
4	77,000	121
5	80,000	134

14.22

The total amount of money spent by West Virginians on shoes over the past four years is given below. Also, an index showing the change in population in West Virginia and an index showing the change in the average price of shoes is given. Adjust shoe sales for both population changes and price changes. What can be said about West Virginians and shoes?

Year	Shoe Sales	Population Index	Shoe Price Index
1	$800,000	100	100
2	820,000	105	110
3	860,000	112	118
4	910,000	118	125

14.23

The average wages received by employees of Dabney Ltd. over the past four years are $5.00, $6.00, $6.80, and $7.20 per hour. The Consumer Price Index has risen by 5 percent each of the years. What is the percentage increase in real wages over this four-year period?

APPENDIX

APPENDIX B
Binomial Distributions

n	x	p	.05	.10	.15	.20	.25	.30	.35	.40	.45	.50	.55	.60	.65	.70	.75	.80	.85	.90	.95
1	0		.9500	.9000	.8500	.8000	.7500	.7000	.6500	.6000	.5500	.5000	.4500	.4000	.3500	.3000	.2500	.2000	.1500	.1000	.0500
	1		.0500	.1000	.1500	.2000	.2500	.3000	.3500	.4000	.4500	.5000	.5500	.6000	.6500	.7000	.7500	.8000	.8500	.9000	.9500
2	0		.9025	.8100	.7225	.6400	.5625	.4900	.4225	.3600	.3025	.2500	.2025	.1600	.1225	.0900	.0625	.0400	.0225	.0100	.0025
	1		.0950	.1800	.2550	.3200	.3750	.4200	.4550	.4800	.4950	.5000	.4950	.4800	.4550	.4200	.3750	.3200	.2550	.1800	.0950
	2		.0025	.0100	.0225	.0400	.0625	.0900	.1225	.1600	.2025	.2500	.3025	.3600	.4225	.4900	.5625	.6400	.7225	.8100	.9025
3	0		.8574	.7290	.6141	.5120	.4219	.3430	.2746	.2160	.1664	.1250	.0911	.0640	.0429	.0270	.0156	.0080	.0034	.0010	.0001
	1		.1354	.2430	.3251	.3840	.4219	.4410	.4436	.4320	.4084	.3750	.3341	.2880	.2389	.1890	.1406	.0960	.0574	.0270	.0071
	2		.0071	.0270	.0574	.0960	.1406	.1890	.2389	.2880	.3341	.3750	.4084	.4320	.4436	.4410	.4219	.3840	.3251	.2430	.1354
	3		.0001	.0010	.0034	.0080	.0156	.0270	.0429	.0640	.0911	.1250	.1664	.2160	.2746	.3430	.4219	.5120	.6141	.7290	.8574
4	0		.8145	.6561	.5220	.4096	.3164	.2401	.1785	.1296	.0915	.0625	.0410	.0256	.0150	.0081	.0039	.0016	.0005	.0001	.0000
	1		.1715	.2916	.3685	.4096	.4219	.4116	.3845	.3456	.2995	.2500	.2005	.1536	.1115	.0756	.0469	.0256	.0115	.0036	.0005
	2		.0135	.0486	.0975	.1536	.2109	.2646	.3105	.3456	.3675	.3750	.3675	.3456	.3105	.2646	.2109	.1536	.0975	.0486	.0135
	3		.0005	.0036	.0115	.0256	.0469	.0756	.1115	.1536	.2005	.2500	.2995	.3456	.3845	.4116	.4219	.4096	.3685	.2916	.1715
	4		.0000	.0001	.0005	.0016	.0039	.0081	.0150	.0256	.0410	.0625	.0915	.1296	.1785	.2401	.3164	.4096	.5220	.6561	.8145
5	0		.7738	.5905	.4437	.3277	.2373	.1681	.1160	.0778	.0503	.0313	.0185	.0102	.0053	.0024	.0010	.0003	.0001	.0000	.0000
	1		.2036	.3281	.3915	.4096	.3955	.3602	.3124	.2592	.2059	.1563	.1128	.0768	.0488	.0284	.0146	.0064	.0022	.0004	.0000
	2		.0214	.0729	.1382	.2048	.2637	.3087	.3364	.3456	.3369	.3125	.2757	.2304	.1811	.1323	.0879	.0512	.0244	.0081	.0011
	3		.0011	.0081	.0244	.0512	.0879	.1323	.1811	.2304	.2757	.3125	.3369	.3456	.3364	.3087	.2637	.2048	.1382	.0729	.0214
	4		.0000	.0004	.0022	.0064	.0146	.0283	.0488	.0768	.1128	.1562	.2059	.2592	.3124	.3601	.3955	.4096	.3915	.3281	.2036
	5		.0000	.0000	.0001	.0003	.0010	.0024	.0053	.0102	.0185	.0312	.0503	.0778	.1160	.1681	.2373	.3277	.4437	.5905	.7738
6	0		.7351	.5314	.3771	.2621	.1780	.1176	.0754	.0467	.0277	.0156	.0083	.0041	.0018	.0007	.0002	.0001	.0000	.0000	.0000
	1		.2321	.3543	.3993	.3932	.3560	.3025	.2437	.1866	.1359	.0938	.0609	.0369	.0205	.0102	.0044	.0015	.0004	.0001	.0000
	2		.0305	.0984	.1762	.2458	.2966	.3241	.3280	.3110	.2780	.2344	.1861	.1382	.0951	.0595	.0330	.0154	.0055	.0012	.0001
	3		.0021	.0146	.0415	.0819	.1318	.1852	.2355	.2765	.3032	.3125	.3032	.2765	.2355	.1852	.1318	.0819	.0415	.0146	.0021
	4		.0001	.0012	.0055	.0154	.0330	.0595	.0951	.1382	.1861	.2344	.2780	.3110	.3280	.3241	.2966	.2458	.1762	.0984	.0305
	5		.0000	.0001	.0004	.0015	.0044	.0102	.0205	.0369	.0609	.0937	.1359	.1866	.2437	.3025	.3560	.3932	.3993	.3543	.2321
	6		.0000	.0000	.0000	.0001	.0002	.0007	.0018	.0041	.0083	.0156	.0277	.0467	.0754	.1176	.1780	.2621	.3771	.5314	.7351

Expanded and Reprinted by permission from William J. Stevenson, *Business Statistics: Concepts and Applications* (New York: Harper & Row, Publishers, 1978), pp. 464–466.

APPENDIX B (continued)
Binomial Distributions

										p										
n	x	.05	.10	.15	.20	.25	.30	.35	.40	.45	.50	.55	.60	.65	.70	.75	.80	.85	.90	.95
7	0	.6983	.4783	.3206	.2097	.1335	.0824	.0490	.0280	.0152	.0078	.0037	.0016	.0006	.0002	.0001	.0000	.0000	.0000	.0000
	1	.2573	.3720	.3960	.3670	.3115	.2471	.1848	.1306	.0872	.0547	.0320	.0172	.0084	.0036	.0013	.0004	.0001	.0000	.0000
	2	.0406	.1240	.2097	.2753	.3115	.3177	.2985	.2613	.2140	.1641	.1172	.0774	.0466	.0250	.0115	.0043	.0012	.0002	.0000
	3	.0036	.0230	.0617	.1147	.1730	.2269	.2679	.2903	.2918	.2734	.2388	.1935	.1442	.0972	.0577	.0287	.0109	.0026	.0002
	4	.0002	.0026	.0109	.0287	.0577	.0972	.1442	.1935	.2388	.2734	.2918	.2903	.2679	.2269	.1730	.1147	.0617	.0230	.0036
	5	.0000	.0002	.0012	.0043	.0115	.0250	.0466	.0774	.1172	.1641	.2140	.2613	.2985	.3177	.3115	.2753	.2097	.1240	.0406
	6	.0000	.0000	.0001	.0004	.0013	.0036	.0084	.0172	.0320	.0547	.0872	.1306	.1848	.2471	.3115	.3670	.3960	.3720	.2573
	7	.0000	.0000	.0000	.0000	.0001	.0002	.0006	.0016	.0037	.0078	.0152	.0280	.0490	.0824	.1335	.2097	.3206	.4783	.6983
8	0	.6634	.4305	.2725	.1678	.1001	.0576	.0319	.0168	.0084	.0039	.0017	.0007	.0002	.0001	.0000	.0000	.0000	.0000	.0000
	1	.2793	.3826	.3847	.3355	.2670	.1977	.1373	.0896	.0548	.0313	.0164	.0079	.0033	.0012	.0004	.0001	.0000	.0000	.0000
	2	.0515	.1488	.2376	.2936	.3115	.2965	.2587	.2090	.1569	.1094	.0703	.0413	.0217	.0100	.0038	.0011	.0002	.0000	.0000
	3	.0054	.0331	.0839	.1468	.2076	.2541	.2786	.2787	.2568	.2188	.1719	.1239	.0808	.0467	.0231	.0092	.0026	.0004	.0000
	4	.0004	.0046	.0185	.0459	.0865	.1361	.1875	.2322	.2627	.2734	.2627	.2322	.1875	.1361	.0865	.0459	.0185	.0046	.0004
	5	.0000	.0004	.0026	.0092	.0231	.0467	.0808	.1239	.1719	.2188	.2568	.2787	.2786	.2541	.2076	.1468	.0839	.0331	.0054
	6	.0000	.0000	.0002	.0011	.0038	.0100	.0217	.0413	.0703	.1094	.1569	.2090	.2587	.2965	.3115	.2936	.2376	.1488	.0515
	7	.0000	.0000	.0000	.0001	.0004	.0012	.0033	.0079	.0164	.0313	.0548	.0896	.1373	.1977	.2670	.3355	.3847	.3826	.2793
	8	.0000	.0000	.0000	.0000	.0000	.0001	.0002	.0007	.0017	.0039	.0084	.0168	.0319	.0576	.1001	.1678	.2725	.4305	.6634
9	0	.6302	.3874	.2316	.1342	.0751	.0404	.0207	.0101	.0046	.0020	.0008	.0003	.0001	.0000	.0000	.0000	.0000	.0000	.0000
	1	.2985	.3874	.3679	.3020	.2253	.1556	.1004	.0605	.0339	.0176	.0083	.0035	.0013	.0004	.0001	.0000	.0000	.0000	.0000
	2	.0629	.1722	.2597	.3020	.3003	.2668	.2162	.1612	.1110	.0703	.0407	.0212	.0098	.0039	.0012	.0003	.0000	.0000	.0000
	3	.0077	.0446	.1069	.1762	.2336	.2668	.2716	.2508	.2119	.1641	.1160	.0743	.0424	.0210	.0087	.0028	.0006	.0001	.0000
	4	.0006	.0074	.0283	.0661	.1168	.1715	.2194	.2508	.2600	.2461	.2128	.1672	.1181	.0735	.0389	.0165	.0050	.0008	.0000
	5	.0000	.0008	.0050	.0165	.0389	.0735	.1181	.1672	.2128	.2461	.2600	.2508	.2194	.1715	.1168	.0661	.0283	.0074	.0006
	6	.0000	.0001	.0006	.0028	.0087	.0210	.0424	.0743	.1160	.1641	.2119	.2508	.2716	.2668	.2336	.1762	.1069	.0446	.0077
	7	.0000	.0000	.0000	.0003	.0012	.0039	.0098	.0212	.0407	.0703	.1110	.1612	.2162	.2668	.3003	.3020	.2597	.1722	.0629
	8	.0000	.0000	.0000	.0000	.0001	.0004	.0013	.0035	.0083	.0176	.0339	.0605	.1004	.1556	.2253	.3020	.3679	.3874	.2986
	9	.0000	.0000	.0000	.0000	.0000	.0000	.0001	.0003	.0008	.0020	.0046	.0101	.0207	.0404	.0751	.1342	.2316	.3874	.6302

APPENDIX B (continued)
Binomial Distributions

n	x	.05	.10	.15	.20	.25	.30	.35	.40	.45	.50	.55	.60	.65	.70	.75	.80	.85	.90	.95
10	0	.5987	.3487	.1969	.1074	.0563	.0282	.0135	.0060	.0025	.0010	.0003	.0001	.0000	.0000	.0000	.0000	.0000	.0000	.0000
	1	.3151	.3874	.3474	.2684	.1877	.1211	.0725	.0403	.0207	.0098	.0042	.0016	.0005	.0001	.0000	.0000	.0000	.0000	.0000
	2	.0746	.1937	.2759	.3020	.2816	.2335	.1757	.1209	.0763	.0439	.0229	.0106	.0043	.0014	.0004	.0001	.0000	.0000	.0000
	3	.0105	.0574	.1298	.2013	.2503	.2668	.2522	.2150	.1665	.1172	.0746	.0425	.0212	.0090	.0031	.0008	.0001	.0000	.0000
	4	.0010	.0112	.0401	.0881	.1460	.2001	.2377	.2508	.2384	.2051	.1596	.1115	.0689	.0368	.0162	.0055	.0012	.0001	.0000
	5	.0001	.0015	.0085	.0264	.0584	.1029	.1536	.2007	.2340	.2461	.2340	.2007	.1536	.1029	.0584	.0264	.0085	.0015	.0001
	6	.0000	.0001	.0012	.0055	.0162	.0368	.0689	.1115	.1596	.2051	.2384	.2508	.2377	.2001	.1460	.0881	.0401	.0112	.0010
	7	.0000	.0000	.0001	.0008	.0031	.0090	.0212	.0425	.0746	.1172	.1665	.2150	.2522	.2668	.2503	.2013	.1298	.0574	.0105
	8	.0000	.0000	.0000	.0001	.0004	.0014	.0043	.0106	.0229	.0439	.0763	.1209	.1757	.2335	.2816	.3020	.2759	.1937	.0746
	9	.0000	.0000	.0000	.0000	.0000	.0001	.0005	.0016	.0042	.0098	.0207	.0403	.0725	.1211	.1877	.2684	.3474	.3874	.3151
	10	.0000	.0000	.0000	.0000	.0000	.0000	.0000	.0001	.0003	.0010	.0025	.0060	.0135	.0282	.0563	.1074	.1969	.3487	.5987
11	0	.5688	.3138	.1673	.0859	.0422	.0198	.0088	.0036	.0014	.0005	.0002	.0000	.0000	.0000	.0000	.0000	.0000	.0000	.0000
	1	.3293	.3835	.3248	.2362	.1549	.0932	.0518	.0266	.0125	.0054	.0021	.0007	.0002	.0000	.0000	.0000	.0000	.0000	.0000
	2	.0867	.2131	.2866	.2953	.2581	.1998	.1395	.0887	.0513	.0269	.0126	.0052	.0018	.0005	.0001	.0000	.0000	.0000	.0000
	3	.0137	.0710	.1517	.2215	.2581	.2568	.2254	.1774	.1259	.0806	.0462	.0234	.0102	.0037	.0011	.0002	.0000	.0000	.0000
	4	.0014	.0158	.0536	.1107	.1721	.2201	.2428	.2365	.2060	.1611	.1128	.0701	.0379	.0173	.0064	.0017	.0003	.0000	.0000
	5	.0001	.0025	.0132	.0388	.0803	.1321	.1830	.2207	.2360	.2256	.1931	.1471	.0985	.0566	.0268	.0097	.0023	.0003	.0000
	6	.0000	.0003	.0023	.0097	.0268	.0566	.0985	.1471	.1931	.2256	.2360	.2207	.1830	.1321	.0803	.0388	.0132	.0025	.0001
	7	.0000	.0000	.0003	.0017	.0064	.0173	.0379	.0701	.1128	.1611	.2060	.2365	.2428	.2201	.1721	.1107	.0536	.0158	.0014
	8	.0000	.0000	.0000	.0002	.0011	.0037	.0102	.0234	.0462	.0806	.1259	.1774	.2254	.2568	.2581	.2215	.1517	.0710	.0137
	9	.0000	.0000	.0000	.0000	.0001	.0005	.0018	.0052	.0126	.0269	.0513	.0887	.1395	.1998	.2581	.2953	.2866	.2131	.0867
	10	.0000	.0000	.0000	.0000	.0000	.0000	.0002	.0007	.0021	.0054	.0125	.0266	.0518	.0932	.1549	.2362	.3248	.3835	.3293
	11	.0000	.0000	.0000	.0000	.0000	.0000	.0000	.0000	.0002	.0005	.0014	.0036	.0088	.0198	.0422	.0859	.1673	.3138	.5688
12	0	.5404	.2824	.1422	.0687	.0317	.0138	.0057	.0022	.0008	.0002	.0001	.0000	.0000	.0000	.0000	.0000	.0000	.0000	.0000
	1	.3413	.3766	.3012	.2062	.1267	.0712	.0368	.0174	.0075	.0029	.0010	.0003	.0001	.0000	.0000	.0000	.0000	.0000	.0000
	2	.0988	.2301	.2924	.2835	.2323	.1678	.1088	.0639	.0339	.0161	.0068	.0025	.0008	.0002	.0000	.0000	.0000	.0000	.0000
	3	.0173	.0852	.1720	.2362	.2581	.2397	.1954	.1419	.0923	.0537	.0277	.0125	.0048	.0015	.0004	.0001	.0000	.0000	.0000
	4	.0021	.0213	.0683	.1329	.1936	.2311	.2367	.2128	.1700	.1208	.0762	.0420	.0199	.0078	.0024	.0005	.0001	.0000	.0000
	5	.0002	.0038	.0193	.0532	.1032	.1585	.2039	.2270	.2225	.1934	.1489	.1009	.0591	.0291	.0115	.0033	.0006	.0000	.0000
	6	.0000	.0005	.0040	.0155	.0401	.0792	.1281	.1766	.2124	.2256	.2124	.1766	.1281	.0792	.0401	.0155	.0040	.0005	.0000
	7	.0000	.0000	.0006	.0033	.0115	.0291	.0591	.1009	.1489	.1934	.2225	.2270	.2039	.1585	.1032	.0532	.0193	.0038	.0002
	8	.0000	.0000	.0001	.0005	.0024	.0078	.0199	.0420	.0762	.1208	.1700	.2128	.2367	.2311	.1936	.1329	.0683	.0213	.0021
	9	.0000	.0000	.0000	.0001	.0004	.0015	.0048	.0125	.0277	.0537	.0923	.1419	.1954	.2397	.2581	.2362	.1720	.0852	.0173
	10	.0000	.0000	.0000	.0000	.0000	.0002	.0008	.0025	.0068	.0161	.0339	.0639	.1088	.1678	.2323	.2835	.2924	.2301	.0988
	11	.0000	.0000	.0000	.0000	.0000	.0000	.0001	.0003	.0010	.0029	.0075	.0174	.0368	.0712	.1267	.2062	.3012	.3766	.3413
	12	.0000	.0000	.0000	.0000	.0000	.0000	.0000	.0000	.0001	.0002	.0008	.0022	.0057	.0138	.0317	.0687	.1422	.2824	.5404

APPENDIX B (continued)
Binomial Distributions

										p										
n	x	.05	.10	.15	.20	.25	.30	.35	.40	.45	.50	.55	.60	.65	.70	.75	.80	.85	.90	.95
13	0	.5133	.2542	.1209	.0550	.0238	.0097	.0037	.0013	.0004	.0001	.0000	.0000	.0000	.0000	.0000	.0000	.0000	.0000	.0000
	1	.3512	.3672	.2774	.1787	.1029	.0540	.0259	.0113	.0045	.0016	.0005	.0001	.0000	.0000	.0000	.0000	.0000	.0000	.0000
	2	.1109	.2448	.2937	.2680	.2059	.1388	.0836	.0453	.0220	.0095	.0036	.0012	.0003	.0001	.0000	.0000	.0000	.0000	.0000
	3	.0214	.0997	.1900	.2457	.2517	.2181	.1651	.1107	.0660	.0349	.0162	.0065	.0022	.0006	.0001	.0000	.0000	.0000	.0000
	4	.0028	.0277	.0838	.1535	.2097	.2337	.2222	.1845	.1350	.0873	.0495	.0243	.0101	.0034	.0009	.0001	.0000	.0000	.0000
	5	.0003	.0055	.0266	.0691	.1258	.1803	.2154	.2214	.1989	.1571	.1089	.0656	.0336	.0142	.0047	.0011	.0001	.0000	.0000
	6	.0000	.0008	.0063	.0230	.0559	.1030	.1546	.1968	.2169	.2095	.1775	.1312	.0833	.0442	.0186	.0058	.0011	.0001	.0000
	7	.0000	.0001	.0011	.0058	.0186	.0442	.0833	.1312	.1775	.2095	.2169	.1968	.1546	.1030	.0559	.0230	.0063	.0008	.0000
	8	.0000	.0000	.0001	.0011	.0047	.0142	.0336	.0656	.1089	.1571	.1989	.2214	.2154	.1803	.1258	.0691	.0266	.0055	.0003
	9	.0000	.0000	.0000	.0001	.0009	.0034	.0101	.0243	.0495	.0873	.1350	.1845	.2222	.2337	.2097	.1535	.0838	.0277	.0028
	10	.0000	.0000	.0000	.0000	.0001	.0006	.0022	.0065	.0162	.0349	.0660	.1107	.1651	.2181	.2517	.2457	.1900	.0997	.0214
	11	.0000	.0000	.0000	.0000	.0000	.0001	.0003	.0012	.0036	.0095	.0220	.0453	.0836	.1388	.2059	.2680	.2937	.2448	.1109
	12	.0000	.0000	.0000	.0000	.0000	.0000	.0000	.0001	.0005	.0016	.0045	.0113	.0259	.0540	.1029	.1787	.2774	.3672	.3512
	13	.0000	.0000	.0000	.0000	.0000	.0000	.0000	.0000	.0000	.0001	.0004	.0013	.0037	.0097	.0238	.0550	.1209	.2542	.5133
14	0	.4877	.2288	.1028	.0440	.0178	.0068	.0024	.0008	.0002	.0001	.0000	.0000	.0000	.0000	.0000	.0000	.0000	.0000	.0000
	1	.3593	.3559	.2539	.1539	.0832	.0407	.0181	.0073	.0027	.0009	.0002	.0001	.0000	.0000	.0000	.0000	.0000	.0000	.0000
	2	.1229	.2570	.2912	.2501	.1802	.1134	.0634	.0317	.0141	.0056	.0019	.0005	.0001	.0000	.0000	.0000	.0000	.0000	.0000
	3	.0259	.1142	.2056	.2501	.2402	.1943	.1366	.0845	.0462	.0222	.0093	.0033	.0010	.0002	.0000	.0000	.0000	.0000	.0000
	4	.0037	.0349	.0998	.1720	.2202	.2290	.2022	.1549	.1040	.0611	.0312	.0136	.0049	.0014	.0003	.0000	.0000	.0000	.0000
	5	.0004	.0078	.0352	.0860	.1468	.1963	.2178	.2066	.1701	.1222	.0762	.0408	.0183	.0066	.0018	.0003	.0000	.0000	.0000
	6	.0000	.0013	.0093	.0322	.0734	.1262	.1759	.2066	.2088	.1833	.1398	.0918	.0510	.0232	.0082	.0020	.0003	.0000	.0000
	7	.0000	.0002	.0019	.0092	.0280	.0618	.1082	.1574	.1952	.2095	.1952	.1574	.1082	.0618	.0280	.0092	.0019	.0002	.0000
	8	.0000	.0000	.0003	.0020	.0082	.0232	.0510	.0918	.1398	.1833	.2088	.2066	.1759	.1262	.0734	.0322	.0093	.0013	.0000
	9	.0000	.0000	.0000	.0003	.0018	.0066	.0183	.0408	.0762	.1222	.1701	.2066	.2178	.1963	.1468	.0860	.0352	.0078	.0004
	10	.0000	.0000	.0000	.0000	.0003	.0014	.0049	.0136	.0312	.0611	.1040	.1549	.2022	.2290	.2202	.1720	.0998	.0349	.0037
	11	.0000	.0000	.0000	.0000	.0000	.0002	.0010	.0033	.0093	.0222	.0462	.0845	.1366	.1943	.2402	.2501	.2056	.1142	.0259
	12	.0000	.0000	.0000	.0000	.0000	.0000	.0001	.0005	.0019	.0056	.0141	.0317	.0634	.1134	.1802	.2501	.2912	.2570	.1229
	13	.0000	.0000	.0000	.0000	.0000	.0000	.0000	.0001	.0002	.0009	.0027	.0073	.0181	.0407	.0832	.1539	.2539	.3559	.3593
	14	.0000	.0000	.0000	.0000	.0000	.0000	.0000	.0000	.0000	.0001	.0002	.0008	.0024	.0068	.0178	.0440	.1028	.2288	.4877

APPENDIX B (continued)
Binomial Distributions

n	x	.05	.10	.15	.20	.25	.30	.35	.40	.45	.50	.55	.60	.65	.70	.75	.80	.85	.90	.95
											(p)									
15	0	.4633	.2059	.0874	.0352	.0134	.0047	.0016	.0005	.0001	.0000	.0000	.0000	.0000	.0000	.0000	.0000	.0000	.0000	.0000
	1	.3658	.3432	.2312	.1319	.0668	.0305	.0126	.0047	.0016	.0005	.0001	.0000	.0000	.0000	.0000	.0000	.0000	.0000	.0000
	2	.1348	.2669	.2856	.2309	.1559	.0916	.0476	.0219	.0090	.0032	.0010	.0003	.0001	.0000	.0000	.0000	.0000	.0000	.0000
	3	.0307	.1285	.2184	.2501	.2252	.1700	.1110	.0634	.0318	.0139	.0052	.0016	.0004	.0001	.0000	.0000	.0000	.0000	.0000
	4	.0049	.0428	.1156	.1876	.2252	.2186	.1792	.1268	.0780	.0417	.0191	.0074	.0024	.0006	.0001	.0000	.0000	.0000	.0000
	5	.0006	.0105	.0449	.1032	.1651	.2061	.2123	.1859	.1404	.0916	.0515	.0245	.0096	.0030	.0007	.0001	.0000	.0000	.0000
	6	.0000	.0019	.0132	.0430	.0917	.1472	.1906	.2066	.1914	.1527	.1048	.0612	.0298	.0116	.0034	.0007	.0001	.0000	.0000
	7	.0000	.0003	.0030	.0138	.0393	.0811	.1319	.1771	.2013	.1964	.1647	.1181	.0710	.0348	.0131	.0035	.0005	.0000	.0000
	8	.0000	.0000	.0005	.0035	.0131	.0348	.0710	.1181	.1647	.1964	.2013	.1771	.1319	.0811	.0393	.0138	.0030	.0003	.0000
	9	.0000	.0000	.0001	.0007	.0034	.0116	.0298	.0612	.1048	.1527	.1914	.2066	.1906	.1472	.0917	.0430	.0132	.0019	.0000
	10	.0000	.0000	.0000	.0001	.0007	.0030	.0096	.0245	.0515	.0916	.1404	.1859	.2123	.2061	.1651	.1032	.0449	.0105	.0006
	11	.0000	.0000	.0000	.0000	.0001	.0006	.0024	.0074	.0191	.0417	.0780	.1268	.1792	.2186	.2252	.1876	.1156	.0428	.0049
	12	.0000	.0000	.0000	.0000	.0000	.0001	.0004	.0016	.0052	.0139	.0318	.0634	.1110	.1700	.2252	.2501	.2184	.1285	.0307
	13	.0000	.0000	.0000	.0000	.0000	.0000	.0001	.0003	.0010	.0032	.0090	.0219	.0476	.0916	.1559	.2309	.2856	.2669	.1348
	14	.0000	.0000	.0000	.0000	.0000	.0000	.0000	.0000	.0001	.0005	.0016	.0047	.0126	.0305	.0668	.1319	.2312	.3432	.3658
	15	.0000	.0000	.0000	.0000	.0000	.0000	.0000	.0000	.0000	.0000	.0001	.0005	.0016	.0047	.0134	.0352	.0874	.2059	.4633
16	0	.4401	.1853	.0743	.0281	.0100	.0033	.0010	.0003	.0001	.0000	.0000	.0000	.0000	.0000	.0000	.0000	.0000	.0000	.0000
	1	.3706	.3294	.2097	.1126	.0535	.0228	.0087	.0030	.0009	.0002	.0001	.0000	.0000	.0000	.0000	.0000	.0000	.0000	.0000
	2	.1463	.2745	.2775	.2111	.1336	.0732	.0353	.0150	.0056	.0018	.0005	.0001	.0000	.0000	.0000	.0000	.0000	.0000	.0000
	3	.0359	.1423	.2285	.2463	.2079	.1465	.0888	.0468	.0215	.0085	.0029	.0008	.0002	.0000	.0000	.0000	.0000	.0000	.0000
	4	.0061	.0514	.1311	.2001	.2252	.2040	.1553	.1014	.0572	.0278	.0115	.0040	.0011	.0002	.0000	.0000	.0000	.0000	.0000
	5	.0008	.0137	.0555	.1201	.1802	.2099	.2008	.1623	.1123	.0667	.0337	.0142	.0049	.0013	.0002	.0000	.0000	.0000	.0000
	6	.0001	.0028	.0180	.0550	.1101	.1649	.1982	.1983	.1684	.1222	.0755	.0392	.0167	.0056	.0014	.0002	.0000	.0000	.0000
	7	.0000	.0004	.0045	.0197	.0524	.1010	.1524	.1889	.1969	.1746	.1318	.0840	.0442	.0185	.0058	.0012	.0001	.0000	.0000
	8	.0000	.0001	.0009	.0055	.0197	.0487	.0923	.1417	.1812	.1964	.1812	.1417	.0923	.0487	.0197	.0055	.0009	.0001	.0000
	9	.0000	.0000	.0001	.0012	.0058	.0185	.0442	.0840	.1318	.1746	.1969	.1889	.1524	.1010	.0524	.0197	.0045	.0004	.0000
	10	.0000	.0000	.0000	.0002	.0014	.0056	.0167	.0392	.0755	.1222	.1684	.1983	.1982	.1649	.1101	.0550	.0180	.0028	.0001
	11	.0000	.0000	.0000	.0000	.0002	.0013	.0049	.0142	.0337	.0667	.1123	.1623	.2008	.2099	.1802	.1201	.0555	.0137	.0008
	12	.0000	.0000	.0000	.0000	.0000	.0002	.0011	.0040	.0115	.0278	.0572	.1014	.1553	.2040	.2252	.2001	.1311	.0514	.0061
	13	.0000	.0000	.0000	.0000	.0000	.0000	.0002	.0008	.0029	.0085	.0215	.0468	.0888	.1465	.2079	.2463	.2285	.1423	.0359
	14	.0000	.0000	.0000	.0000	.0000	.0000	.0000	.0001	.0005	.0018	.0056	.0150	.0353	.0732	.1336	.2111	.2775	.2745	.1463
	15	.0000	.0000	.0000	.0000	.0000	.0000	.0000	.0000	.0001	.0002	.0009	.0030	.0087	.0228	.0535	.1126	.2097	.3294	.3706
	16	.0000	.0000	.0000	.0000	.0000	.0000	.0000	.0000	.0000	.0000	.0001	.0003	.0010	.0033	.0100	.0281	.0743	.1853	.4401

APPENDIX B (continued)
Binomial Distributions

p

n	x	.05	.10	.15	.20	.25	.30	.35	.40	.45	.50	.55	.60	.65	.70	.75	.80	.85	.90	.95
17	0	.4181	.1668	.0631	.0225	.0075	.0023	.0007	.0002	.0000	.0000	.0000	.0000	.0000	.0000	.0000	.0000	.0000	.0000	.0000
	1	.3741	.3150	.1893	.0957	.0426	.0169	.0060	.0019	.0005	.0001	.0000	.0000	.0000	.0000	.0000	.0000	.0000	.0000	.0000
	2	.1575	.2800	.2673	.1914	.1136	.0581	.0260	.0102	.0035	.0010	.0003	.0001	.0000	.0000	.0000	.0000	.0000	.0000	.0000
	3	.0415	.1556	.2359	.2393	.1893	.1245	.0701	.0341	.0144	.0052	.0016	.0004	.0001	.0000	.0000	.0000	.0000	.0000	.0000
	4	.0076	.0605	.1457	.2093	.2209	.1868	.1320	.0796	.0411	.0182	.0068	.0021	.0005	.0001	.0000	.0000	.0000	.0000	.0000
	5	.0010	.0175	.0668	.1361	.1914	.2081	.1849	.1379	.0875	.0472	.0215	.0081	.0024	.0006	.0001	.0000	.0000	.0000	.0000
	6	.0001	.0039	.0236	.0680	.1276	.1784	.1991	.1839	.1432	.0944	.0525	.0242	.0090	.0026	.0005	.0001	.0000	.0000	.0000
	7	.0000	.0007	.0065	.0267	.0668	.1201	.1685	.1927	.1841	.1484	.1008	.0571	.0263	.0095	.0025	.0004	.0000	.0000	.0000
	8	.0000	.0001	.0014	.0084	.0279	.0644	.1134	.1606	.1883	.1855	.1540	.1070	.0611	.0276	.0093	.0021	.0003	.0000	.0000
	9	.0000	.0000	.0003	.0021	.0093	.0276	.0611	.1070	.1540	.1855	.1883	.1606	.1134	.0644	.0279	.0084	.0014	.0001	.0000
	10	.0000	.0000	.0000	.0004	.0025	.0095	.0263	.0571	.1008	.1484	.1841	.1927	.1685	.1201	.0668	.0267	.0065	.0007	.0000
	11	.0000	.0000	.0000	.0001	.0005	.0026	.0090	.0242	.0525	.0944	.1432	.1839	.1991	.1784	.1276	.0680	.0236	.0039	.0001
	12	.0000	.0000	.0000	.0000	.0001	.0006	.0024	.0081	.0215	.0472	.0875	.1379	.1849	.2081	.1914	.1361	.0668	.0175	.0010
	13	.0000	.0000	.0000	.0000	.0000	.0001	.0005	.0021	.0068	.0182	.0411	.0796	.1320	.1868	.2209	.2093	.1457	.0605	.0076
	14	.0000	.0000	.0000	.0000	.0000	.0000	.0001	.0004	.0016	.0052	.0144	.0341	.0701	.1245	.1893	.2393	.2359	.1556	.0415
	15	.0000	.0000	.0000	.0000	.0000	.0000	.0000	.0000	.0003	.0010	.0035	.0102	.0263	.0581	.1136	.1914	.2673	.2800	.1575
	16	.0000	.0000	.0000	.0000	.0000	.0000	.0000	.0000	.0000	.0001	.0005	.0019	.0060	.0169	.0426	.0957	.1893	.3150	.3741
	17	.0000	.0000	.0000	.0000	.0000	.0000	.0000	.0000	.0000	.0000	.0000	.0002	.0007	.0023	.0075	.0225	.0631	.1668	.4181
18	0	.3972	.1501	.0536	.0180	.0056	.0016	.0004	.0001	.0000	.0000	.0000	.0000	.0000	.0000	.0000	.0000	.0000	.0000	.0000
	1	.3763	.3002	.1704	.0811	.0338	.0126	.0042	.0012	.0003	.0001	.0000	.0000	.0000	.0000	.0000	.0000	.0000	.0000	.0000
	2	.1683	.2835	.2556	.1723	.0958	.0458	.0190	.0069	.0022	.0006	.0001	.0000	.0000	.0000	.0000	.0000	.0000	.0000	.0000
	3	.0473	.1680	.2406	.2297	.1704	.1046	.0547	.0246	.0095	.0031	.0009	.0002	.0000	.0000	.0000	.0000	.0000	.0000	.0000
	4	.0093	.0700	.1592	.2153	.2130	.1681	.1104	.0614	.0291	.0117	.0039	.0011	.0002	.0000	.0000	.0000	.0000	.0000	.0000
	5	.0014	.0218	.0787	.1507	.1988	.2017	.1664	.1146	.0666	.0327	.0134	.0045	.0012	.0002	.0000	.0000	.0000	.0000	.0000
	6	.0002	.0052	.0301	.0816	.1436	.1873	.1941	.1655	.1181	.0708	.0354	.0145	.0047	.0012	.0002	.0000	.0000	.0000	.0000
	7	.0000	.0010	.0091	.0350	.0820	.1376	.1792	.1892	.1657	.1214	.0742	.0374	.0151	.0046	.0010	.0001	.0000	.0000	.0000
	8	.0000	.0002	.0022	.0120	.0376	.0811	.1327	.1734	.1864	.1669	.1248	.0771	.0385	.0149	.0042	.0008	.0001	.0000	.0000
	9	.0000	.0000	.0004	.0033	.0139	.0386	.0794	.1284	.1694	.1855	.1694	.1284	.0794	.0386	.0139	.0033	.0004	.0000	.0000
	10	.0000	.0000	.0001	.0008	.0042	.0149	.0385	.0771	.1248	.1669	.1864	.1734	.1327	.0811	.0376	.0120	.0022	.0002	.0000
	11	.0000	.0000	.0000	.0001	.0010	.0046	.0151	.0374	.0742	.1214	.1657	.1892	.1792	.1376	.0820	.0350	.0091	.0010	.0000
	12	.0000	.0000	.0000	.0000	.0002	.0012	.0047	.0145	.0354	.0708	.1181	.1655	.1941	.1873	.1436	.0816	.0301	.0052	.0002
	13	.0000	.0000	.0000	.0000	.0000	.0002	.0012	.0045	.0134	.0327	.0666	.1146	.1664	.2017	.1988	.1507	.0787	.0218	.0014
	14	.0000	.0000	.0000	.0000	.0000	.0000	.0002	.0011	.0039	.0117	.0291	.0614	.1104	.1681	.2130	.2153	.1592	.0700	.0093
	15	.0000	.0000	.0000	.0000	.0000	.0000	.0000	.0002	.0009	.0031	.0095	.0246	.0547	.1046	.1704	.2297	.2406	.1680	.0473
	16	.0000	.0000	.0000	.0000	.0000	.0000	.0000	.0000	.0001	.0006	.0022	.0069	.0190	.0458	.0958	.1723	.2556	.2835	.1683
	17	.0000	.0000	.0000	.0000	.0000	.0000	.0000	.0000	.0000	.0001	.0003	.0012	.0042	.0126	.0338	.0811	.1704	.3002	.3763
	18	.0000	.0000	.0000	.0000	.0000	.0000	.0000	.0000	.0000	.0000	.0000	.0001	.0004	.0016	.0056	.0180	.0536	.1501	.3972

APPENDIX B: Binomial Distributions (continued)

n	x	.05	.10	.15	.20	.25	.30	.35	.40	.45	.50	.55	.60	.65	.70	.75	.80	.85	.90	.95
19	0	.3774	.1351	.0456	.0144	.0042	.0011	.0003	.0001	.0000	.0000	.0000	.0000	.0000	.0000	.0000	.0000	.0000	.0000	.0000
	1	.3774	.2852	.1529	.0685	.0268	.0093	.0029	.0008	.0002	.0000	.0000	.0000	.0000	.0000	.0000	.0000	.0000	.0000	.0000
	2	.1787	.2852	.2428	.1540	.0803	.0358	.0138	.0046	.0013	.0003	.0001	.0000	.0000	.0000	.0000	.0000	.0000	.0000	.0000
	3	.0533	.1796	.2428	.2182	.1517	.0869	.0422	.0175	.0062	.0018	.0005	.0001	.0000	.0000	.0000	.0000	.0000	.0000	.0000
	4	.0112	.0798	.1714	.2182	.2023	.1491	.0909	.0467	.0203	.0074	.0022	.0005	.0001	.0000	.0000	.0000	.0000	.0000	.0000
	5	.0018	.0266	.0907	.1636	.2023	.1916	.1468	.0933	.0497	.0222	.0082	.0024	.0006	.0001	.0000	.0000	.0000	.0000	.0000
	6	.0002	.0069	.0374	.0955	.1574	.1916	.1844	.1451	.0949	.0518	.0233	.0085	.0024	.0005	.0000	.0000	.0000	.0000	.0000
	7	.0000	.0014	.0122	.0443	.0974	.1525	.1844	.1797	.1443	.0961	.0529	.0237	.0083	.0022	.0004	.0000	.0000	.0000	.0000
	8	.0000	.0002	.0032	.0166	.0487	.0981	.1489	.1797	.1771	.1442	.0970	.0532	.0233	.0077	.0018	.0003	.0000	.0000	.0000
	9	.0000	.0000	.0007	.0051	.0198	.0514	.0980	.1464	.1771	.1762	.1449	.0976	.0528	.0220	.0066	.0013	.0001	.0000	.0000
	10	.0000	.0000	.0001	.0013	.0066	.0220	.0528	.0976	.1449	.1762	.1771	.1464	.0980	.0514	.0198	.0051	.0007	.0000	.0000
	11	.0000	.0000	.0000	.0003	.0018	.0077	.0233	.0532	.0970	.1442	.1771	.1797	.1489	.0981	.0487	.0166	.0032	.0002	.0000
	12	.0000	.0000	.0000	.0000	.0004	.0022	.0083	.0237	.0529	.0961	.1443	.1797	.1844	.1525	.0974	.0443	.0122	.0014	.0000
	13	.0000	.0000	.0000	.0000	.0001	.0005	.0024	.0085	.0233	.0518	.0949	.1451	.1844	.1916	.1574	.0955	.0374	.0069	.0002
	14	.0000	.0000	.0000	.0000	.0000	.0001	.0006	.0024	.0085	.0222	.0497	.0933	.1468	.1916	.2023	.1636	.0907	.0266	.0018
	15	.0000	.0000	.0000	.0000	.0000	.0000	.0001	.0006	.0022	.0074	.0203	.0467	.0909	.1491	.2023	.2182	.1714	.0798	.0112
	16	.0000	.0000	.0000	.0000	.0000	.0000	.0000	.0001	.0005	.0018	.0062	.0175	.0422	.0869	.1517	.2182	.2428	.1796	.0533
	17	.0000	.0000	.0000	.0000	.0000	.0000	.0000	.0000	.0001	.0003	.0013	.0046	.0138	.0358	.0803	.1540	.2428	.2852	.1787
	18	.0000	.0000	.0000	.0000	.0000	.0000	.0000	.0000	.0000	.0000	.0002	.0008	.0029	.0093	.0268	.0685	.1529	.2852	.3774
	19	.0000	.0000	.0000	.0000	.0000	.0000	.0000	.0000	.0000	.0000	.0000	.0001	.0003	.0011	.0042	.0144	.0456	.1351	.3774
20	0	.3585	.1216	.0388	.0115	.0032	.0008	.0002	.0000	.0000	.0000	.0000	.0000	.0000	.0000	.0000	.0000	.0000	.0000	.0000
	1	.3774	.2702	.1368	.0576	.0211	.0068	.0020	.0005	.0001	.0000	.0000	.0000	.0000	.0000	.0000	.0000	.0000	.0000	.0000
	2	.1887	.2852	.2293	.1369	.0669	.0278	.0100	.0031	.0008	.0002	.0000	.0000	.0000	.0000	.0000	.0000	.0000	.0000	.0000
	3	.0596	.1901	.2428	.2054	.1339	.0716	.0323	.0123	.0040	.0011	.0002	.0000	.0000	.0000	.0000	.0000	.0000	.0000	.0000
	4	.0133	.0898	.1821	.2182	.1897	.1304	.0738	.0350	.0139	.0046	.0013	.0003	.0000	.0000	.0000	.0000	.0000	.0000	.0000
	5	.0022	.0319	.1028	.1746	.2023	.1789	.1272	.0746	.0365	.0148	.0049	.0013	.0003	.0000	.0000	.0000	.0000	.0000	.0000
	6	.0003	.0089	.0454	.1091	.1686	.1916	.1712	.1244	.0746	.0370	.0150	.0049	.0012	.0002	.0000	.0000	.0000	.0000	.0000
	7	.0000	.0020	.0160	.0545	.1124	.1643	.1844	.1659	.1221	.0739	.0366	.0146	.0045	.0010	.0002	.0000	.0000	.0000	.0000
	8	.0000	.0004	.0046	.0222	.0609	.1144	.1614	.1797	.1623	.1201	.0727	.0355	.0136	.0039	.0008	.0001	.0000	.0000	.0000
	9	.0000	.0001	.0011	.0074	.0271	.0654	.1158	.1597	.1771	.1602	.1185	.0710	.0336	.0120	.0030	.0005	.0000	.0000	.0000
	10	.0000	.0000	.0002	.0020	.0099	.0308	.0686	.1171	.1593	.1762	.1593	.1171	.0686	.0308	.0099	.0020	.0002	.0000	.0000
	11	.0000	.0000	.0000	.0005	.0030	.0120	.0336	.0710	.1185	.1602	.1771	.1597	.1158	.0654	.0271	.0074	.0011	.0001	.0000
	12	.0000	.0000	.0000	.0001	.0008	.0039	.0136	.0355	.0727	.1201	.1623	.1797	.1614	.1144	.0609	.0222	.0046	.0004	.0000
	13	.0000	.0000	.0000	.0000	.0002	.0010	.0045	.0146	.0366	.0739	.1221	.1659	.1844	.1643	.1124	.0545	.0160	.0020	.0000
	14	.0000	.0000	.0000	.0000	.0000	.0002	.0012	.0049	.0150	.0370	.0746	.1244	.1712	.1916	.1686	.1091	.0454	.0089	.0003
	15	.0000	.0000	.0000	.0000	.0000	.0000	.0003	.0013	.0049	.0148	.0365	.0746	.1272	.1789	.2023	.1746	.1028	.0319	.0022
	16	.0000	.0000	.0000	.0000	.0000	.0000	.0000	.0003	.0013	.0046	.0139	.0350	.0738	.1304	.1897	.2182	.1821	.0898	.0133
	17	.0000	.0000	.0000	.0000	.0000	.0000	.0000	.0000	.0002	.0011	.0040	.0123	.0323	.0716	.1339	.2054	.2428	.1901	.0596
	18	.0000	.0000	.0000	.0000	.0000	.0000	.0000	.0000	.0000	.0002	.0008	.0031	.0100	.0278	.0669	.1369	.2293	.2852	.1887
	19	.0000	.0000	.0000	.0000	.0000	.0000	.0000	.0000	.0000	.0000	.0001	.0005	.0020	.0068	.0211	.0576	.1368	.2702	.3774
	20	.0000	.0000	.0000	.0000	.0000	.0000	.0000	.0000	.0000	.0000	.0000	.0000	.0002	.0008	.0032	.0115	.0388	.1216	.3585

p

APPENDIX C
Chi-Square Distributions

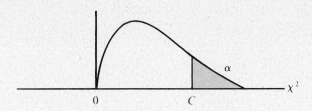

Degrees of Freedom, d	α			
	.10	.05	.01	.005
1	2.71	3.84	6.63	7.88
2	4.61	5.99	9.21	10.60
3	6.25	7.81	11.34	12.84
4	7.78	9.49	13.28	14.86
5	9.24	11.07	15.09	16.75
6	10.6	12.6	16.8	18.5
7	12.0	14.1	18.5	20.3
8	13.4	15.5	20.1	22.0
9	14.7	16.9	21.7	23.6
10	16.0	18.3	23.2	25.2
11	17.3	19.7	24.7	26.8
12	18.5	21.0	26.2	28.3
13	19.8	22.4	27.7	29.8
14	21.1	23.7	29.1	31.3
15	22.3	25.0	30.6	32.8
16	23.5	26.3	32.0	34.3
17	24.8	27.6	33.4	35.7
18	26.0	28.9	34.8	37.2
19	27.2	30.1	36.2	38.6
20	28.4	31.4	37.6	40.0
21	29.6	32.7	38.9	41.4
24	33.2	36.4	43.0	45.6
25	34.4	37.7	44.3	46.9
27	36.7	40.1	47.0	49.6
28	37.9	41.3	48.3	51.0
30	40.3	43.8	50.9	53.7
40	51.8	55.8	63.7	66.8
50	63.2	67.5	76.2	79.5
70	85.5	90.5	100.4	104.2
100	118.5	124.3	135.8	140.2

APPENDIX F
F Distributions

Light type gives critical value for $\alpha = .05$
Bold type gives critical value for $\alpha = .01$

d_2	\multicolumn{24}{c}{d_1 = Degrees of Freedom for Numerator}	d_2
	1	2	3	4	5	6	7	8	9	10	11	12	14	16	20	24	30	40	50	75	100	200	500	∞	
1	161 / 4,052	200 / 4,999	216 / 5,403	225 / 5,625	230 / 5,764	234 / 5,859	237 / 5,928	239 / 5,981	241 / 6,022	242 / 6,056	243 / 6,082	244 / 6,106	245 / 6,142	246 / 6,169	248 / 6,208	249 / 6,234	250 / 6,261	251 / 6,286	252 / 6,302	253 / 6,323	253 / 6,334	254 / 6,352	254 / 6,361	254 / 6,366	1
2	18.51 / 98.49	19.00 / 99.00	19.16 / 99.17	19.25 / 99.25	19.30 / 99.30	19.33 / 99.33	19.36 / 99.36	19.37 / 99.37	19.38 / 99.39	19.39 / 99.40	19.40 / 99.41	19.41 / 99.42	19.42 / 99.43	19.43 / 99.44	19.44 / 99.45	19.45 / 99.46	19.46 / 99.47	19.47 / 99.48	19.47 / 99.48	19.48 / 99.49	19.49 / 99.49	19.49 / 99.49	19.50 / 99.50	19.50 / 99.50	2
3	10.13 / 34.12	9.55 / 30.82	9.28 / 29.46	9.12 / 28.71	9.01 / 28.24	8.94 / 27.91	8.88 / 27.67	8.84 / 27.49	8.81 / 27.34	8.78 / 27.23	8.76 / 27.13	8.74 / 27.05	8.71 / 26.92	8.69 / 26.83	8.66 / 26.69	8.64 / 26.60	8.62 / 26.50	8.60 / 26.41	8.58 / 26.35	8.57 / 26.27	8.56 / 26.23	8.54 / 26.18	8.54 / 26.14	8.53 / 26.12	3
4	7.71 / 21.20	6.94 / 18.00	6.59 / 16.69	6.39 / 15.98	6.26 / 15.52	6.16 / 15.21	6.09 / 14.98	6.04 / 14.80	6.00 / 14.66	5.96 / 14.54	5.93 / 14.45	5.91 / 14.37	5.87 / 14.24	5.84 / 14.15	5.80 / 14.02	5.77 / 13.93	5.74 / 13.83	5.71 / 13.74	5.70 / 13.69	5.68 / 13.61	5.66 / 13.57	5.65 / 13.52	5.64 / 13.48	5.63 / 13.46	4
5	6.61 / 16.26	5.79 / 13.27	5.41 / 12.06	5.19 / 11.39	5.05 / 10.97	4.95 / 10.67	4.88 / 10.45	4.82 / 10.29	4.78 / 10.15	4.74 / 10.05	4.70 / 9.96	4.68 / 9.89	4.64 / 9.77	4.60 / 9.68	4.56 / 9.55	4.53 / 9.47	4.50 / 9.38	4.46 / 9.29	4.44 / 9.24	4.42 / 9.17	4.40 / 9.13	4.38 / 9.07	4.37 / 9.04	4.36 / 9.02	5
6	5.99 / 13.74	5.14 / 10.92	4.76 / 9.78	4.53 / 9.15	4.39 / 8.75	4.28 / 8.47	4.21 / 8.26	4.15 / 8.10	4.10 / 7.98	4.06 / 7.87	4.03 / 7.79	4.00 / 7.72	3.96 / 7.60	3.92 / 7.52	3.87 / 7.39	3.84 / 7.31	3.81 / 7.23	3.77 / 7.14	3.75 / 7.09	3.72 / 7.02	3.71 / 6.99	3.69 / 6.94	3.68 / 6.90	3.67 / 6.88	6
7	5.59 / 12.25	4.74 / 9.55	4.35 / 8.45	4.12 / 7.85	3.97 / 7.46	3.87 / 7.19	3.79 / 7.00	3.73 / 6.84	3.68 / 6.71	3.63 / 6.62	3.60 / 6.54	3.57 / 6.47	3.52 / 6.35	3.49 / 6.27	3.44 / 6.15	3.41 / 6.07	3.38 / 5.98	3.34 / 5.90	3.32 / 5.85	3.29 / 5.78	3.28 / 5.75	3.25 / 5.70	3.24 / 5.67	3.23 / 5.65	7
8	5.32 / 11.26	4.46 / 8.65	4.07 / 7.59	3.84 / 7.01	3.69 / 6.63	3.58 / 6.37	3.50 / 6.19	3.44 / 6.03	3.39 / 5.91	3.34 / 5.82	3.31 / 5.74	3.28 / 5.67	3.23 / 5.56	3.20 / 5.48	3.15 / 5.36	3.12 / 5.28	3.08 / 5.20	3.05 / 5.11	3.03 / 5.06	3.00 / 5.00	2.98 / 4.96	2.96 / 4.91	2.94 / 4.88	2.93 / 4.86	8
9	5.12 / 10.56	4.26 / 8.02	3.86 / 6.99	3.63 / 6.42	3.48 / 6.06	3.37 / 5.80	3.29 / 5.62	3.23 / 5.47	3.18 / 5.35	3.13 / 5.26	3.10 / 5.18	3.07 / 5.11	3.02 / 5.00	2.98 / 4.92	2.93 / 4.80	2.90 / 4.73	2.86 / 4.64	2.82 / 4.56	2.80 / 4.51	2.77 / 4.45	2.76 / 4.41	2.73 / 4.36	2.72 / 4.33	2.71 / 4.31	9
10	4.96 / 10.04	4.10 / 7.56	3.71 / 6.55	3.48 / 5.99	3.33 / 5.64	3.22 / 5.39	3.14 / 5.21	3.07 / 5.06	3.02 / 4.95	2.97 / 4.85	2.94 / 4.78	2.91 / 4.71	2.86 / 4.60	2.82 / 4.52	2.77 / 4.41	2.74 / 4.33	2.70 / 4.25	2.67 / 4.17	2.64 / 4.12	2.61 / 4.05	2.59 / 4.01	2.56 / 3.96	2.55 / 3.93	2.54 / 3.91	10
11	4.84 / 9.65	3.98 / 7.20	3.59 / 6.22	3.36 / 5.67	3.20 / 5.32	3.09 / 5.07	3.01 / 4.88	2.95 / 4.74	2.90 / 4.63	2.86 / 4.54	2.82 / 4.46	2.79 / 4.40	2.74 / 4.29	2.70 / 4.21	2.65 / 4.10	2.61 / 4.02	2.57 / 3.94	2.53 / 3.86	2.50 / 3.80	2.47 / 3.74	2.45 / 3.70	2.42 / 3.66	2.41 / 3.62	2.40 / 3.60	11
12	4.75 / 9.33	3.88 / 6.93	3.49 / 5.95	3.26 / 5.41	3.11 / 5.06	3.00 / 4.82	2.92 / 4.65	2.85 / 4.50	2.80 / 4.39	2.76 / 4.30	2.72 / 4.22	2.69 / 4.16	2.64 / 4.05	2.60 / 3.98	2.54 / 3.86	2.50 / 3.78	2.46 / 3.70	2.42 / 3.61	2.40 / 3.56	2.36 / 3.49	2.35 / 3.46	2.31 / 3.41	2.31 / 3.38	2.30 / 3.36	12
13	4.67 / 9.07	3.80 / 6.70	3.41 / 5.74	3.18 / 5.20	3.02 / 4.86	2.92 / 4.62	2.84 / 4.44	2.77 / 4.30	2.72 / 4.19	2.67 / 4.10	2.63 / 4.02	2.60 / 3.96	2.55 / 3.85	2.51 / 3.78	2.46 / 3.67	2.42 / 3.59	2.38 / 3.51	2.34 / 3.42	2.32 / 3.37	2.28 / 3.30	2.26 / 3.27	2.24 / 3.21	2.22 / 3.18	2.21 / 3.16	13

d_2 = Degrees of Freedom for Denominator

Reprinted by permission from *Statistical Methods*, 6th edition, by George W. Snedecor and William C. Cochran, © 1967 by the Iowa State University Press, Ames, Iowa.

APPENDIX F (continued)
F Distributions

d_1 = Degrees of Freedom for Numerator

d_2	1	2	3	4	5	6	7	8	9	10	11	12	14	16	20	24	30	40	50	75	100	200	500	∞	d_2
14	4.60 / 8.86	3.74 / 6.51	3.34 / 5.56	3.11 / 5.03	2.96 / 4.69	2.85 / 4.46	2.77 / 4.28	2.70 / 4.14	2.65 / 4.03	2.60 / 3.94	2.56 / 3.86	2.53 / 3.80	2.48 / 3.70	2.44 / 3.62	2.39 / 3.51	2.35 / 3.43	2.31 / 3.34	2.27 / 3.26	2.24 / 3.21	2.21 / 3.14	2.19 / 3.11	2.16 / 3.06	2.14 / 3.02	2.13 / 3.00	14
15	4.54 / 8.68	3.68 / 6.36	3.29 / 5.42	3.06 / 4.89	2.90 / 4.56	2.79 / 4.32	2.70 / 4.14	2.64 / 4.00	2.59 / 3.89	2.55 / 3.80	2.51 / 3.73	2.48 / 3.67	2.43 / 3.56	2.39 / 3.48	2.33 / 3.36	2.29 / 3.29	2.25 / 3.20	2.21 / 3.12	2.18 / 3.07	2.15 / 3.00	2.12 / 2.97	2.10 / 2.92	2.08 / 2.89	2.07 / 2.87	15
16	4.49 / 8.53	3.63 / 6.23	3.24 / 5.29	3.01 / 4.77	2.85 / 4.44	2.74 / 4.20	2.66 / 4.03	2.59 / 3.89	2.54 / 3.78	2.49 / 3.69	2.45 / 3.61	2.42 / 3.55	2.37 / 3.45	2.33 / 3.37	2.28 / 3.25	2.24 / 3.18	2.20 / 3.10	2.16 / 3.01	2.13 / 2.96	2.09 / 2.98	2.07 / 2.86	2.04 / 2.80	2.02 / 2.77	2.01 / 2.75	16
17	4.45 / 8.40	3.59 / 6.11	3.20 / 5.18	2.96 / 4.67	2.81 / 4.34	2.70 / 4.10	2.62 / 3.93	2.55 / 3.79	2.50 / 3.68	2.45 / 3.59	2.41 / 3.52	2.38 / 3.45	2.33 / 3.35	2.29 / 3.27	2.23 / 3.16	2.19 / 3.08	2.15 / 3.00	2.11 / 2.92	2.08 / 2.86	2.04 / 2.79	2.02 / 2.76	1.99 / 2.70	1.97 / 2.67	1.96 / 2.65	17
18	4.41 / 8.28	3.55 / 6.01	3.16 / 5.09	2.93 / 4.58	2.77 / 4.25	2.66 / 4.01	2.58 / 3.85	2.51 / 3.71	2.46 / 3.60	2.41 / 3.51	2.37 / 3.44	2.34 / 3.37	2.29 / 3.27	2.25 / 3.19	2.19 / 3.07	2.15 / 3.00	2.11 / 2.91	2.07 / 2.83	2.04 / 2.78	2.00 / 2.71	1.98 / 2.68	1.95 / 2.62	1.93 / 2.59	1.92 / 2.57	18
19	4.38 / 8.18	3.52 / 5.93	3.13 / 5.01	2.90 / 4.50	2.74 / 4.17	2.63 / 3.94	2.55 / 3.77	2.48 / 3.63	2.43 / 3.52	2.38 / 3.43	2.34 / 3.36	2.31 / 3.30	2.26 / 3.19	2.21 / 3.12	2.15 / 3.00	2.11 / 2.92	2.07 / 2.84	2.02 / 2.76	2.00 / 2.70	1.96 / 2.63	1.94 / 2.60	1.91 / 2.54	1.90 / 2.51	1.88 / 2.49	19
20	4.35 / 8.10	3.49 / 5.85	3.10 / 4.94	2.87 / 4.43	2.71 / 4.10	2.60 / 3.87	2.52 / 3.71	2.45 / 3.56	2.40 / 3.45	2.35 / 3.37	2.31 / 3.30	2.28 / 3.23	2.23 / 3.13	2.18 / 3.05	2.12 / 2.94	2.08 / 2.86	2.04 / 2.77	1.99 / 2.69	1.96 / 2.63	1.92 / 2.56	1.90 / 2.53	1.87 / 2.47	1.85 / 2.44	1.84 / 2.42	20
21	4.32 / 8.02	3.47 / 5.78	3.07 / 4.87	2.84 / 4.37	2.68 / 4.04	2.57 / 3.81	2.49 / 3.65	2.42 / 3.51	2.37 / 3.40	2.32 / 3.31	2.28 / 3.24	2.25 / 3.17	2.20 / 3.07	2.15 / 2.99	2.09 / 2.88	2.05 / 2.80	2.00 / 2.72	1.96 / 2.63	1.93 / 2.58	1.89 / 2.51	1.87 / 2.47	1.84 / 2.42	1.82 / 2.38	1.81 / 2.36	21
22	4.30 / 7.94	3.44 / 5.72	3.05 / 4.82	2.82 / 4.31	2.66 / 3.99	2.55 / 3.76	2.47 / 3.59	2.40 / 3.45	2.35 / 3.35	2.30 / 3.26	2.26 / 3.18	2.23 / 3.12	2.18 / 3.02	2.13 / 2.94	2.07 / 2.83	2.03 / 2.75	1.98 / 2.67	1.93 / 2.58	1.91 / 2.53	1.87 / 2.46	1.84 / 2.42	1.81 / 2.37	1.80 / 2.33	1.78 / 2.31	22
23	4.28 / 7.88	3.42 / 5.66	3.03 / 4.76	2.80 / 4.26	2.64 / 3.94	2.53 / 3.71	2.45 / 3.54	2.38 / 3.41	2.32 / 3.30	2.28 / 3.21	2.24 / 3.14	2.20 / 3.07	2.14 / 2.97	2.10 / 2.89	2.04 / 2.78	2.00 / 2.70	1.96 / 2.62	1.91 / 2.53	1.88 / 2.48	1.84 / 2.41	1.82 / 2.37	1.79 / 2.32	1.77 / 2.28	1.76 / 2.26	23
24	4.26 / 7.82	3.40 / 5.61	3.01 / 4.72	2.78 / 4.22	2.62 / 3.90	2.51 / 3.67	2.43 / 3.50	2.36 / 3.36	2.30 / 3.25	2.26 / 3.17	2.22 / 3.09	2.18 / 3.03	2.13 / 2.93	2.09 / 2.85	2.02 / 2.74	1.98 / 2.66	1.94 / 2.58	1.89 / 2.49	1.86 / 2.44	1.82 / 2.36	1.80 / 2.33	1.76 / 2.27	1.74 / 2.23	1.73 / 2.21	24
25	4.24 / 7.77	3.38 / 5.57	2.99 / 4.68	2.76 / 4.18	2.60 / 3.86	2.49 / 3.63	2.41 / 3.46	2.34 / 3.32	2.28 / 3.21	2.24 / 3.13	2.20 / 3.05	2.16 / 2.99	2.11 / 2.89	2.06 / 2.81	2.00 / 2.70	1.96 / 2.62	1.92 / 2.54	1.87 / 2.45	1.84 / 2.40	1.80 / 2.32	1.77 / 2.29	1.74 / 2.23	1.72 / 2.19	1.71 / 2.17	25
26	4.22 / 7.72	3.37 / 5.53	2.98 / 4.64	2.74 / 4.14	2.59 / 3.82	2.47 / 3.59	2.39 / 3.42	2.32 / 3.29	2.27 / 3.17	2.22 / 3.09	2.18 / 3.02	2.15 / 2.96	2.10 / 2.86	2.05 / 2.77	1.99 / 2.66	1.95 / 2.58	1.90 / 2.50	1.85 / 2.41	1.82 / 2.36	1.78 / 2.28	1.76 / 2.25	1.72 / 2.19	1.70 / 2.15	1.69 / 2.13	26

d_2 = Degrees of Freedom for Denominator

APPENDIX N
Normal Distribution

Each entry gives the area (as shaded) between the mean and the value which is Z standard deviation units above the mean. For example, the area or probability between the mean which is $Z = 0$, and $Z = 1.34$ is .4099.

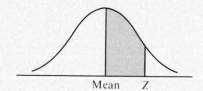

Mean Z

Z	0.00	0.01	0.02	0.03	0.04	0.05	0.06	0.07	0.08	0.09
0.0	0.0000	0.0040	0.0080	0.0120	0.0160	0.0199	0.0239	0.0279	0.0319	0.0359
0.1	0.0398	0.0438	0.0478	0.0517	0.0557	0.0596	0.0636	0.0675	0.0714	0.0753
0.2	0.0793	0.0832	0.0871	0.0910	0.0948	0.0987	0.1026	0.1064	0.1103	0.1141
0.3	0.1179	0.1217	0.1255	0.1293	0.1331	0.1368	0.1406	0.1443	0.1480	0.1517
0.4	0.1554	0.1591	0.1628	0.1664	0.1700	0.1736	0.1772	0.1808	0.1844	0.1879
0.5	0.1915	0.1950	0.1985	0.2019	0.2054	0.2088	0.2123	0.2157	0.2190	0.2224
0.6	0.2257	0.2291	0.2324	0.2357	0.2389	0.2422	0.2454	0.2486	0.2518	0.2549
0.7	0.2580	0.2612	0.2642	0.2673	0.2704	0.2734	0.2764	0.2794	0.2823	0.2852
0.8	0.2881	0.2910	0.2939	0.2967	0.2995	0.3023	0.3051	0.3078	0.3106	0.3133
0.9	0.3159	0.3186	0.3212	0.3238	0.3264	0.3289	0.3315	0.3340	0.3365	0.3389
1.0	0.3413	0.3438	0.3461	0.3485	0.3508	0.3531	0.3554	0.3577	0.3599	0.3621
1.1	0.3643	0.3665	0.3686	0.3708	0.3729	0.3749	0.3770	0.3790	0.3810	0.3830
1.2	0.3849	0.3869	0.3888	0.3907	0.3925	0.3944	0.3962	0.3980	0.3997	0.4015
1.3	0.4032	0.4049	0.4066	0.4082	0.4099	0.4115	0.4131	0.4147	0.4162	0.4177
1.4	0.4192	0.4207	0.4222	0.4236	0.4251	0.4265	0.4279	0.4292	0.4306	0.4319
1.5	0.4332	0.4345	0.4357	0.4370	0.4382	0.4394	0.4406	0.4418	0.4429	0.4441
1.6	0.4452	0.4463	0.4474	0.4484	0.4495	0.4505	0.4515	0.4525	0.4535	0.4545
1.7	0.4554	0.4564	0.4573	0.4582	0.4591	0.4599	0.4608	0.4616	0.4625	0.4633
1.8	0.4641	0.4649	0.4656	0.4664	0.4671	0.4678	0.4686	0.4693	0.4699	0.4706
1.9	0.4713	0.4719	0.4726	0.4732	0.4738	0.4744	0.4750	0.4756	0.4761	0.4767
2.0	0.4772	0.4778	0.4783	0.4788	0.4793	0.4798	0.4803	0.4808	0.4812	0.4817
2.1	0.4821	0.4826	0.4830	0.4834	0.4838	0.4842	0.4846	0.4850	0.4854	0.4857
2.2	0.4861	0.4864	0.4868	0.4871	0.4875	0.4878	0.4881	0.4884	0.4887	0.4890
2.3	0.4893	0.4896	0.4898	0.4901	0.4904	0.4906	0.4909	0.4911	0.4913	0.4916
2.4	0.4918	0.4920	0.4922	0.4925	0.4927	0.4929	0.4931	0.4932	0.4934	0.4936
2.5	0.4938	0.4940	0.4941	0.4943	0.4945	0.4946	0.4948	0.4949	0.4951	0.4952
2.6	0.4953	0.4955	0.4956	0.4957	0.4959	0.4960	0.4961	0.4962	0.4963	0.4964
2.7	0.4965	0.4966	0.4967	0.4968	0.4969	0.4970	0.4971	0.4972	0.4973	0.4974
2.8	0.4974	0.4975	0.4976	0.4977	0.4977	0.4978	0.4979	0.4979	0.4980	0.4981
2.9	0.4981	0.4982	0.4982	0.4983	0.4984	0.4984	0.4985	0.4985	0.4986	0.4986
3.0	0.4986	0.4987	0.4987	0.4988	0.4988	0.4989	0.4989	0.4989	0.4990	0.4990
3.1	0.4990	0.4991	0.4991	0.4991	0.4992	0.4992	0.4992	0.4992	0.4993	0.4993
3.2	0.4993	0.4993	0.4994	0.4994	0.4994	0.4994	0.4994	0.4995	0.4995	0.4995
3.3	0.4995	0.4995	0.4995	0.4996	0.4996	0.4996	0.4996	0.4996	0.4996	0.4997
3.4	0.4997	0.4997	0.4997	0.4997	0.4997	0.4997	0.4997	0.4997	0.4998	0.4998
3.5	0.4998	0.4998	0.4998	0.4998	0.4998	0.4998	0.4998	0.4998	0.4998	0.4998
3.6	0.4998	0.4998	0.4999	0.4999	0.4999	0.4999	0.4999	0.4999	0.4999	0.4999
3.7	0.4999	0.4999	0.4999	0.4999	0.4999	0.4999	0.4999	0.4999	0.4999	0.4999
3.8	0.4999	0.4999	0.4999	0.4999	0.4999	0.4999	0.4999	0.5000	0.5000	0.5000
3.9	0.5000	0.5000	0.5000	0.5000	0.5000	0.5000	0.5000	0.5000	0.5000	0.5000

Reprinted by permission from William J. Stevenson, *Business Statistics: Concepts and Applications* (New York: Harper & Row, Publishers, 1978), p. 483.

APPENDIX P
Poisson Distributions

x	0.005	0.01	0.02	0.03	λ 0.04	0.05	0.06	0.07	0.08	0.09
0	.9950	.9900	.9802	.9704	.9608	.9512	.9418	.9324	.9231	.9139
1	.0050	.0099	.0192	.0291	.0384	.0476	.0565	.0653	.0738	.0823
2	.0000	.0000	.0002	.0004	.0008	.0012	.0017	.0023	.0030	.0037
3	.0000	.0000	.0000	.0000	.0000	.0000	.0000	.0001	.0001	.0001

x	0.10	0.20	0.30	0.40	λ 0.50	0.60	0.70	0.80	0.90	1.00
0	.9048	.8187	.7408	.6703	.6065	.5488	.4966	.4493	.4066	.3679
1	.0905	.1637	.2222	.2681	.3033	.3293	.3476	.3595	.3659	.3679
2	.0045	.0164	.0333	.0536	.0758	.0988	.1217	.1438	.1647	.1839
3	.0002	.0011	.0033	.0072	.0126	.0198	.0284	.0383	.0494	.0613
4	.0000	.0001	.0003	.0007	.0016	.0030	.0050	.0077	.0111	.0153
5	.0000	.0000	.0000	.0001	.0002	.0004	.0007	.0012	.0020	.0031
6	.0000	.0000	.0000	.0000	.0000	.0000	.0001	.0002	.0003	.0005
7	.0000	.0000	.0000	.0000	.0000	.0000	.0000	.0000	.0000	.0001

x	1.10	1.20	1.30	1.40	λ 1.50	1.60	1.70	1.80	1.90	2.00
0	.3329	.3012	.2725	.2466	.2231	.2019	.1827	.1653	.1496	.1353
1	.3662	.3614	.3543	.3452	.3347	.3230	.3106	.2975	.2842	.2707
2	.2014	.2169	.2303	.2417	.2510	.2584	.2640	.2678	.2700	.2707
3	.0738	.0867	.0998	.1128	.1255	.1378	.1496	.1607	.1710	.1804
4	.0203	.0260	.0324	.0395	.0471	.0551	.0636	.0723	.0812	.0902
5	.0045	.0062	.0084	.0111	.0141	.0176	.0216	.0260	.0309	.0361
6	.0008	.0012	.0018	.0026	.0035	.0047	.0061	.0078	.0098	.0120
7	.0001	.0002	.0003	.0005	.0008	.0011	.0015	.0020	.0027	.0034
8	.0000	.0000	.0001	.0001	.0001	.0002	.0003	.0005	.0006	.0009
9	.0000	.0000	.0000	.0000	.0000	.0000	.0001	.0001	.0001	.0002

x	2.10	2.20	2.30	2.40	λ 2.50	2.60	2.70	2.80	2.90	3.00
0	.1225	.1108	.1003	.0907	.0821	.0743	.0672	.0608	.0550	.0498
1	.2572	.2438	.2306	.2177	.2052	.1931	.1815	.1703	.1596	.1494
2	.2700	.2681	.2652	.2613	.2565	.2510	.2450	.2384	.2314	.2240
3	.1890	.1966	.2033	.2090	.2138	.2176	.2205	.2225	.2237	.2240
4	.0992	.1082	.1169	.1254	.1336	.1414	.1488	.1557	.1622	.1680
5	.0417	.0476	.0538	.0602	.0668	.0735	.0804	.0872	.0940	.1008
6	.0146	.0174	.0206	.0241	.0278	.0319	.0362	.0407	.0455	.0504
7	.0044	.0055	.0068	.0083	.0099	.0118	.0139	.0163	.0188	.0216
8	.0011	.0015	.0019	.0025	.0031	.0038	.0047	.0057	.0068	.0081
9	.0003	.0004	.0005	.0007	.0009	.0011	.0014	.0018	.0022	.0027
10	.0001	.0001	.0001	.0002	.0002	.0003	.0004	.0005	.0006	.0008
11	.0000	.0000	.0000	.0000	.0000	.0001	.0001	.0001	.0002	.0002
12	.0000	.0000	.0000	.0000	.0000	.0000	.0000	.0000	.0000	.0001

x	3.10	3.20	3.30	3.40	λ 3.50	3.60	3.70	3.80	3.90	4.00
0	.0450	.0408	.0369	.0334	.0302	.0273	.0247	.0224	.0202	.0183
1	.1397	.1304	.1217	.1135	.1057	.0984	.0915	.0850	.0789	.0733
2	.2165	.2087	.2008	.1929	.1850	.1771	.1692	.1615	.1539	.1465
3	.2237	.2226	.2209	.2186	.2158	.2125	.2087	.2046	.2001	.1954
4	.1733	.1781	.1823	.1858	.1888	.1912	.1931	.1944	.1951	.1954

Reprinted by permission from William J. Stevenson, *Business Statistics: Concepts and Applications* (New York: Harper & Row, 1978), pp. 474–477.

APPENDIX P (continued)

Poisson Distributions

X	3.10	3.20	3.30	3.40	λ 3.50	3.60	3.70	3.80	3.90	4.00
5	.1075	.1140	.1203	.1264	.1322	.1377	.1429	.1477	.1522	.1563
6	.0555	.0608	.0662	.0716	.0771	.0826	.0881	.0936	.0989	.1042
7	.0246	.0278	.0312	.0348	.0385	.0425	.0466	.0508	.0551	.0595
8	.0095	.0111	.0129	.0148	.0169	.0191	.0215	.0241	.0269	.0298
9	.0033	.0040	.0047	.0056	.0066	.0076	.0089	.0102	.0116	.0132
10	.0010	.0013	.0016	.0019	.0023	.0028	.0033	.0039	.0045	.0053
11	.0003	.0004	.0005	.0006	.0007	.0009	.0011	.0013	.0016	.0019
12	.0001	.0001	.0001	.0002	.0002	.0003	.0003	.0004	.0005	.0006
13	.0000	.0000	.0000	.0000	.0001	.0001	.0001	.0001	.0002	.0002
14	.0000	.0000	.0000	.0000	.0000	.0000	.0000	.0000	.0000	.0001

X	4.10	4.20	4.30	4.40	λ 4.50	4.60	4.70	4.80	4.90	5.00
0	.0166	.0150	.0136	.0123	.0111	.0101	.0091	.0082	.0074	.0067
1	.0679	.0630	.0583	.0540	.0500	.0462	.0427	.0395	.0365	.0337
2	.1393	.1323	.1254	.1188	.1125	.1063	.1005	.0948	.0894	.0842
3	.1904	.1852	.1798	.1743	.1687	.1631	.1574	.1517	.1460	.1404
4	.1951	.1944	.1933	.1917	.1898	.1875	.1849	.1820	.1789	.1755
5	.1600	.1633	.1662	.1687	.1708	.1725	.1738	.1747	.1753	.1755
6	.1093	.1143	.1191	.1237	.1281	.1323	.1362	.1398	.1432	.1462
7	.0640	.0686	.0732	.0778	.0824	.0869	.0914	.0959	.1002	.1044
8	.0328	.0360	.0393	.0428	.0463	.0500	.0537	.0575	.0614	.0653
9	.0150	.0168	.0188	.0209	.0232	.0255	.0281	.0307	.0334	.0363
10	.0061	.0071	.0081	.0092	.0104	.0118	.0132	.0147	.0164	.0181
11	.0023	.0027	.0032	.0037	.0043	.0049	.0056	.0064	.0073	.0082
12	.0008	.0009	.0011	.0013	.0016	.0019	.0022	.0026	.0030	.0034
13	.0002	.0003	.0004	.0005	.0006	.0007	.0008	.0009	.0011	.0013
14	.0001	.0001	.0001	.0001	.0002	.0002	.0003	.0003	.0004	.0005
15	.0000	.0000	.0000	.0000	.0001	.0001	.0001	.0001	.0001	.0002

X	5.10	5.20	5.30	5.40	λ 5.50	5.60	5.70	5.80	5.90	6.00
0	.0061	.0055	.0050	.0045	.0041	.0037	.0033	.0030	.0027	.0025
1	.0311	.0287	.0265	.0244	.0225	.0207	.0191	.0176	.0162	.0149
2	.0793	.0746	.0701	.0659	.0618	.0580	.0544	.0509	.0477	.0446
3	.1348	.1293	.1239	.1185	.1133	.1082	.1033	.0985	.0938	.0892
4	.1719	.1681	.1641	.1600	.1558	.1515	.1472	.1428	.1383	.1339
5	.1753	.1748	.1740	.1728	.1714	.1697	.1678	.1656	.1632	.1606
6	.1490	.1515	.1537	.1555	.1571	.1584	.1594	.1601	.1605	.1606
7	.1086	.1125	.1163	.1200	.1234	.1267	.1298	.1326	.1353	.1377
8	.0692	.0731	.0771	.0810	.0849	.0887	.0925	.0962	.0998	.1033
9	.0392	.0423	.0454	.0486	.0519	.0552	.0586	.0620	.0654	.0688
10	.0200	.0220	.0241	.0262	.0285	.0309	.0334	.0359	.0386	.0413
11	.0093	.0104	.0116	.0129	.0143	.0157	.0173	.0190	.0207	.0225
12	.0039	.0045	.0051	.0058	.0065	.0073	.0082	.0092	.0102	.0113
13	.0015	.0018	.0021	.0024	.0028	.0032	.0036	.0041	.0046	.0052
14	.0006	.0007	.0008	.0009	.0011	.0013	.0015	.0017	.0019	.0022
15	.0002	.0002	.0003	.0003	.0004	.0005	.0006	.0007	.0008	.0009
16	.0001	.0001	.0001	.0001	.0001	.0002	.0002	.0002	.0003	.0003
17	.0000	.0000	.0000	.0000	.0000	.0001	.0001	.0001	.0001	.0001

X	6.10	6.20	6.30	6.40	λ 6.50	6.60	6.70	6.80	6.90	7.00
0	.0022	.0020	.0018	.0017	.0015	.0014	.0012	.0011	.0010	.0009
1	.0137	.0126	.0116	.0106	.0098	.0090	.0082	.0076	.0070	.0064
2	.0417	.0390	.0364	.0340	.0318	.0296	.0276	.0258	.0240	.0223
3	.0848	.0806	.0765	.0726	.0688	.0652	.0617	.0584	.0552	.0521
4	.1294	.1249	.1205	.1161	.1118	.1076	.1034	.0992	.0952	.0912
5	.1579	.1549	.1519	.1487	.1454	.1420	.1385	.1349	.1314	.1277
6	.1605	.1601	.1595	.1586	.1575	.1562	.1546	.1529	.1511	.1490
7	.1399	.1418	.1435	.1450	.1462	.1472	.1480	.1486	.1489	.1490
8	.1066	.1099	.1130	.1160	.1188	.1215	.1240	.1263	.1284	.1304
9	.0723	.0757	.0791	.0825	.0858	.0891	.0923	.0954	.0985	.1014
10	.0441	.0469	.0498	.0528	.0558	.0588	.0618	.0649	.0679	.0710
11	.0244	.0265	.0285	.0307	.0330	.0353	.0377	.0401	.0426	.0452
12	.0124	.0137	.0150	.0164	.0179	.0194	.0210	.0227	.0245	.0263
13	.0058	.0065	.0073	.0081	.0089	.0099	.0108	.0119	.0130	.0142
14	.0025	.0029	.0033	.0037	.0041	.0046	.0052	.0058	.0064	.0071

APPENDIX P (continued)

Poisson Distributions

x	6.10	6.20	6.30	6.40	λ 6.50	6.60	6.70	6.80	6.90	7.00
15	.0010	.0012	.0014	.0016	.0018	.0020	.0023	.0026	.0029	.0033
16	.0004	.0005	.0005	.0006	.0007	.0008	.0010	.0011	.0013	.0014
17	.0001	.0002	.0002	.0002	.0003	.0003	.0004	.0004	.0005	.0006
18	.0000	.0001	.0001	.0001	.0001	.0001	.0001	.0002	.0002	.0002
19	.0000	.0000	.0000	.0000	.0000	.0000	.0001	.0001	.0001	.0001

x	7.10	7.20	7.30	7.40	λ 7.50	7.60	7.70	7.80	7.90	8.00
0	.0008	.0007	.0007	.0006	.0006	.0005	.0005	.0004	.0004	.0003
1	.0059	.0054	.0049	.0045	.0041	.0038	.0035	.0032	.0029	.0027
2	.0208	.0194	.0180	.0167	.0156	.0145	.0134	.0125	.0116	.0107
3	.0492	.0464	.0438	.0413	.0389	.0366	.0345	.0324	.0305	.0286
4	.0874	.0836	.0799	.0764	.0729	.0696	.0663	.0632	.0602	.0573
5	.1241	.1204	.1167	.1130	.1094	.1057	.1021	.0986	.0951	.0916
6	.1468	.1445	.1420	.1394	.1367	.1339	.1311	.1282	.1252	.1221
7	.1489	.1486	.1481	.1474	.1465	.1454	.1442	.1428	.1413	.1396
8	.1321	.1337	.1351	.1363	.1373	.1381	.1388	.1392	.1395	.1396
9	.1042	.1070	.1096	.1121	.1144	.1167	.1187	.1207	.1224	.1241
10	.0740	.0770	.0800	.0829	.0858	.0887	.0914	.0941	.0967	.0993
11	.0478	.0504	.0531	.0558	.0585	.0613	.0640	.0667	.0695	.0722
12	.0283	.0303	.0323	.0344	.0366	.0388	.0411	.0434	.0457	.0481
13	.0154	.0168	.0181	.0196	.0211	.0227	.0243	.0260	.0278	.0296
14	.0078	.0086	.0095	.0104	.0113	.0123	.0134	.0145	.0157	.0169
15	.0037	.0041	.0046	.0051	.0057	.0062	.0069	.0075	.0083	.0090
16	.0016	.0019	.0021	.0024	.0026	.0030	.0033	.0037	.0041	.0045
17	.0007	.0008	.0009	.0010	.0012	.0013	.0015	.0017	.0019	.0021
18	.0003	.0003	.0004	.0004	.0005	.0006	.0006	.0007	.0008	.0009
19	.0001	.0001	.0001	.0002	.0002	.0002	.0003	.0003	.0003	.0004
20	.0000	.0000	.0001	.0001	.0001	.0001	.0001	.0001	.0001	.0002
21	.0000	.0000	.0000	.0000	.0000	.0000	.0000	.0000	.0001	.0001

x	8.10	8.20	8.30	8.40	λ 8.50	8.60	8.70	8.80	8.90	9.00
0	.0003	.0003	.0002	.0002	.0002	.0002	.0002	.0002	.0001	.0001
1	.0025	.0023	.0021	.0019	.0017	.0016	.0014	.0013	.0012	.0011
2	.0100	.0092	.0086	.0079	.0074	.0068	.0063	.0058	.0054	.0050
3	.0269	.0252	.0237	.0222	.0208	.0195	.0183	.0171	.0160	.0150
4	.0544	.0517	.0491	.0466	.0443	.0420	.0398	.0377	.0357	.0337
5	.0882	.0849	.0816	.0784	.0752	.0722	.0692	.0663	.0635	.0607
6	.1191	.1160	.1128	.1097	.1066	.1034	.1003	.0972	.0941	.0911
7	.1378	.1358	.1338	.1317	.1294	.1271	.1247	.1222	.1197	.1171
8	.1395	.1392	.1388	.1382	.1375	.1366	.1356	.1344	.1332	.1318
9	.1256	.1269	.1280	.1290	.1299	.1306	.1311	.1315	.1317	.1318
10	.1017	.1040	.1063	.1084	.1104	.1123	.1140	.1157	.1172	.1186
11	.0749	.0776	.0802	.0828	.0853	.0878	.0902	.0925	.0948	.0970
12	.0505	.0530	.0555	.0579	.0604	.0629	.0654	.0679	.0703	.0728
13	.0315	.0334	.0354	.0374	.0395	.0416	.0438	.0459	.0481	.0504
14	.0182	.0196	.0210	.0225	.0240	.0256	.0272	.0289	.0306	.0324
15	.0098	.0107	.0116	.0126	.0136	.0147	.0158	.0169	.0182	.0194
16	.0050	.0055	.0060	.0066	.0072	.0079	.0086	.0093	.0101	.0109
17	.0024	.0026	.0029	.0033	.0036	.0040	.0044	.0048	.0053	.0058
18	.0011	.0012	.0014	.0015	.0017	.0019	.0021	.0024	.0026	.0029
19	.0005	.0005	.0006	.0007	.0008	.0009	.0010	.0011	.0012	.0014
20	.0002	.0002	.0002	.0003	.0003	.0004	.0004	.0005	.0005	.0006
21	.0001	.0001	.0001	.0001	.0001	.0002	.0002	.0002	.0002	.0003
22	.0000	.0000	.0000	.0000	.0001	.0001	.0001	.0001	.0001	.0001

x	9.10	9.20	9.30	9.40	λ 9.50	9.60	9.70	9.80	9.90	10.00
0	.0001	.0001	.0001	.0001	.0001	.0001	.0001	.0001	.0001	.0000
1	.0010	.0009	.0009	.0008	.0007	.0007	.0006	.0005	.0005	.0005
2	.0046	.0043	.0040	.0037	.0034	.0031	.0029	.0027	.0025	.0023
3	.0140	.0131	.0123	.0115	.0107	.0100	.0093	.0087	.0081	.0076
4	.0319	.0302	.0285	.0269	.0254	.0240	.0226	.0213	.0201	.0189
5	.0581	.0555	.0530	.0506	.0483	.0460	.0439	.0418	.0398	.0378
6	.0881	.0851	.0822	.0793	.0764	.0736	.0709	.0682	.0656	.0631
7	.1145	.1118	.1091	.1064	.1037	.1010	.0982	.0955	.0928	.0901
8	.1302	.1286	.1269	.1251	.1232	.1212	.1191	.1170	.1148	.1126
9	.1317	.1315	.1311	.1306	.1300	.1293	.1284	.1274	.1263	.1251

APPENDIX P (continued)

Poisson Distributions

x	9.10	9.20	9.30	9.40	λ 9.50	9.60	9.70	9.80	9.90	10.00
10	.1198	.1210	.1219	.1228	.1235	.1241	.1245	.1249	.1250	.1251
11	.0991	.1012	.1031	.1049	.1067	.1083	.1098	.1112	.1125	.1137
12	.0752	.0776	.0799	.0822	.0844	.0866	.0888	.0908	.0928	.0948
13	.0526	.0549	.0572	.0594	.0617	.0640	.0662	.0685	.0707	.0729
14	.0342	.0361	.0380	.0399	.0419	.0439	.0459	.0479	.0500	.0521
15	.0208	.0221	.0235	.0250	.0265	.0281	.0297	.0313	.0330	.0347
16	.0118	.0127	.0137	.0147	.0157	.0168	.0180	.0192	.0204	.0217
17	.0063	.0069	.0075	.0081	.0088	.0095	.0103	.0111	.0119	.0128
18	.0032	.0035	.0039	.0042	.0046	.0051	.0055	.0060	.0065	.0071
19	.0015	.0017	.0019	.0021	.0023	.0026	.0028	.0031	.0034	.0037
20	.0007	.0008	.0009	.0010	.0011	.0012	.0014	.0015	.0017	.0019
21	.0003	.0003	.0004	.0004	.0005	.0006	.0006	.0007	.0008	.0009
22	.0001	.0001	.0002	.0002	.0002	.0002	.0003	.0003	.0004	.0004
23	.0000	.0001	.0001	.0001	.0001	.0001	.0001	.0001	.0002	.0002
24	.0000	.0000	.0000	.0000	.0000	.0000	.0000	.0001	.0001	.0001

APPENDIX R

Random Numbers

73310	60288	63577	73455	37934	03129	40925	78395
01847	56844	08198	78401	86756	77247	92110	36216
11415	60919	37282	58414	17041	46406	65948	33433
59904	14566	17560	01207	08524	78466	54385	85977
91949	26871	24194	23557	03087	73521	57892	17521
23508	00921	41837	91474	02823	54046	60816	30407
61959	24468	29867	28336	58566	06874	55020	32109
25331	71533	13363	41962	63996	22425	74337	00253
65397	87789	17863	13223	14485	51935	12155	86530
57357	84246	35832	75425	99208	67379	66887	58634
56889	70257	45315	41428	50166	32962	71446	73229
75802	24387	52183	02935	94143	68424	94263	64390
04778	93048	51135	28714	25696	22690	52141	68005
37211	67903	49585	32749	97035	53820	29382	38981
57133	17416	19555	22474	42718	33142	59996	52763
86062	21176	37823	47127	36676	07243	23397	43173
61226	03677	00086	22723	57463	63959	59465	49627
40075	12613	09780	87206	90447	41887	06312	83332
61073	58323	59741	70270	18884	85794	32504	47781
34624	10187	80102	91149	12205	67151	39922	78558
79690	31099	40885	50813	00054	21900	36653	86715
28587	24620	72831	08156	79211	70752	59096	84209
07064	91427	16180	21018	46865	04522	36743	07116
77293	08441	51742	74868	06431	77105	90106	01449
42198	42693	14800	25939	84468	48466	06070	94096

Reprinted by permission from David Heinze, *Management Science – Introductory Concepts and Applications*, (Cincinnati: South-Western Publishing Co., 1978), p. 450.

APPENDIX T

t Distributions for One-Sample Tests

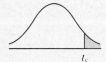

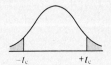

Critical Values, t_c, for Upper-Tailed Tests (Critical Values for Lower-Tailed Tests are the Negatives)

Critical Values, $-t_c$ and $+t_c$, for Two-Tailed Tests (These t Values also may be used for 90%, 95%, and 99% Confidence Intervals)

$d*$ $(n-1)$	Level of Significance (α) .10	.05	.01	Level of Significance (α) .10	.05	.01
1	3.078	6.314	31.821	±6.314	±12.706	±63.657
2	1.886	2.920	6.965	±2.920	±4.303	±9.925
3	1.638	2.353	4.541	±2.353	±3.182	±5.841
4	1.533	2.132	3.747	±2.132	±2.776	±4.604
5	1.476	2.015	3.365	±2.015	±2.571	±4.032
6	1.440	1.943	3.143	±1.943	±2.447	±3.707
7	1.415	1.895	2.998	±1.895	±2.365	±3.499
8	1.397	1.860	2.896	±1.860	±2.306	±3.355
9	1.383	1.833	2.821	±1.833	±2.262	±3.250
10	1.371	1.812	2.764	±1.812	±2.228	±3.169
11	1.363	1.796	2.718	±1.796	±2.201	±3.106
12	1.356	1.782	2.681	±1.782	±2.179	±3.055
13	1.350	1.771	2.650	±1.771	±2.160	±3.012
14	1.345	1.761	2.624	±1.761	±2.145	±2.977
15	1.341	1.753	2.602	±1.753	±2.131	±2.947
16	1.337	1.746	2.583	±1.746	±2.120	±2.921
17	1.333	1.740	2.567	±1.740	±2.110	±2.898
18	1.330	1.734	2.552	±1.734	±2.101	±2.878
19	1.328	1.729	2.539	±1.729	±2.093	±2.861
20	1.325	1.725	2.528	±1.725	±2.086	±2.845
21	1.323	1.721	2.518	±1.721	±2.080	±2.831
22	1.321	1.717	2.508	±1.717	±2.074	±2.819
23	1.319	1.714	2.500	±1.714	±2.069	±2.801
24	1.318	1.711	2.492	±1.711	±2.064	±2.797

*The degrees of freedom, d, equals $n - 1$ for all the applications in this text. In other applications d may not equal $n - 1$.

Reprinted by permission from Table III of Fisher & Yates, *Statistical Tables for Biological, Agricultural and Medical Research*, (6th ed. London: Longman Group, 1974).

INDEX